AUTHORS DIGEST

ROSSITER JOHNSON, Ph.D., LL.D.

AUTHORS PRESS

CONTENTS

in the year two thousand, and you have slept exactly one hundred and thirteen years, three months and eleven days."

Julian, dazed, drank a cup of broth and fell into a sleep, from which he awoke refreshed with a clear mind and renewed strength. His mysterious host soon informed him that three days before, while the garden was being excavated for foundations for a laboratory that he was about to build, his daughter had called his attention to the corner of a curious mass of masonry that had been laid bare. The workmen then unearthed an oblong vault set in the corner of what had evidently been the foundation walls of an ancient house. A layer of ashes and charcoal on the top of the vault showed that the house had perished by fire. The vault was intact, and the doctor, by removing one of the flagstones that formed the roof, descended into a bedroom, where, to his astonishment, a young man was lying, as he supposed, dead. The extraordinary preservation of the body, however, excited the doctor's interest; and, as soon as the medical friends he sent for to view the curiosity had left, he began a systematic attempt to resuscitate the sleeper. To accomplish his purpose the better, he had him removed to his house.

Julian West refused to believe this incredible story; and, to convince him of its truth, Dr. Leete led the way up three flights of stairs to the house-top. A new Boston burst upon his gaze! Miles of broad streets shaded by trees and lined with fine buildings, open squares filled with sparkling fountains, and statues gleaming amongst the shrubbery, public buildings of colossal size and of architectural grandeur, were framed in the well-known setting—"that blue ribbon winding away to the sunset, was it not the sinuous Charles?" And, on looking east, Boston harbor gladdened the eyes of the sleeper awakened.

"If you had told me," he said to his host, "that a thousand years instead of a hundred had elapsed since I last looked on this city, I should now believe you."

The two men exchanged names; and Dr. Leete of the Twentieth Century offered the hospitality of his home (on the site of Julian's), to Julian West of the Nineteenth.

After a little conversation, Dr. Leete escorted his guest below to introduce him to his wife and daughter. The latter was a beautiful girl, a charming product of the New Age, and, by a coincidence, bore the name of Edith. After the ladies had retired for the night, Dr. Leete and his guest again enjoyed a talk, during which Julian referred to the labor question, which led to a discussion of the social conditions of the two centuries. Julian had much to learn. He soon found that the United States had passed through an extraordinary and bloodless revolution; that the whole nation had organized as one great business corporation, and that all living was carried on upon a coöperative system.

"Early in the last century," Dr. Leete told him, "the evolution was completed by the final consolidation of the entire capital of the nation. The industry and commerce of the country, ceasing to be conducted by a set of irresponsible corporations and syndicates of private persons at their caprice and for their profit, were intrusted to a single syndicate representing the people, to be conducted in the common interest for the common profit. The nation, that is to say, organized as the one great business corporation in which all other corporations were absorbed; it became the one capitalist in the place of all other capitalists, the sole employer, the final monopoly in which all previous and lesser monopolies were swallowed up, a monopoly in the profits and economies of which all citizens shared. The epoch of trusts had ended in The Great Trust. In a word, the people of the United States determined to assume the conduct of their own business, just as one hundred-odd years before they had assumed the conduct of their own government, organizing now for industrial purposes on precisely the same grounds that they had then organized for political purposes."

"In my day," I replied, "it was considered that the proper functions of governments, strictly speaking, were limited to keeping the peace and defending the people against the public enemy, that is, to the military and police powers."

"And, in Heaven's name, who are the public enemies?" exclaimed Dr. Leete. "Are they France, England, Germany, or hunger, cold, and nakedness? In your day governments were accustomed, on the slightest international misunderstanding, to seize upon the bodies of citizens and deliver them over by hundreds of thousands to death and mutilation, wasting their treasures the while like water; and all this oftenest for no imaginable profit to the victims. We have no wars now, and our governments no war powers, but in order to protect every citizen against hunger, cold, and nakedness, and provide for all his physical and mental needs, the function is assumed by directing his industry for a term of years."

"But you have not yet told me how you have settled the labor problem. It is the problem of capital which we have been discussing," I said.

"The moment the nation assumed the responsibilities of capital those difficulties vanished," replied Dr. Leete.

"When the nation became the sole employer, all the citizens, by virtue of their citizenship, became employees, to be distributed according to the needs of industry."

"That is," I suggested, "you have simply applied the principle of universal military service, as it was understood in our day, to the labor question."

"Yes," said Dr. Leete, "that was something which followed as a matter of course as soon as the nation had become the sole capitalist. The people were already accustomed to the idea that the obligation of every citizen, not physically disabled, to contribute his military services to the defense of the nation was equal and absolute. That it was equally the duty of every citizen to contribute his quota of industrial or intellectual services to the maintenance of the nation was equally evident, though it was not until the nation became the employer of labor that citizens were able to render this sort of service with any pretense either of universality or of equity."

"Is the term of service in this industrial army for life?"

"Oh, no; it both begins later and ends earlier than the average working period in your day. Your workshops were filled with children and old men, but we hold the period of youth sacred to education and the period of maturity, when the physical forces begin to flag, equally sacred to ease and agreeable relaxation. The period of industrial service is twenty-four years, beginning at the close of the course of education at twenty-one and terminating at forty-five. After forty-five, while discharged from labor, the citizen still remains liable to special calls in case of emergencies causing a sudden great increase in the demand for labor, till he reaches the age of fifty-five, but such calls are rarely, in fact almost never, made. The fifteenth day of October of every year is what we call Muster Day, because those who have reached the age of twenty-one are then mustered into the industrial service, and at the same time those who, after twenty-four years' service, have reached the age of forty-five, are honorably mustered out. It is the great day of the year with us, whence we reckon all other events, our Olympiad, save that it is annual."

After their conversation the doctor gave his guest an opiate, and he awoke the following morning in health and spirits. Returning to the house after an early ramble, he encountered Edith, who showed considerable emotional interest in the strange visitor. She took him shopping with her and was greatly interested to learn of the methods of a past age, while she explained the new system of distribution. The electric button was not used solely for practical shopping. On their return home, Edith asked Julian whether he liked music. He replied in the affirmative, whereupon she led him into a bare room and handed him a program, dated "September 12, 2000." When he made his choice, she touched a few stops and the room was flooded with exquisite music. Julian learned that all the houses were supplied with telephone attachments by which music could be ordered at pleasure.

The Leetes next took their guest to the general dining-house of their ward; and here he learned something about the system of catering and cooking that had supplanted the old domestic housekeeping. Edith was puzzled at the word "menial" used by Julian; it was unknown to her. It was as difficult for her to grasp the idea of class divisions as it was for Julian to comprehend that no sort of difference between the dignity of the different sorts of work required by the nation was recognized. "The individual," explained Dr. Leete, "is never regarded, nor regards himself, as the servant of those he serves, nor is he in any way dependent upon them. It is always the nation that he is serving."

One afternoon Julian visited the underground vault with Edith Leete. Here he showed her Edith Bartlett's picture, and told her about his love affair. Edith was much affected, but reminded him that "her heartache was over long ago."

A cultivated and sympathetic cicerone was Dr. Leete, who showed Julian all the new institutions of the age, including schools and colleges; and answered his questions from a full mind. The vast economy of labor, the noble public spirit, the comfort, the general culture and happiness, were self-evident and striking.

In Dr. Leete's opinion the want of money was the root of all evil.

"In your day," he remarked to his guest, "fully nineteen-twentieths of the crime, using the word broadly to include all sorts of misdemeanors, resulted from the inequality in the possessions of individuals; want tempted the poor, lust of greater gains, or the desire to preserve former gains, tempted the well-to-do. Directly, or indirectly, the desire for money, which then meant every good thing, was the motive of all this crime, the taproot of a vast poison growth, which the machinery of law, courts, and police could barely prevent from choking your civilization outright. When we made the nation the sole trustee of the wealth of the people, and guaranteed to all abundant maintenance, on the one hand abolishing want, and on the other checking the accumulation of riches, we cut this root, and the poison tree that overshadowed your society withered, like Jonah's gourd, in a day.

"In your day riches debauched one class with idleness of mind and body, while poverty sapped the vitality of the masses by overwork, bad food, and pestilent homes. The labor required of children and the burdens laid on women enfeebled the very springs of life. Instead of these maleficent circumstances, all now enjoy the most favorable conditions of physical life."

One evening Julian questioned Edith about certain mysterious words that he remembered hearing whispered as he was waking from his long sleep. He remembered that Edith's voice extracted a promise that a secret should be kept from the sleeper. He wished to know what that was. She refused to tell him, and made him promise that he would not ask this question again. Yes: perhaps some day she would tell him of her own accord. On Sunday, Julian was diverted by a sermon

heard on the telephone, which was inspired by his own singular
return to life. The clergyman used the circumstance as the
theme for a comparative study of the two centuries, in which
the old state of society did not appear to advantage. From
this clergyman's point of view, the people of the Nineteenth
Century were "beasts of prey," and in the old society, "the
generous, the just, and the tender-hearted had been placed at
a disadvantage by the possession of those qualities." He partially excused the display of brutal qualities at this period.
"It is not hard to understand," he said, "the desperation with
which men and women who under other conditions would have
been full of gentleness and truth, fought and tore one another
in the scramble for gold, when we realize what it meant to miss
it, what poverty was in that day. For the body it was hunger
and thirst, torment by heat and frost, in sickness neglect, in
health unremitting toil; for the moral nature it meant oppression,
contempt, and the patient endurance of indignity, brutish associations from infancy, the loss of all the innocence of childhood,
the grace of womanhood, the dignity of manhood; for the mind
it meant the end of ignorance, the torpor of all those faculties
which distinguish us from brutes, the reduction of life to a
round of bodily functions."

This sermon depressed Julian, who felt his isolation. He
also made a discovery: he loved Edith.

One afternoon, in a melancholy mood, he strayed to the
subterranean chamber. Edith followed. First he told her of
his loneliness; and finally, encouraged by her, of his love.
When they returned to the house to inform Edith's parents of
their happiness, Mrs. Leete told Julian that Edith was the
great-granddaughter of Edith Bartlett. Long before Julian
West had been discovered, Edith Leete's imagination had been
fired by the portrait of Edith Bartlett, which had been preserved with her letters from Julian West as family heirlooms.
From these Edith had formed a romantic idea of Julian's per-
sonality, and had half jestingly vowed that she would not marry
until she found a lover like Julian West. When he was discovered—for the picture of Edith Bartlett in a locket on his
breast proved his identity—Edith Leete knew her fate was
linked with his.

The happy Julian felt that his lost love had become reëmbodied, and he was delighted to find that Edith really regarded herself as a reincarnation of Edith Bartlett. The mystery was that Edith Leete, when watching Julian's return to life, begged her parents not to let the stranger know by what ties they were connected.

Julian West, who had found the new world "a paradise of order, equity, and felicity," was now radiantly happy; but, to his great distress, he heard Sawyer trying to wake him. With a sad heart, he drank Dr. Pillsbury's prescribed glass of sherry, and left his underground chamber to stroll once more about the streets of Boston. Full of his dream of the "enlightened and care-free race of men," of their simple institutions, of the new Boston with its domes and pinnacles, its gardens and fountains, and its universal peace and prosperity, and with tender memories of his genial host and his betrothed Edith, he returned to the Boston of the Nineteenth Century. He was depressed by the horrible babel and clamor and even more by the general moral repulsiveness of his native city, in which he seemed to have suddenly become a stranger.

"The squalor and malodorousness of the town struck me," he said, "from the moment I stood upon the street, as facts I had never before observed. But yesterday, moreover, it had seemed quite a matter of course that some of my fellow-citizens should wear silks and others rags, that some should look wellfed, and others hungry. Now, on the contrary, the glaring disparities in the dress and condition of the men and women who brushed each other on the sidewalks shocked me at every step, and yet more the entire indifference which the prosperous showed to the plight of the unfortunate. Were these human beings, who could behold the wretchedness of their fellows without so much as a change of countenance? And yet, all the while, I knew well that it was I who had changed and not my contemporaries. I had dreamed of a city whose people fared all alike as children of one family, and were one another's keepers in all things.

"Another feature of the real Boston, which assumed the extraordinary effect of strangeness that marks familiar things seen in a new light, was the prevalence of advertising. There had been no personal advertising in the Boston of the Twentieth Century, because there was no need of any; but here the walls of the buildings, the windows, the broadsides of the newspapers on every hand, the very pavements, everything in fact in sight, save the sky, were covered with the appeals of individuals who sought, under innumerable pretexts, to attract the contributions of others to their support. However the wording might vary, the tenor of all these appeals was the same:

" 'Help John Jones. Never mind the rest. They are frauds. I, John Jones, am the right one. Buy of me. Employ me. Visit me. Hear me, John Jones. Look at me. Make no mistake, John Jones is the man and nobody else. Let the rest starve, but for God's sake remember John Jones!'

"Whether the pathos or the moral repulsiveness of the spectacle most impressed me, so suddenly become a stranger in my own city, I know not. Wretched men, I was moved to cry, who, because they will not learn to be helpers of one another, are doomed to be beggars of one another from the least to the greatest! This horrible babel of shameless self-assertion and mutual depreciation, this stunning clamor of conflicting boasts, appeals and adjurations, this stupendous system of brazen beggary, what was it all but the necessity of a society in which the opportunity to serve the world according to his gifts, instead of being secured to every man as the first object of social organization, had to be fought for!"

While watching his fellow-citizens march by, he exclaimed: "For thirty years I had lived among them, and yet I seemed to have never noted before how drawn and anxious were their faces, of the rich as of the poor, the refined, acute faces of the educated as well as the dull masks of the ignorant. And well it might be so, for I saw now, as never before I had seen so plainly, that each as he walked constantly turned to catch the whispers of a specter at his ear, the specter of Uncertainty. 'Do your work never so well,' the specter was whispering— 'rise early and toil till late, rob cunningly or serve faithfully, you shall never know security. Rich you may be now and still come to poverty at last. Leave never so much wealth to your children, you cannot buy the assurance that your son may not be the servant of your servant, or that your daughter will not have to sell herself for bread.'"

When he joined the Bartletts at a dinner party in their Commonwealth Avenue house, the richly appointed table and the sumptuously dressed guests, blazing with jewels, pained Julian to such a degree that he broke out in a tirade upon modern luxury and oppression, setting forth with enthusiasm the mental enlightenment, physical felicity, and moral elevation of the new world—that Utopia in which he had dwelt.

In mortification and anger, Edith Bartlett and her father drove him out of the house, denouncing him as a madman and an enemy to society; but he awoke suddenly to find himself once again in Dr. Leete's house with the morning sun shining through the open window.

As with an escaped convict who dreams that he has been recaptured and brought back to his dark and reeking dungeon, and opens his eyes to see the heaven's vault spread above him, so it was with me as I realized that my return to the Nineteenth Century had been the dream and my presence in the Twentieth was the reality. . . . But in that moment, while yet I mused with unspeakable thankfulness upon the greatness of the world's salvation and my privilege in beholding it, there suddenly pierced me like a knife a pang of shame, remorse, and wondering self-reproach, that bowed my head upon my breast. . . . What had I done to help on the deliverance whereat I now presumed to rejoice? . . . So far as my personal influence went, it had been exerted rather to hinder than to help forward the enfranchisement of the race which was even then preparing. What right had I to hail a salvation which reproached me, to rejoice in a day whose dawning I had mocked?

"Better for you, better for you," a voice within me rang, "had this evil dream been the reality, and this fair reality the dream; better your part pleading for crucified humanity with a scoffing generation than here drinking of wells you digged not and eating of trees whose husbandmen you stoned"; and my spirit answered: "Better truly."

THE DUKE OF STOCKBRIDGE (1900)

This story was written at the request of an editor of a local paper in Great Barrington, Massachusetts. Its scenes concern themselves with the revolt of the debtor-farmers in 1786 against the intolerable tyranny of the State government and their grasping creditors. One finds, in the general attitude taken by the author in this historical tale, the same trend of mind afterward so clearly expressed in *Looking Backward;* that sympathy with the coöperative social system to which he devoted the rest of his life. It was this devotion which prevented the publishing in book form of this story during the author's life. Refusing the demands of the publishers on the completion of the novel, he determined to delay its appearance until after the publication of *Looking Backward*, which was then in formation. But he never returned to fiction, and left this story buried in the files of the village newspaper; from which it was finally rescued by his cousin, Francis Bellamy.

THE dawn's first glow was illuminating the village of Stockbridge on August 17, 1777, when a horseman at full gallop pulled rein before Squire Woodbridge's house. Almost immediately the Squire came out and was joined by Deacon Nash and Squire Edwards from neighboring houses, all with guns in hand; and on the village green the Sabbath calm was broken by three musket-shots. Immediately the village was in a commotion, and open doors disgorged minute-men, who gathered on the green to join Gen. John Stark, who was at that hour fighting Baum and his Hessians on the Hoosac.

Among the men who were going out to fight were Abner Rathbun, George Fennell, and Perez and Reuben Hamlin. The chief citizens went about, encouraging those that were departing and those that remained. Squire Edwards assured Mrs. Hamlin that she need not worry about the mortgage on her house, and Deacon Nash added that he would see that her crops should be saved. George Fennell was also assured that the family left behind would be supplied from Squire Edwards's store; and every soldier plow-boy was honored by a word from the magnates who never before had recognized his existence.

Perez Hamlin was in love with Desire, the fifteen-year-old daughter of Squire Edwards. Although better bred than the other boys, he was only a farmer's son, and as such she looked down upon him. But among the general affectionate farewells, and moved by the emotion of the hour, she came to bid him good-by and granted his trembling request for a farewell kiss, and he marched away to take part in the great Revolution.

Nine years later a group of farmers and laborers were gathered in the bar-room of Stockbridge tavern, discussing the hard times. They harped upon the limited markets, the low prices for farm-produce, the extortions and multiplying numbers of lawyers and sheriffs, the oppressions of creditors, the enormous, grinding taxes, the last sheriff's sale, and who was the next to be sold out, the last batch of debtors taken to jail and who was next to go, the utter dearth of money of any sort, the impossibility of getting work, the gloomy and hopeless prospect for the coming winter, and in general the wretched failure of the military triumph of the colonies to bring about the public and private prosperity that was so confidently expected to follow the successful revolt against Great Britain. The village political economists harangued sympathetic ears. Abner Rathbun, in particular, was very bitter over the fact that Reuben Hamlin and George Fennell were in jail at Great Barrington, having been sold out for non-payment of taxes. The consensus of opinion was that the courts should be forcibly closed, as had been the case in Revolutionary days; and the assembled company were inclined to agree with a taunting Tory, who unfavorably compared the existing conditions with those of monarchical rule. Abner closed the discussion with the remark: "I used to think there was no such vermin as a Tory, but I didn't know anything about lawyers and sheriffs in those times. I calculate you could cut five Tories out of one lawyer, and make a dozen skunks out of what was left over."

The next day Perez Hamlin, after nine years' absence, reached Great Barrington. His uniform showed that he had been a captain in the late Continental Army. On the disbandment of General Greene's troops in South Carolina, he had been left to find his way home as best he could. Part of the premises of the inn at which he put up was used as a jail, and the landlord was the jailer. On paying for his meal, he was dismayed to find that his five thousand dollars in Continental bills were worthless in the landlord's eyes. One thousand was grumblingly accepted, and soon Perez learned that George Fennell, who had fought by his side, was confined in the jail. He induced the brutal keeper to consent to an interview. On entering Fennell's filthy, dark cell, he found not only George Fennell, in the last stages of consumption, but his own brother, Reuben.

That same day the Stockbridge magnates were assembled on the piazza of Squire Edwards's store, awaiting the arrival of Squire Sedgwick, who was expected back that afternoon from the county convention that had been sitting at Lenox to devise remedies for the popular distress. Most of the farmers of the neighborhood were collected on the green, anxious for the first tidings of the result of the deliberations. The "gentry" resentfully discussed the prevailing spirit of discontent and sedition. When Squire Sedgwick arrived, he contemptuously informed the "yokels" that the convention had very wisely done nothing at all except to resolve to support the courts, enforce the laws, and punish all disorderly persons; and he further impressed upon them the fact that it would be well for them to leave matters of government to their betters.

Perez Hamlin was not happy in his home-coming. He learned that his parents were about to be dispossessed for debt that very week; but this was little compared with Reuben's imprisonment and grave illness. He conspired with Abner Rathbun, his old comrade, to kidnap Deacon Nash, who had put Reuben in jail; but this was rendered unnecessary by important news that arrived that fifteen hundred men, under Captain Daniel Shays, had stopped the courts in Hampshire County. Down at the tavern this news had been like dropping a match into a powder-barrel. As Tuesday was court day at Great Barrington, there would certainly be great happenings; and Abner concluded: "When that court's stopped, that jail's coming open."

Before leaving for Boston on business, Squire Sedgwick called on Squire Woodbridge, to impress upon him the unruly spirit of the people and the advisability of vigilance—advice which was received with very ill grace.

Perez Hamlin was regarded with suspicion by the farmers; but when he bitterly told the tavern company: "Yesterday I came home to find my father and mother waiting to be sold out by the sheriff, and my brother Reub rotting to death in Barrington jail," his hearers were satisfied that he shared their sympathies.

The morning after the news from Hampshire was known, a hundred men and boys, armed with muskets and cudgels, mustered on the green in consequence of an understanding that those intending to witness the goings-on at Barrington should gather at the tavern. When they were ready to start, the five selectmen appeared, headed by Squire Woodbridge. Perez saw that the crowd was already half intimidated by the mere presence and glances of the men of authority, and that a threatening speech would suffice to scatter them like whipped curs. His eye fell on a German drummer in the crowd, and at the first words of Squire Woodbridge, he drew his sword and shouted in imperious tones: "Drum!" The German drummer immediately obeyed the uniformed captain, and the amazed and indignant Squire was reduced to silence. The selectmen ignominiously retired, and Perez was forced to lead the mob.

On their march to Great Barrington, they overtook young Prudence Fennell. Perez dismounted and forced her to take his seat and lead the column. On the eyes of the men, she was an embodiment of the spirit of suffering and outraged humanity which had nerved them for the day's work.

When the judges at Great Barrington left their lodging to proceed to court, a thousand men barred their way; and so threatening and violent was the attitude of the mob that they had to beat a retreat, and the prestige of the Honorable Justices of the Court of Common Pleas was gone. Leaders of the mob followed them to the house where they were being entertained, and forced them to sign a promise "not to act under our commissions until the grievances of which the people complain are redressed." Having prevented the meeting of the court, Perez next led his followers to the jail. The brutal landlord-jailer, Cephas Bement, was easily intimidated, but his wife was made of sterner stuff, and hid the keys of the jail in her bosom, and it needed the attack of a virago to get them.

Then the jail was filled with cries of horror and indignation, for each opening door revealed the same heartrending scenes. The deliverers recoiled before the ghastly figures that rose before them from pallets of putrid straw. Sickness and confinement had worked such terrible changes on the prisoners that even brothers could not recognize brothers. Perez led Prudence to the cell where her father and Reuben were confined.

In the first outburst of indignation over the horrible condition of the prison and prisoners, there was a yell for the jailer; and unless he had hidden himself it would have gone hard with him. But the mob soothed their disappointment by helping themselves to his liquor. Perez took his brother and Fennell to his mother's home, where the women tenderly cared for them. That night the village of Stockbridge was kept awake with unearthly noises. The mob returned drunk from Great Barrington, rigged up a "horse-fiddle," and hunted up tin pans and serenaded the "silk-stockings," as they called the aristocratic element, particularly Squire Woodbridge. The next day there was hardly anyone in the town who went to work except those who had farms of their own. Most of the labor had been that of debtors working out their debts at such allowance for wages as their creditor-employers chose to make. If they considered it too small, they could go to jail as an alternative. But now the spirit of revolt was in the air. There was a vague impression of impending changes that were to better the condition of the poor. Preparations were made to entertain Squire Woodbridge and other "silk-stockings" with a concert that would eclipse the entertainment of the night before.

Mrs. Woodbridge had long been very ill, and the uproar had left her in such a prostrated condition as to require medical attention. The doctor told her niece, Desire Edwards, that another sleepless night would be the end of her. His suggestion that Desire should make a personal appeal to the leader of the mob to stop the annoyance was treated by her with scorn; but after his departure she thought better of it, and made her way to Perez Hamlin's home. Perez had not seen her since she had kissed him good-by, and in the presence of her beauty and charm his former love flamed up anew. He promised to prevent the annoyance. With some difficulty he induced the mob not to make the intended demonstration at the Woodbridge house, though consenting that the sheriff should be treated to a little music.

The armed uprising at Great Barrington had occurred on Tuesday, but this was not followed by violent disturbances, although throughout those quiet and industrious communities the entire government machinery was at a standstill. Not a local magistrate undertook to sit, not a constable ventured to attempt an arrest, not a sheriff dared to serve a process or make an execution. On Friday evening the crowd at the tavern was in a far more jubilant mood than on the previous Friday. The "silk-stockings" were cowed, and not the least cause for rejoicing was the widely known fact that Desire Edwards had practically gone down upon her knees to ask a favor of Hamlin, the leader of the rebellion. On the following Sabbath, however, there was much comment on the fact that when Perez raised his hat to Desire as she came out of meeting, on the arm of her father, she cut him dead.

This painful shock, which so sharply ended Hamlin's brief delusion that Desire might possibly accept his devotion, roused him to a recognition of his critical situation and that of his family. He therefore determined to leave the State without delay, for the house that was to have been sold would undoubtedly go as soon as the insurrection quieted down; Reuben was liable to rearrest and imprisonment, and his own life was forfeit to the gallows for his part in the rebellion. Once across the State line, however, they would be safe.

Squire Woodbridge was anxious to recover the control of reins and whip before the return of Squire Sedgwick, whose warnings he had disdained. He took the first step toward this end by selling out a pestilent Baptist, with whom no one in the community could be expected to have any sympathy. But the effect was disappointing, for the mob reinstated the dispossessed man, and restored to him all his goods that had been bought in by the "silk-stockings" at auction. News came that practically the whole State was flaming with revolt on the question of "sueing and selling and sending to jail," and anarchy was practically organized. Orchards were robbed, fences burned, and an ingenious variety of petty outrages perpetrated. The "silk-stockings" hardly dared to go abroad, the least of the dangers they met being unripe apples and overripe eggs.

One day, when the "Regulators" met at the tavern, the landlady complained of their exclusive custom, and induced them to go over to Squire Edwards's store. There the drunken crowd forced the Squire and his son to treat them with rum and his daughter Desire to entertain them with the piano.

The next day Israel Goodrich and Ezra Phelps, two of the chief malcontents, called on Perez, to induce him to use his influence to prevent things from going too far. They said that Abner Rathbun didn't care how far the boys went against the aristocrats, and that Paul Hubbard, with his gang from the West Stockbridge iron-works, was egging on the fellows to burn fences and stone houses, and had actually tried to get them to tar-and-feather the Squire. The village doctor also came on the same errand, but Perez gave them all the same answer: he intended to take his family to York State, and must refuse to interfere. At this crisis news arrived of further rebel victories in the lower counties. The Government's weakness was manifest in the fact that it did not dare call upon the militia. Shays's Rebellion had manifested strength and boldness within a few hours' march of Boston; and the jubilation of the Stockbridge mob was expressed in further excesses. In the midst of the pandemonium Mrs. Woodbridge died; but her brother, Squire Edwards, dared not refuse to serve the mob with liquor when they again invaded his store. The funeral brought together all the gentry of the county, and this afforded an opportunity for a council of war after the obsequies, at which the widower outlined a plan for arresting Perez, Abner, and others, and making a public example of them. The news of the plot was conveyed to Perez by an Indian girl friendly to the Hamlin household. A counterplot was quickly formed. Perez woke up fifty of the most determined rebels; and when morning dawned armed men were on guard at the street corners, the arms and ammunition of the militia had been seized, and the hated aristocrats were the prisoners of their intended victims! When Perez faced the villagers in the morning, a shout of acclamation was the popular ratification of the night's work.

But the rebels were horrified when he announced his intention of publicly whipping the "silk-stockings," as they had planned to whip him. He was not to be turned from his purpose by the entreaties of the parson, and it needed the personal entreaties of Desire Edwards to save her father, uncle, and the other gentry from the lash, stocks, and pillory. Knowing his infatuation for her, she offered to let Perez kiss her if he would release her father; but it required all his influence over the mob to force it to do his will, when he yielded to her prayer.

When Squire Sedgwick returned with grave news of the progress of the Shays Rebellion at Springfield and elsewhere, he was mockingly introduced by the town doctor to the Duke of Stockbridge, Captain Hamlin, to whom the court party temporarily were indebted for their lives and liberties. Thenceforward Perez was known as " the Duke of Stockbridge."

Squire Sedgwick reported that the militia had gone over to the insurgents, and that weakness left the Government no choice but to adopt a temporary policy of conciliation with the rabble. An extra session of the legislature had been called to pass measures for relief.

The elation which the news produced among the people was prodigious. Perez doubled the patrols to keep order, but even then had to wink at many acts of lawlessness. Squire Edwards was glad to purchase immunity by indiscriminate treating of the crowd.

The upper classes indeed had come to regard "the Duke" in the light of a protector, and appealed to him on all occasions when they were likely to suffer from the persecutions of the mob. Squire Edwards was glad of his presence and good-will on several occasions, and did not even resent his conduct when once he had the audacity to kiss Desire in her mother's presence.

"There was really a good deal more than a joke in calling Perez 'the Duke of Stockbridge.' The guard-house was often half full of a morning with gentlemen, and those of lower degree as well, waiting to see him with requests. Some wanted passes, or authority to go out of town, or to carry goods away.

In addition to this, he had the military affairs of the insurgent train-band to direct, besides transacting business with messengers from Captain Shays, who already had begun to call on the Berkshire towns for quotas to swell the rebel forces, of which a regular military organization was now being attempted."

When Perez visited her father's store, Desire usually kept out of his way. Finally, however, she wheedled out of him a pass for a trip to Pittsfield; but her carriage was stopped and she was brought back by Perez's devoted Indian follower, who had learned how broken-hearted his chief was at her departure. On one occasion Squire Edwards induced Desire to attend a husking-bee for the sake of currying favor with the lower orders, in order to help his business interests. While there, Perez protected her from insult and escorted her home, after which she began to regard him more favorably.

On Thanksgiving Day the parson ended his sermon by reading a proclamation by the Governor, offering pardon to all who would take the oath of allegiance to the State before January the first, with a threat of dire penalties to those that failed to do so. The mob burned the Governor in effigy on the green that night, but the feeling of the community was growing lukewarm toward rebellion. In the lower counties, all the talk was of pardon and terms of submission. The rebels lost ground daily in Stockbridge, and Hamlin was losing control over his own followers. Laws were passed that alleviated the worst of the popular distress, and the people had had quite enough of anarchy. One by one, all but the most desperate of Perez's followers fell away, till one day he found the guard-house in possession of the deputy-sheriff. Mounting his horse and calling at the store to insist on a moment's farewell of Desire, he just managed to escape to the hills.

Up in the hills the rebels held out for a while, but when the militia advanced against them, though practically trapped, the latter were saved by the presence of mind of Squire Sedgwick, whose harangue resulted in the rebels throwing down their arms. The militia returned to Stockbridge with a hundred prisoners to grace the triumph of a bloodless victory. But severity to the conquered would have been a fatal policy; and

the prisoners were released that very afternoon on taking the
oath of allegiance to the State. As a climax, news was received
the same evening of the rout of the rebels under Shays at
Springfield.

The victorious muster represented the wealth, culture, and
aristocracy of all Berkshire; and there was such an excess of
beaux in Stockbridge that every girl of family had half a dozen.
As for Desire Edwards, she captivated the whole army. The
young militia officers and gentlemen privates thought her
adorable, and she found it very agreeable to queen it over so
devoted a court. She came to regard her former tolerance of
Perez's attentions with self-contemptuous reproach. Nevertheless, when she overheard, one snowy night, plans for an
expedition to surprise and capture Perez and his remaining
followers, she slipped out of the back door in her evening-dress,
with only a shawl thrown over her head, and tramped through
deep snow to the Hamlin home to give warning of the expedition, and to supply Reuben with the countersign.

Reuben reached his brother in the hills in time to warn him
of the expected attack at dawn. When the troops arrived,
therefore, they found the rebels drawn up to receive them. To
their dismay, they were crowded together in a road between
high snow-banks and in front of them was a cannon with a
brazier of coals by the breech, beside which Abner Rathbun
was brandishing a pair of tongs in readiness to discharge it.
The column halted and Perez came forward for a parley. The
commander of the attacking force, being caught at such a disadvantage, was glad to agree to the terms imposed, namely,
that the rebels should be allowed to disperse and go home, and
be immune from future arrest or molestation. Perez agreed
also to surrender the artillery, which, on examination, proved
to be merely a yarn-beam mounted on a pair of ox-cart wheels,
with the tongue of the cart resting on the ground behind.

Not long afterward, Perez made a sudden descent on
Stockbridge with his few remaining followers. In a night raid
they looted the houses of the wealthy, and Perez appealed in
vain to Desire Edwards to accompany him across the border.
With a broken heart, he again sought the fastnesses of the hills.
On his way through Great Barrington he emptied the jail of

imprisoned debtors a second time, and found his brother
Reuben dead.   The militia were soon hot on the trail of the
rebels, who, being surrounded, made a last stand in the snow.
There, Abner Rathbun and the fallen "Duke of Stockbridge,"
his passionate, troubled heart freed forever from its burden,
met their death.

THÉRÈSE BENTZON

(MADAME BLANC)

(France, 1840–1907)

JACQUELINE (1893)

The French Academy officially crowned the novel *Jacqueline* as the greatest masterpiece of fiction produced in France in 1893. The author, Madame Blanc, or Thérèse Bentzon as she has always called herself in literature, was already recognized as the foremost living woman novelist in France. Three of her novels had previously received the Academy's crown, each as the most notable work of its class written during the year of its publication, and her translations of Dickens, Bret Harte, Aldrich, and Ouida into French had added notably to her reputation as a scholar. *Jacqueline*, in company with the other Academy-crowned novels, has been sumptuously published both in French and in English under the sanction and supervision of the Academy.

JACQUELINE was the fifteen-year-old daughter of the Baron de Nailles. Her stepmother, whom she wellnigh worshiped, dressed and treated her as a child two or three years younger. The Baroness, a typical Parisienne a little more than thirty years old, had no mind to let her stepdaughter, who promised to be radiantly beautiful, develop too soon a womanhood that might rival and even eclipse her own. But she petted the girl beyond reason, and the two were comrades of the most lovingly intimate sort, except in society, from whose contamination the elder woman jealously guarded the younger, under the plea that she was only a child.

The Baron was completely subject to his womankind. At his wife's suggestion and largely by her influence, he had become a deputy in the Corps Legislatif, though personally he cared nothing for politics. Also at her instigation, though she concealed the fact even from him, he became a speculator on

the Bourse. He had before been content with his ample country estate, but it became necessary to speculate in order to meet
the cost of his wife's way of living.

In a half childish, half womanly way, Jacqueline had fallen
in love with Hubert Marien, a great painter, who was an intimate of the family. He had petted her in her actual childhood, but of late he had adopted a coldly critical and sarcastic
tone in his intercourse with her. Under tutelage of an English
novel which she had been allowed to read, Jacqueline attributed
Marien's changed manner to a consciousness of love for a girl
too far above him in rank for him to have hope of winning.
Around this thought her inexperienced fancy built up a romance
that prompted her to keep as souvenirs of him an old glove, a
cigarette stump, and other objects that had been glorified to
her imagination by his touch.

At one of the Baroness's receptions, where Jacqueline was
kept in a bow-window in company with a number of other
girls too young to be permitted to listen to the scandalous gossip
of the salon, Marien stared admiringly at the girl, and when
she challenged him to explain, he suggested that she seemed
old enough now to justify him in painting her portrait as a young
woman. He immediately added something, however, which
seemed to postpone the matter to some indefinite time in the
future, but the girl cherished the thought and resolved to bring
about the thing she so ardently desired. To have her portrait
painted by the great master, to appear in it as a young woman
of ravishing beauty, would emancipate her from her bondage
to childhood. And—who could tell?—in posing to Marien,
might she not reveal to him a charm of which he was only half
conscious, and teach him to understand his own feeling regarding her?

She laid her plans accordingly, making her father her co-
conspirator. They would have the portrait painted in secret
and present it to her "little mamma" on her birthday.

When the Baron discussed the matter with Marien, the
painter strangely and strongly objected, but the Baron's in-
sistence was so great that his consent was unavoidable.

Secretly Jacqueline prepared her costume for the posing,
and so great was the change wrought by it in her appearance

that the painter completely fell in love with his sitter, and in effect told her so at the last, though with a reserve and embarrassment which her romantic fancy found it easy to explain.

When the picture was unveiled before the Baroness, that lady fell into an inexplicable passion which reduced both Jacqueline and her father to a state of apologetic contrition. It was decreed that the portrait should be banished to their country home, by way of appeasing a wrath on the part of the Baroness which neither of the other persons concerned could understand. The Baroness was unrelenting in her offended mood, and Jacqueline, in her distress, determined to creep upon her "mamma," throw her arms about her, and caress her into forgiveness.

In her effort to do this, Jacqueline overheard a passionate interview between the Baroness and Marien, in which the latter was pleading for forgiveness for painting the unlucky portrait, and employing many terms of endearment inconsistent with any conception that the girl possessed of relations proper or possible between a married woman and a man not her husband.

Even then the girl did not fully understand. Her acquaintance with wickedness was too slight for that, for the reason that she had read none but English novels. But she understood enough. She was passionately angry with the Baroness for the wrong done to her father. But she said clearly that to go to the Baron with her information would be only to make matters worse.

Marien, in his eagerness to placate the Baroness, had said contemptuous, belittling things of Jacqueline, which she had overheard, and her girlish love changed to hate. She burned her souvenirs of him and resolved to be mistress of the situation. As reconciliation slowly came to the rest, Jacqueline avenged herself and made the guilty pair afraid by sly utterances that revealed her possession of some secret, without revealing the extent of the limitations of her knowledge.

Marien, meanwhile, had his punishment apart from the pin pricks of Jacqueline's inflicting. He really loved the girl, whom he must ostentatiously give up, and he had grievously tired of his *liaison* with the Baroness, who was in no wise minded to let him escape from her jealous clutches. She

planned a family excursion to Italy, in which he should be an
unwilling participant.

Unable to understand fully the relations between her stepmother and Marien, Jacqueline abstracted French novels from
the library shelves and read them, at once to her enlightenment
and her sore disgust.

In her distress of mind—partly wholesome and partly sentimental—she visited her cousin Giselle de Monredon, who was
a pupil in a Bénédictine convent, and deeply imbued with conventual ideas. Giselle gave her good advice, and for a time
she was disposed not only to follow it but to go further and retire for all time into a convent.

The Baroness, warned by Jacqueline's persistence in making remarks which revealed her possession of dangerous knowledge, decided at last upon placative measures, and under her
instruction the Baron set about to make his daughter happy.
He took her to a riding-school, ordered riding costumes for her
which emphasized the beauty of her figure, and quickly weaned
her soul from its impulse toward the conventual life. Then he
proposed for her a season of sea bathing and enjoyment at
Tréport.

There she fell in with other girls, and the little company ran
wild, to the scandalizing of all the dowagers, though in fact they
did nothing wrong. They were nicknamed "the Blue Band."

Within a mile or two of Tréport lay Lizerolles, the estate
of Madame d'Argy, a distant cousin to Jacqueline. Jacqueline
had long ago discovered that Madame d'Argy and the Baroness
de Nailles were not congenial, though they maintained the
fiction of friendship and even of intimacy. It was apparent
that Madame d'Argy disapproved of Madame de Nailles, and
only now did Jacqueline begin to guess the reason.

Madame d'Argy's son Fred, a young naval officer, was at
home on furlough at this time, and he was much with the girls
of the Blue Band. He fell madly in love with his cousin Jacqueline, who persisted in regarding him as a mere boy, not in
the reckoning with older men, who had seen something of the
world and could talk glibly of their actress acquaintances and
the like.

Giselle de Monredon—the convent-bred girl into whose ears

Jacqueline had recently poured her woes, and to whom she had revealed her momentary impulse to take the veil—was brought to Tréport by her grandmother, who had betrothed her to Monsieur de Talbrun, owner of an estate adjoining her own. M. de Talbrun was thirty-five years old, prematurely bald, coarse in fiber, and altogether repulsive in the eyes of the *spirituelle* Giselle, who nevertheless entertained no thought of resisting her grandmother's will in the matter of this unwelcome marriage. M. de Talbrun held it to be the duty of women to be always well and lively, and Giselle's grandmother hoped to make her so by a season at Tréport, where she might also become acquainted with her future husband in the greater freedom of intercourse permitted at the seaside.

M. de Talbrun was therefore thrown into the society of the Blue Band girls, and his presence quickly undermined young Fred d'Argy's favor, while it in no way changed Giselle from the shrinking convent-bred, submissive girl that she was. Her efforts were directed solely to the object of avoiding close association with the man she was presently to marry. His manifest admiration for Jacqueline pleased Giselle instead of offending her, but it grievously offended Fred d'Argy.

Madame de Villegry, a gay Parisienne, was also at Tréport. So was the Count de Cymier, her admirer, her worshiper indeed, so far as the Count could worship anybody but himself. For reasons of prudence Madame de Villegry wished to detach Cymier from herself, and to that end she sought to interest him in Jacqueline, whom he greatly admired for her beauty, and concerning whose *dot* he made quiet inquiries of the banker Wermant. Strongly supported by Madame de Villegry, and not less strongly, for reasons of her own, by Madame de Nailles, Cymier made fierce love to Jacqueline, taking care, however, not to committ himself to any definite proposal of marriage. Fred d'Argy went back to his ship disconsolate, his mother meantime urging his suit for him in every way she could, partly for his sake and partly in the hope that he might give up his place in the navy and settle down, with Jacqueline as his wife, at Lizerolles. Separation from her boy, and the thought that he might be exposed to danger, were the nightmares of Madame d'Argy's soul.

It was arranged that Jacqueline should pass some months at Lizerolles, as the guest of Madame d'Argy, while her father and the Baroness should make the Italian journey in company with Marien. During that time she corresponded with Fred in a fashion that drove him wellnigh mad because of the enigmatical attitude she assumed. In his vexed perturbation of spirit, poor Fred wrote poetry, which Jacqueline cruelly criticized in a letter after rejoining her parents in Paris.

There, when his cruise was done, Fred met her again at a charity bazaar. She was more beautiful than ever, dazzlingly, dangerously beautiful, Fred thought, and his judgment was confirmed by the admirers that swarmed about her, among whom the Count de Cymier was most in evidence, most aggressive, most impudent, Fred thought. Jacqueline was engrossed in social frivolity and had formed the dangerous acquaintance of a bohemian set—a certain Madame Wanda Strahlberg, her mother, Madame Odinska, and her sister Colette, with others of their kind.

Fred, feeling himself repulsed at his first meeting with Jacqueline, betook himself to his old friend Giselle (now Madame de Talbrun), who was about to become a mother; and at her hands he received soothing advice and encouragement. Above all else she urged him to consider Jacqueline's youth, and advised him to go away and win his commission as ensign before venturing again to approach the subject of marriage. Fred acted upon the advice, and during his long absence both Giselle and Madame d'Argy urged his suit with the Baron and Baroness de Nailles. It was all to no purpose, for the reason that they had every hope of achieving the greater alliance with the Count de Cymier, who continued, in an inconclusive way, to pay court to Jacqueline.

After an absence of two years Fred returned, bearing a routine promotion, and, in spite of her efforts to prevent it, he declared his love to Jacqueline. She rejected him, and, with a heart that he sincerely believed to be broken, he sought and secured orders to go to Tonquin, where fierce war was then in progress, and where, as he romantically hoped, he might meet a welcome death.

Jacqueline's feelings over this were mixed. She was

childishly vain of the fact that she had power thus to drive a young man to desperation, and she hoped that the fact might enhance her value as a prize in the eyes of the Count de Cymier. But she sincerely cared for Fred d'Argy, and in secret bewailed the event she had brought about. Added to this regret was her consciousness that her course had angered both Madame d'Argy and Giselle, and had seriously displeased her father.

She found relief in participation in some private theatricals which Madame d'Avrigny was planning, after her frequent custom. She was to play a leading part with the Count de Cymier, in which he was to kiss her twice, a part of the performance which he insisted upon acting realistically at rehearsal. She was to sing a song, the words of which seemed to her stupid only because she was too innocent to understand them as did those others, who greeted them with ribald and uproarious applause.

Just as she was rendering this song at dress rehearsal she was hastily summoned home, and there she found her father dead of a sudden attack of heart trouble.

As she knelt in passionate grief by the bed on which her dead father lay, she was wounded to the heart by the sight of Hubert Marien there, still posing as a "friend of the family."

The death of the Baron was quickly followed by the revelation that not only his own fortune but Jacqueline's also had gone, swallowed up in the speculations by which the dead man had desperately tried to provide the means for that style of living upon which Madame de Nailles had insisted.

In the midst of her grief and terror, Jacqueline was ashamed to find herself wondering how Gérard de Cymier would behave at this crisis, and hoping that he would now generously come forward with the proposal of marriage which had been so unmistakably promised by his attentions to her during two years.

But the Count de Cymier found himself suddenly called to Vienna, as he told her stepmother in an over-effusive letter of sympathy and meaningless condolence.

Foreseeing that her stepmother would presently compel Marien to marry her—for she understood the relations of these two now—Jacqueline felt that she could no longer live with

Madame de Nailles, yet she knew not whither she could go. Giselle urged her to go to Lizerolles and so did its mistress, Madame d'Argy, who was eager to end the estrangement now that sorrow had fallen upon Jacqueline, and especially now that Fred had so distinguished himself in battle as to have won the ribbon of Chevalier of the Legion of Honor.

But Jacqueline declined the invitation, feeling that she could not seem to seek, at a time of misfortune, that which she had rejected at a happier time. Madame d'Argy attributed her refusal to unworthy motives, and her feeling of offense was deep.

Under Giselle's advice, Jacqueline retired to a convent and began a course of study which was to qualify her as a teacher. For three months she did not quit the place except when Giselle came with her little boy to take her for a drive. Then she began her work as a teacher, going to the house of one old acquaintance after another to give lessons. After a little time her employers grew indifferent, and one by one they dismissed her upon various pretexts.

When the time came for Giselle de Talbrun to leave town, she begged Jacqueline to go with her to the Château de Fresne, and there the girl rapidly recovered her health and spirits. M. de Talbrun promptly fell in love with the guest, after a brutal fashion, and one day, a month or two later, he made insulting approaches during a horseback journey. When she repelled his advances he endeavored to embrace her by force; she struck him across the face with her riding-whip, and rode at speed toward the château, with De Talbrun in close pursuit.

She could explain nothing to Giselle; she could only take her leave and return to Paris, excusing her sudden departure by the fiction that her old nurse, Modeste, was very ill—a story Giselle did not believe, because she knew her husband too well.

Without fault of her own, Jacqueline was now cut off even from her intimacy with Giselle, and no friendship was left to her in all the world but that of old Modeste; while her stepmother, thanks to the compulsory generosity of Hubert Marien, was living luxuriously.

Jacqueline returned to the convent and tried to resume her music teaching, but her pupils were few for lack of influence.

One day, as she was returning to the convent after a lesson, she encountered her old bohemian acquaintance, Wanda Strahlberg, the daughter of Madame Odinska and sister of Colette. Madame Strahlberg immediately carried her to the ill-regulated Odinska residence, where music, feasting, and unrestrained jollity dominated at all hours. Jacqueline was fairly forced to take a part in the entertainment, at the end of which she found that it was past the hour at which the convent required all its inmates to be within the gates. Notwithstanding her explanations and pleadings next day, the poor girl was forbidden to resume her residence there, except for a few days, during which she might search for some other refuge.

She found it with a family of rich, vulgar Americans, a Mr. Sparks, who had begun life as a barkeeper in California, and his daughters, whom Jacqueline had learned to know as members of the Blue Band at Tréport. They were going to Bellagio. Miss Sparks, who did not want an elderly chaperone, employed Jacqueline to go with her as a companion. Madame de Nailles did not interfere, as Marien urged her to do. She knew that Jacqueline knew too much of her affairs for safety; she wished to be rid of the girl, but she did not wish for an open rupture. In that case Jacqueline might tell certain things. It would be more convenient to let the wayward girl ruin herself. Marien grieved, and his conscience reproached him; but he dared not do anything.

About this time Fred d'Argy was ordered home. His mother, indignant with Jacqueline, told him everything as she understood it. He went again to Giselle (Madame de Talbrun) for consolation, and in all sincerity she gave it. But by this time she was herself an unloved and unhappy wife, and her intimacy with Fred was dangerous to her peace of mind, in spite of her own resolute loyalty to her marital obligations. It was only after a time, however, that the good Giselle discovered her own danger and struggled with it.

Jacqueline soon found herself in revolt against the servitude of her position as the companion of Nora Sparks, whose conduct she disapproved, greatly to that young person's displeasure.

When the rupture came, Jacqueline decided to study for the musical stage, and to that end she wished to consult Wanda

Strahlberg, who was staying at Monaco, surrounded as usual
by her bohemian circle. She received Jacqueline effusively,
but presently Jacqueline found herself in a trap. By Wanda
Strahlberg's procurement, Gérard de Cymier was an inmate
of the household. He had abandoned all pretense of a desire
to make Jacqueline his wife, but he had abated no part of his
desire to possess her in a less honorable relation, and Jacqueline
was quick to discover that all arrangements had been made
for her entrapment. She slipped out of the house, abandoning
her personal belongings, and fled to the protection of her old
nurse, Modeste, as she had no other refuge.

Then came a story in the newspapers that a duel had occurred between Fred d'Argy and Gérard de Cymier, in which
Fred had received a sword wound in the arm. The newspapers
quickly revealed the truth that Jacqueline was the subject of
the quarrel, that De Cymier had boasted of her as a prospective conquest, that Fred had given him the lie, and that
Fred, implacable, had demanded a second meeting, to be held
as soon as his wound should be healed.

Jacqueline was shocked and frightened. She hurried to
the house of Madame d'Argy, only to be repulsed. Only Giselle
remained to her, and when Jacqueline went to her residence
and refused to accept "Not at home" as an answer, Giselle
sent word that she would not see her visitor. Giselle was already
incensed at Jacqueline's rejection of Fred's honest, manly love,
and she was outraged now that Jacqueline's conduct, of which
she believed the worst, had involved Fred in danger and scandal.
The platonic friendship between Giselle and Fred d'Argy had
grown warmer on the woman's part than she had realized until
now; but Giselle was tender-hearted, and, though she had
refused to receive Jacqueline, she went to her at last in her
distress. Her motives were complex, but the visit brought
about explanations that cleared Jacqueline from the worst suspicions, and awakened in the mind of the conscientious Giselle
a new realization of the necessity of saving herself from the
consequences of her own still innocent but perilous relations
with Fred d'Argy. Discovering that Jacqueline really loved
Fred, and knowing already that Fred's love for Jacqueline was
unabated, Giselle set herself to bring about reconciliation and

marriage between the two. The task was difficult, for Madame d'Argy had become implacably resentful toward Jacqueline; but with the aid of a good priest, and by the exercise of a diplomacy worthy of a far more worldly woman, Giselle succeeded at last in saving both herself and those she loved. The marriage of M. Frédéric d'Argy, Chevalier of the Legion of Honor, to Mademoiselle Jacqueline de Nailles was announced, and there was everywhere rejoicing in what was so obviously a love match, a thing so rare in France in modern times.

Nora Sparks sent a costly wedding present from New York. The Count de Cymier sent to Fred d'Argy a written apology and retraction of his utterance concerning Jacqueline, which averted all necessity of a second duel. Madame the Baroness de Nailles behaved with exquisite propriety, issuing wedding announcements in her own name. Fred d'Argy, to his mother's delight, resigned his commission in the navy, and settled himself at Lizerolles in summer and at his Paris home in winter.

Giselle de Talbrun was the least demonstrative of all those who rejoiced in the happy event.

BESANT AND RICE

(Walter Besant, England, 1836-1901; James Rice, 1846-1882)

READY-MONEY MORTIBOY (1871)

This novel, written in collaboration with James Rice, was the first work by Walter Besant (afterward Sir Walter Besant) to attract attention. Later he ceased collaborating and produced alone some of his best known works.

R. RICHARD MATTHEW MORTIBOY, better known as "Ready-Money Mortiboy," was already the richest banker and most stingy and grasping man in his native town of Market Basing, England, when his sister died and left him twenty-five thousand pounds, with the sole condition that he should keep her memory alive by placing a memorial window in the parish church. Mortiboy was past sixty and a widower; he had driven his only son from home twelve years before, with only ten pounds in his pocket, for the crime of forging a small check, so the old man was not oppressed by family expenses; yet the possible expense of a memorial window troubled him so greatly that on the night following his sister's funeral he went into the churchyard to estimate the size and cost of this money-wasting requirement.

Just as he turned to retrace his steps, a hand like a blacksmith's fell on his shoulder, held him in a vise, and guided him homeward. Mortiboy might have shouted for help, had not the stranger intimated that he could tell something about the absent son, for whom, strange though it would have seemed to anyone in Market Basing, the father cherished steadily a strong affection and longing. The hand, which by the light of a clouded moon was seen to belong to a bearded stranger, tall and strong, in a pilot-jacket and with a stout stick in his hand,

34

guided the banker into his own house and through it to the
kitchen, where the stranger sat down before the fire and asked:

"Would you like to hear that your son Dick, very early in
his history after leaving you, saw the many errors of his way and
reformed; that he became steady, industrious, and respectable;
that, in short, he got money and is consequently much revered
and respected by all good men?"

"I should!" the old man exclaimed. "Good heavens
man! if this is what you have to tell me, be quick about it."

Little by little the stranger disclosed his identity and proved
that he himself was the long-lost Dick; his most convincing
evidence was full payment, with compound interest, of the
forged check and also of the ten-pound note with which he was
cast off. The father was convinced and shook hands with his
son, but not quite cordially; suppose that Dick were a ne'er-
do-well and had come home to borrow money and perhaps
live on his father? But when the young man, whose face and
manner were impressive, talked like a man of affairs, spoke of
mining interests, of some money invested in Mexico, and a half
interest in a cotton plantation of three thousand acres, carelessly displayed a traveler's money-belt heavy with gold coin,
and expressed willingness to make some modest investments
under parental advice, the banker's heart grew warm.

Dick had been a great traveler before he settled down to
cotton-planting, and he showed his father curiosities from many
parts of the world; gay apparel from Nicaragua, an Indian's
poisoned arrows, the pistol with which he had shot the Indian;
a dagger given him by the King of Dahomey; cotton-bolls from
his plantation; silver ore from a mine owned by himself and
his partner, which would make them rich as soon as they could
spare ten thousand pounds with which to work it; a great
nugget of pure gold, and, most interesting of all, a chart showing
the position of a wrecked treasure-ship containing gold and
silver bullion worth half a million dollars. Dick said he had
seen the ship himself, and would recover the treasure as soon
as he could divert from the plantation's funds six or seven
thousand dollars with which to charter a ship and employ divers.

The banker's imagination took possession of the silver mine
and sunken treasure and held them fast. Even a well-to-do

cotton planter perhaps could not easier spare enough of his working capital to finance enterprises so large, so why should not old Mortiboy himself take them in hand as banker, director, manager, and perhaps owner, in the course of time? Besides, Dick's confidence in his business projects was infectious; his insight, audacity, and vigor dazzled the old man. Dick was handsome and hearty, too; everybody in Market Basing admired him at sight; he was friendly to all his old acquaintances, affectionate to his many relatives, and respectful and deferential to his father.

It is sad to relate that Dick was also an adventurer, a gambler, a ruffian, and perhaps a murderer; he had no mining or plantation interests anywhere nor much money besides that in his pocket and his belt, and he had come to England with a heart full of hatred for his father and a determination to get by trickery or robbery a large portion of the old man's money. He had for accomplice one Alcide Lafleur, the man to whom he frequently alluded as his partner; Lafleur and he had been jailbirds together in the West Indies and slavers afterward. Lafleur had devised a "system" that should break any gambling house in the world; it had already succeeded in a small way, but the partners never had had enough capital for great operations; hence the desire for some of old Mortiboy's surplus. They never had quarreled with each other, for Lafleur always needed a strong man to lean upon, while Dick, despite a genius for lying, was never untrue to a promise; he never was suspicious, and his energy, courage, and good temper were unfailing. What rogue could quarrel with such a partner?

But some unexpected incidents suddenly dulled old Mortiboy's acquisitive spirit and weakened his grasp of business details. Mr. Melliship, his brother-in-law and only rival in the banking business, committed suicide, and a run on his bank reduced his family to poverty. A sympathetic run on Mortiboy's own bank gave the old man a great fright until Dick devised a trick which dazzled and pacified the depositors. Mortiboy's gratitude was unbounded, but his purse-strings remained as tightly drawn as ever; he even made Dick pay for his food and shelter under the paternal roof. Meanwhile, Lafleur was urgent in his demands for money with which to play the System on a large scale. If the old man would not invest in any of Dick's glittering enterprises, some of his money must be taken without his consent.

So the partners planned, as coolly as if one of them was not the banker's only son, that Dick should give Lafleur casts of his father's keys, and on a certain night he was to drop a sleeping potion, not dangerously strong, into the old man's grog; then Lafleur, whose ways were soft and cat-like, should enter the house, unlock an iron-doored closet in Mortiboy's room, and help himself to some of the coin which the banker, miser-like, always kept where he could look at it and gloat over it.

But on the very day of the contemplated *coup* Dick was startled into temporary irresolution by his father making over to him in full legal form, and before witnesses, all his property, including the bank and its holdings of every description. This transfer made the young man worth half a million pounds, yet he could not take possession quickly enough to comply with Lafleur's demand, which was for a very large sum. Besides, he doubted his father's sincerity as he had always doubted his affection; much mental reviewing of his youth and his father's coldness, meanness, and cruelty to him had caused him to look forward gleefully to the old man's misery when he should learn of the robbery. In his excitement he forgot to administer the sleeping potion, but as he was a man of his word he took Lafleur's keys, opened the iron doors himself, and began to toss bags of gold on the table. The noise roused the old man, who shouted:

"Thieves! Murder! Dick! Murder! Dick!"

"Yes, it is Dick. Don't be alarmed, father. I am helping myself to a little of my own property; that is all." Then he seated himself on the edge of the bed, candlestick in hand, looked into the old man's face, and continued:

"It is quite as well, father, that we should understand each other. All your property is mine; I can do what I like with it; consequently, what I like with you. I shall not be hard on you. What you gave me when I was nineteen I will give you now that you are getting on toward seventy; an old man does not want so much as a boy, so the bargain is a good one for you. A pound a week shall be paid to you, with your board and lodging, and as much drink as you can put away. The pound begins to-morrow."

Dick said much more. He admitted that he had lied industriously ever since his return, and that he had no mine, no cotton plantation, no investments. He compared his own life with his father's, and asserted that he had been the better man of the two. But before he finished his father had groaned and become a speechless paralytic. Naturally, he did not come down to breakfast in the morning; except for his breathing he would have been called dead. Dick called in all the physicians in the place, and when they declared the case hopeless he expressed great sorrow and arranged for careful nursing. All men praised Dick for his filial goodness and congratulated old "Ready-Money," or his memory, on having a son gifted with such a remarkable sweetness of disposition, and so singular an affection for a father in whom no one else had ever been able to discern anything lovable.

Yet Dick had a heart and a good share of common-sense, and he began at once to use both for the benefit of everyone who had suffered by his father's meanness. He raised all salaries at the bank; helped out of trouble a young forger whose experience had been very like his own; was charitable in a large-hearted yet practical manner, and made everybody his friend as well as his admirer. He was unwearying in efforts to help his cousin Frank Melliship, son of the banker-suicide, for the elder Melliship's troubles had come of greater generosity than the resources of his bank could maintain. He fell in love with Frank's sweetheart, but when the girl refused him he continued to love her in an honorable manner. He suppressed all the bad inclinations which twelve years of lawlessness had fixed in his nature, and longed to become entirely honest as well as respectable. Conscience gave him no pangs, for he was unaware of the existence of such a thing.

Only two people blocked his progress toward a blameless future. One was a woman whom he had married secretly before his father drove him from home; the other was his partner Lafleur, to whom the System had been unkind, in spite of the great sum with which he had backed it. The woman was disposed of by proof that she already had a husband when she married Dick. But Lafleur still needed some one to lean upon; he knew that Dick's changed circumstances made it necessary that the partnership should be dissolved, yet he begged that Dick, with plenty of money, should accompany him to one of the greatest gambling-places in Europe where together they would break the bank. Dick refused; he offered Lafleur a large sum of money if he would go to America and remain there. Regarding the System he said:

"I am not surprised that it has broken down; they always do. No man ever yet could invent, or will invent, a scheme to meet the chances of luck. When it isn't luck it is skill."

Lafleur turned white. Tell a gambler that his scheme is a mistake and a delusion and you will madden him. Lafleur felt compelled to accept Dick's offer, with its conditions, yet he lingered. He begged a glass of brandy and then asked for a game of euchre, saying it might be that they never would have another opportunity to play together. Dick consented, but the Frenchman lost steadily; he took more brandy, but he continued to lose. Suddenly Dick brought down his hand heavily on the sleeve of his adversary's coat, from which he took a knave, the best card at euchre.

"Swindler!" Dick cried. "You would cheat even me!" He pushed back his chair, turned over the table, and flung the cards in Lafleur's face. "Give me back my check! I am done with you."

There was a struggle; Lafleur fired a pistol-shot from his pocket, and Dick fell forward on his face. Assuring himself that his partner was dead, and placing the pistol in the fallen man's hand Lafleur stole softly away. Yet Dick still had a few moments to live when he was found by some boys whom he had befriended. A physician was summoned and he pronounced the wound fatal; to him Dick slowly dictated:

"I—Richard—Melliship—Mortiboy—declare that I—have —accidentally shot myself while preparing to clean my pistol." Loyal to his old partner to the very last, he died with a lie on his lips to save him. He also dictated a letter which was in effect his will, giving everything to Frank Melliship's sweetheart, whom Dick still loved, with the request that Frank and the bank's manager should be partners and "Let the money go back to the poor as much as may be." Then he gasped in broken sentences:

"Tell my father—ah, it's no use now to tell him anything. I shall tell him myself."

On the afternoon of that same day old Mortiboy fell very ill, but at the very hour of Dick's taking-off his power of speech was restored. He spoke but three words:—"My—son—Dick!" and lay there dead.

WALTER BESANT

(England, 1836-1901)

ALL SORTS AND CONDITIONS OF MEN (1884)

The People's Palace of London, an institution for the instruction and entertainment of the working-classes, owes its origin to this book, which roused a very wide interest on its appearance, and caused Mr. Besant to be knighted. This institution has a great significance among the movements of the time and is credited with accomplishing much toward uplifting the lives of the poor by introducing an element of beauty, comfort, and inspiration otherwise unattainable.

 FEW years ago, when the higher education of women was the newest of new things in old England, Miss Angela Messenger, of Newnham College, astonished her fellow-students by pouring contempt upon political economy, in which science she had just passed a brilliant examination. She asserted that it was not a science at all, but a collection of theories impossible of proof; it treated men and women as skittles, ignored the principles of action, and had been put together by doctrinaires who lived apart and knew nothing about men and less about women.

Such an announcement by an ordinary Newnham girl might have been attributed to uncertain nerves, temper, age, prospects, or a combination of these. But Angela Messenger was young, healthy, cheerful, and so fair to look upon that a young curate said her face made him understand what Solomon meant when he compared his love's temples to a piece of pomegranate within her locks. She had inherited a great London brewery employing almost a thousand men, and with an output in steady demand by hundreds of thousands more, while her rent-roll, securities, bank balances, and other possessions

41

were worth millions of pounds. Her social position, too, was all that a rich and brilliant girl could desire. Yet, in speaking of political economy, she exclaimed to a friend:

"I am weary of theories, facts, statistics. I want flesh and blood. I want to feel myself a part of this striving, eager, anxious humanity on whose labors I live in comfort, by whom I have been educated, to whom I owe all and for whom I have done nothing."

So, pretending to go to the country for a few months, Angela effaced herself by going to London's "East End," that great huddle of almost two million people, whose homes, surroundings, occupations and amusements are so commonplace as to attract the attention of no one in greater London or anywhere else. She made her home in a very decent and dreary boarding-house, and under an assumed name opened a dressmaking business for which everybody in the vicinity, her own employés included, predicted failure, for she gave facilities and time for recreation twice a day, provided her girls' dinners, gave them a sitting-room, with piano, for use in their leisure hours, and a share of the profits of the business in addition to their regular wages.

She endeavored to soften some of the asperities of life in her boarding-house also, where the people were as commonplace and shabby as the house itself. While doing so she was puzzled at finding something congenial in Harry Goslett, a young cabinet-maker with ideas and manners to which she had imagined all mechanics were strangers; still, he had been in the United States, where perhaps workingmen came of a higher strain of blood. Goslett, who had reasons for not telling the story of his life, was son of an army sergeant who was killed in the Crimean war. He had been brought up from infancy as an aristocrat and by an aristocrat, Lord Jocelyn le Breton, as an experiment, and the result had been quite satisfactory to the experimenter.

But when Harry learned of his extraction he insisted on going back to his own class, if for only a little while, to learn how they differed from the circle in which he had been reared. Some amateur handiness with tools qualified him to assume the trade at which no one in the East End had known him to practise, but he was unwearying in sympathy and assistance to Angela, the dressmaker, after he learned that she was philanthropist as well as tradeswoman, and that she wished that the lives of all people in the East End, as well as those of her own employés, might be made less monotonous and more enjoyable through means that were as honest a part of life as labor itself.

A charming woman with a soul can impart no end of inspiration to a young man of sense and heart, so when Harry suggested to Angela the dressmaker that it would be of great service to humanity if someone were to found what he called a "Palace of Delight,"—a building in which all the better arts, acquirements, and recreations known to the upper classes should be brought within reach of the mass of East End people who were too poor to provide such cheer for themselves, the heart of Angela the heiress was warmed to white heat, especially when Harry asked, with much feeling in his voice, whether the rich Miss Messenger, who had assisted the dressmaking enterprise, might not be persuaded to give a bit of the income of her brewery, her miles of houses at rental, and her millions of interest-drawing surplus, for a purpose so beneficent.

This brilliant idea was discussed in delightful detail for weeks by Harry and Angela, but the girl discovered, not without some dismay, that the young man was in her mind quite as much as the Palace of Delight. As for Harry, a clean-hearted youth, reared as a gentleman and accustomed to the society of ladies, could not help falling in love with the only rose in the garden of vegetables and weeds into which he had placed himself. Angela could not avoid seeing that he held her in at least as high esteem as the Palace of Delight, of which he could not speak without reverential longing, so she found it necessary to warn him, kindly but firmly, that they two were not "keeping company" in the East End sense of the expression, but were merely and honestly society for each other. And Harry accepted the situation manfully.

Meanwhile Angela the heiress and descendant of her grandfather, who, she said, was hard as nails, took counsel of her head, her lawyers, and her architects, and counted the cost of the Palace of Delight. Then an entire square of her houses in the East End disappeared, and a new and great building began to arise. Harry did not see it or hear of it, for

the East End is a city in area and without a building, park,
place of amusement or other structure that would incite a man
of taste to walk out and view it, or justify the city newspapers in mentioning it.

The details of construction and cost seem to have troubled
the dual Angela but little, for she found time to worry much
over Harry's apparent idleness. She made him understand
that she wished he would go to work; he replied that he was
willing, but he was not yet certain that the East End was his
proper place. He aspired to a shop in which he would be the
only worker; he might find one in some great establishment
elsewhere in London, or some other city. Or, there was America.
Then Angela discovered that she could not spare him, though
she did not say so. He admitted that he was willing to
remain in the East End if he could find satisfactory employment; the next day he was astonished by an offer of a shop
to himself in the great Messenger brewery.

The train of thought in which this offer placed him carried
him to his guardian, Lord Jocelyn, to whom he explained
frankly that he must remain near the scene of his birth, and all
for love of a lady — "a lady," Harry insisted, although she
was a dressmaker and would not allow him to unburden his
heart to her.

Lord Jocelyn was a man of the world; he had known all
sorts of young men to discover all sorts of perfections in all
sorts of girls, through the eyes of love. But he loved Harry
dearly, and his heart was so greatly troubled on his account
that on meeting Angela the heiress in society he told her the
story of his runaway ward, who was now a cabinet-maker in
Miss Messenger's own brewery, at tenpence an hour, and all for
love of a dressmaker who he declared was a lady and would
give him no encouragement. As he had declined to accept
any more of Lord Jocelyn's money, would not Miss Messenger
tax the resources of the brewery to raise the poor boy's hourly
wage to a full shilling?

But mere talk can not quiet a heart that contains a real
trouble. Lord Jocelyn's love for his ward was so sincere that
he journeyed to the East End to behold the counterfeit paragon
who had bewitched the boy. When he discovered that Angela

the dressmaker was also Angela the heiress, he rose to the
sympathy as well as the dignity appropriate to the occasion,
and listened with delight to much earnest talk about the Palace
of Delight and its real founder, who she insisted was Harry.

Lord Jocelyn's disclosure of Harry's infatuation and its
conditions taught Angela the heiress that she was being loved
for herself alone instead of for her money — an assurance for
which few rich girls dare hope. This assurance made the heart
of Angela the dressmaker much less obdurate; she promised
Harry, of her own accord, that if ever the time should come
when she and he might be more than mere acquaintances she
would tell him. Harry was greatly encouraged by another
incident: he recovered from a rascally uncle three houses
which his mother had inherited years before she died; he also
got two thousand pounds in satisfaction of rentals on these
houses for many years that had passed. By a strange coincidence, one of these buildings, the one in which Mr. Messenger,
founder of the fortune of Angela the heiress, was born, was that
in which Angela the dressmaker was conducting business, so
the young man hastened joyously to present the house to the
associated dressmakers and to offer his two thousand pounds
to begin the building of the long-planned Palace of Delight.

Angela declined the money; with tremulous voice she called
it a sacrifice, but she assured him that the palace which he—
really he—had planned would yet be an accomplished fact,
adding: "Perhaps the opening of this Palace will be the
beginning of a new happiness for all of us." So clearly does
heart speak to heart that Harry constructed "all of us" to
signify merely Angela and himself.

Soon afterward Angela asked Harry and her working girls
to accompany her for an evening walk. She guided them to
an immense building that none of them had ever seen before;
at a signal from her to some workmen in the vestibule, the building was flooded with light; and Angela conducted the wondering party through the various rooms of the completed Palace
of Delight — reception-room, theater, concert-hall, library,
gymnasium, smoking-room, billiard-room, art gallery, besides
rooms for instruction in arts, sciences, and accomplishments,
and she gave Harry full credit for it all and informed him that

he was to be the managing trustee. Apparently she had some special communication to make to him regarding the work, for she sent away her girls and the workmen, and had the lights extinguished so that only moonbeams lighted the room in which she and Harry stood. Then she whispered softly that on the Palace's opening day he and she might be married, if he liked.

So they were made husband and wife at a little East End church, before the sewing-girls and their friends, the boarding-house company, and Lord Jocelyn, who gave away the bride. Angela explained to her husband that out of respect for the great heiress, owner of the brewery, whose money had paid for the Palace, she must spend the time until the formal opening hour with Miss Messenger, after which she would rejoin him.

At seven in the evening the great hall was full of East End people. Harry (in evening dress for the last time, he informed himself with a pang) and all the wedding guests assembled in the vestibule to receive the august patroness of their friend the dressmaker and the founder of the Palace itself. But the handsome figure in satin, lace, and diamonds that descended from Miss Messenger's carriage, and approached them on the arm of Lord Jocelyn, had a face which was familiar and dear to all of them, and Harry learned that Angela the dressmaker and Angela the heiress were one.

He raised her veil and kissed her forehead before them all. but he could not speak, because all in a moment the sense of what this would mean poured upon his brain in a great wave, and he would have given anything, excepting Angela, to be alone with himself for a few minutes.

HERR PAULUS (1888)

Much discussion, involving considerable anger and no little amusement, was aroused in England, on the appearance of this novel, among believers and non-believers in the so-called phenomena of spiritualism. The author was severely censured by the former class and applauded by the latter; and the excitement it caused extended to the United States, where, as well as in England, it is *taboo*, in spiritualist "circles."

R. CYRUS BRUDENEL, a man of wealth and leisure, had been for many years the leader of the spiritualistic world in London. His wife, the Lady Augusta, had eagerly adopted her husband's beliefs as her own, and was the undoubted queen of the Spiritualists and maintained her court with admirable graciousness and hospitality. Her name was well known in London, New York, Paris, St. Petersburg, and all other centers of the faith, and every "medium" who could reach London made straight for her drawing-room. Yet Lady Augusta and her husband had suffered many disappointments. Some world-renowned mediums had been unmasked as arrant tricksters; others had "lost their power," a significant expression in the profession; none had placed the cult on what Mr. Brudenel was pleased to term The Solid Rock.

But hope springs eternal in the human breast, and the Brudenels were human. One evening their drawing-room was filled with guests, selected from the highest circle of Spiritualists, to meet Herr Paulus, introduced to Lady Augusta by a noted Russian adept in the occult, who wrote:

"He makes a new departure. His soul is candoritself. He is as pure as the white leaf of a lily. He is as incapable of deception as one of the lofty spirits with whom he holds habitual communion. He is above and beyond all considerations of money. My dear sister, we are on the eve of one of the most stupendous revolutions of thought that the world has ever

47

seen. It will begin in England—Christian, bigoted, prejudiced, conservative England."

Lady Augusta believed that something of the sort was desirable, for she said to the guests nearest her:

"We want a new departure. Everything has grown stale. All the answers to all the questions have failed. All the old systems are breaking down. We are on the eve of a universal collapse of systems and faiths, and nothing really new has been proposed. In fact, we need, we must have, a new gospel. I pray that this stranger may preach it to the world—and in my drawing-room."

At that instant Herr Paulus appeared and everybody gasped, so unlike was he to any other high authority on the spirit world and kindred mysteries. He was not bearded, bald, grizzled, spectacled, oddly clothed, or unkempt. He did not diffuse the odor of tobacco or alcohol nor did he evince unfamiliarity with soap, razors and hair-brushes. He was a young man of fine figure, delicate and regular features, and was in faultless evening dress. Except that his black eyes were unusually deep-set, keen, swift, and full of light, he would have passed for a conventional young gentleman of good society. He greeted his hostess without hesitation, and said with a voice soft and musical:

"Lady Augusta, I have seen you already, while I was in St. Petersburg. I came here in the spirit. I am assured already that our souls will be in sympathy."

He held Lady Augusta's hand in the long, warm grasp of one who greets a long absent friend, and his eyes met hers with a steady glow of affection and friendship which moved her strangely. Could he—oh, could he be the long looked-for prophet? He greeted Mr. Brudenel, looking curiously into his face as if trying to read something there, and said:

"I was with you in the spirit. Yesterday morning it was, Mr. Brudenel, in your library. You were reading a novel by Ouida, called *Moths*. You turned the page down at 144, and you resumed the reading this morning until you arrived at page 280."

Everybody knew that Herr Paulus had arrived only that day from St. Petersburg, but nobody expressed the least surprise;

in this house anything might happen. Mr. Brudenel's face flushed. Herr Paulus apologized for being late; he had been delayed by a message—not by telegraph, however—from friends in the heart of Abyssinia; he said it without the least appearance of boastfulness, but as if such a thing was common. Greater and more visible wonders occurred in the course of the evening, but first Herr Paulus explained his situation after lifting his right hand so suddenly and unexpectedly that everybody jumped.

"I have come to this country," he said, "with a message. My mission is to teach to those who are worthy the old wisdom, the Ancient Way. As it is well to prove that I am what I profess to be, I have asked for and obtained certain powers. Do not think, I pray you, that these powers constitute my message. They do no more than illustrate it. Listen!"

No lights were turned down, accomplices were impossible, yet soft music was heard; it came nearer and sounded louder until it appeared to be directly over the head of Herr Paulus. This was followed by the tinkling of silver bells; Herr Paulus threw up both arms, and lo, a miracle!—for fluttering into his hands were seen two thin packets of silver paper which he entrusted to Lady Augusta. Then he surveyed his audience slowly, as if searching for something. The faces represented all stages of bewilderment, from the cataleptic condition of those who believe all they see to the irritated and puzzled expression of those who see yet preserve something of the critical faculty. The young man's eye caught that of Hetty Medlock, the paid companion of Mr. Brudenel's blind ward, Cicely Langston, and Hetty meekly walked across the room and seated herself by the magician, who appeared to breathe softly over her head. The girl seemed to become insensible, yet she answered questions as to what she saw. Herr Paulus took one of the packets from Lady Augusta, opened it, and displayed to the audience a scene described by Hetty and containing Hetty's portrait also. Blind Cicely followed Hetty, and her sight was restored for several moments; she saw Herr Paulus and described him minutely; saw her cousin Tom Langston and her cousin Sybil Brudenel, the only doubters in the room. Still greater was the amazement of everyone when, in answer to the question whether anybody desired a message of consolation or hope, the blind girl asked for word about her brother, and Paulus said:

"Your brother? Who is your brother? Oh, now I know. He has been gone for five years, and has sent no letter, and you fear he is dead. Yes, I understand. He has been at sea. His name is Percival; Sir Percival Langston. He is not dead. He lives. He is well." Taking from Lady Augusta's hands the remaining packet, still unopened, he continued: "What do you see?"

"A ship, rolling on a rough sea. At the wheel I see my brother; he is steering the ship. He does not think of me at all; his mind is full of religion. I know it is my brother, but I cannot tell why. Percival!" she cried, holding out her arms, "Speak to me! Look at me!"

Doubting, Sybil stepped forward and protested against her afflicted cousin's feelings being played with; Paulus opened the packet, showed her a picture of a ship at sea in a storm, and asked her who was the man at the wheel; she was obliged to reply that the face was that of Sir Percival Langston. Then a great awe fell upon the multitude. To Sybil the wonder-worker was even more definite, for he named the ship on which the missing baronet was, described her position at sea, and said that she was bound for London and would arrive soon.

From that evening Herr Paulus was an inmate of the Brudenel mansion and treated as a member of the family. Lady Augusta, blind Cicely, and her companion Hetty accepted him unquestioningly for all he professed to be. Mr. Brudenel had been deceived so many times that he was skeptical for a few hours; but when he asked, after a long conversation, that a copy of an East Indian newspaper of that day and date be placed in his hands and the request was instantly complied with, his confidence became complete.

From day to day the young man told much of the Ancient Way and the manner in which it had been handed down to his friends, a select circle of believers, The Accepted, in the heart of Abyssinia, and the tale was more wonderful than any in the Arabian Nights. He took Mr. Brudenel, in the spirit, to Abyssinia, where the good man communed with The Accepted to his great comfort, although he never could describe the experiences to others. He begged that he might be called Paul; he addressed the ladies by their Christian names and was as familiar and affectionate as if he were a relative, yet he never was offensive in the slightest degree in act, word, or look. He even healed the little ailments of everyone, including the servants.

But to Sybil and her lover, Tom Langston, the new prophet was merely a puzzle, although a great one. Sybil, destined by her father to be a vestal or priestess of the new faith, when it should establish itself on The Solid Rock, was not of the stuff of which such dignitaries are made. She was of generous stature and shapely figure, with laughing eyes and lips always ready to laugh, light curly hair and plenty of it, a cheek warmed with sunshine, and her whole face was full of suggestions of a Venus. Tom, who like his cousin Cicely was a ward of Mr. Brudenel, was a young but practical scientist and the deviser of many new things mechanical and electrical. He and Sybil had seen the rise and fall of so many mediums and prophets that they heartily detested the family hobby. But Tom found this prophet so decent, non-acquisitive, and companionable that he could not help liking him, though he watched him closely and frankly told him so.

Great wonders followed one another so rapidly that they seemed to exceed Tom's powers of watchfulness. The strangest of these affected the financial status of several members of the family. Mr. Brudenel had invested the private fortunes of his two wards and his daughter in the shares of a reputable company which nevertheless went to pieces suddenly and just as the young people should have come into possession of their own. He shocked the family by announcing that he was disgraced and ruined. Paul alone remained cheerful; he insisted that Mr. Brudenel's bankbook be sent for; the book showed that Brudenel had sold the shares while they were still good and had banked the money, although he had no recollection of the transaction; it had probably occurred, at the suggestion of The Accepted, while he was in the spirit in Abyssinia. But he had also drawn checks for the full amount, and he could not remember why, to the order of three men whose names were unknown to him. Would not Paul's "friends," The Accepted Ones in

Abyssinia, unravel the mystery and save a respected name and family? They would, Paul replied. if Mr. Brudenel would permit his daughter Sybil to wed his ward Tom Langston. Although this consent had been beyond hope, for vestals and priestesses should not marry, Mr. Brudenel yielded, and the lost money was quickly forthcoming from the hands of The Accepted's agent, Herr Paulus. Then blind Cicely's brother Percival returned; he admitted that he had been a common sailor, and his manner showed that his mind was full of religion to the exclusion of everything else, as Cicely had learned in her vision of him.

After a time the prophet began to lose his power and was conscious of it. It seems to be a law of occultism that no medium, prophet, seer, or other worker of supra-natural wonders can retain his power after surrendering his will to that of any other human being. Cicely's companion Hetty, although a simple, modest, good girl, had dark lustrous eyes with possibilities of grand passion in them, and Paul had looked into them too often for his own safety. He could no longer foretell anything; he could not send Mr. Brudenel in the spirit to Abyssinia; he could not even banish a housemaid's toothache.

Greater humiliations awaited him. Sir Percival, although almost maniacal in his religious frenzy, identified him as the assistant of a medium whom he had consulted in New York three years before: the medium was now in retirement in London, but Tom had traced him and his antecedents. Paul regarded this medium as his banker, who held much money for him; but when the old man learned that his pupil had lost his power and was determined to drop the business he denied any indebtedness, and the matter was not exactly one which a man would care to take into court. So Paul was penniless and without occupation.

He suffered a severer blow when Tom took him to the roof of the house and into a dark chamber with a brilliantly lighted white table, on which, by means of an arrangement of mirrors and lenses, he showed the ex-prophet the interior of Mr. Brudenel's study, the large windows of which were within range of the dark chamber. And Tom said:

"I have occupied myself here in a very interesting series

of observations, the nature of which you can guess. I have seen our dear old friend there, morning after morning, reduced to insensibility. I have then seen you, Paul, take his keys out of his pocket, unlock and ransack his safe, open and read his letters and examine his papers. I have seen you, not heard you, put questions to him and receive answers from him. I have seen you order him to write letters which you dictated. By the help of a magnifying-glass I was able to read those letters. In this way I acquired information which was very useful to me. In fact, I knew all along what you were doing, though I confess there were some things which I did not quite understand; for instance, the appearance of the day's paper."

Paul groaned and fell across the table; he had fainted. Tom revived him.

"Sit up, Paul! So. Look me in the face! So. Keep your eyes fixed in mine!"

A strange giddiness fell upon Paul; then he stiffened in all his limbs and sat upright. He who had mesmerized so many others was himself mesmerized. When he was restored to self-control Tom said to him:

"You have told me everything, Paul. You have been in a mesmeric trance, and you have told me how you did the Indian paper miracle and the musical bells and everything. You are a prestidigitateur, a ventriloquist and a mesmerist—all in one! Thank you very much."

It was even as Tom had said. Shame and love soon combined to make Paul so penitent that he made partial confession to Tom, also to Hetty, who loved him the more for his disgust at the "profession" from which he was retiring, for her own mother was a medium and Hetty had known some of the tricks of the trade. But his most comprehensive confession, made before a great gathering in London of well-known Spiritualists from all parts of Europe, contained the following explanation:

"I understood in practice what you call the art of mesmerism. I had worked for seven years on the subject, making experiments of all kinds. I succeeded in making those persons who became subject to me think and do exactly as I pleased. I also succeeded in making them remember what I made them think; that was the foundation of everything. I made the blind girl see her brother; I knew where the man was and had prepared his portrait beforehand. All that was done by me in that house was sheer pretense and trickery. You ask me how I dare to stand before you and make this confession? I dare it becau e I have left the ranks of the charlatans."

He had gone from America to Europe for fame, not money, but he was to return without either, although the Brudenel family offered generous financial assistance; they owed the saving of their fortunes to him, one of his tricks having resulted in the discovery that Mr. Brudenel's investments were in danger; his affection for the family had prompted him to the farther trickery of compelling Mr. Brudenel, while under mesmeric influence, to order his banker to sell the shares, and to the additional trick of having the money covered by checks which he retained that he might reproduce the money as if by miracle. He was so fond even of the doubters, Sybil and Tom, as to exact Brudenel's permission for their marriage. But he could not accept money from a family that knew him for a trickster, although a lovable one. So he married Hetty and sold all his belongings to get money to take him and his wife back to his birthplace, a little New England town in which his father, Deacon Trinder, had long kept a general store and accumulated dollars; perhaps the old man might make a place in the store for an assistant.

ROBERT MONTGOMERY BIRD

(United States, 1803-1854)

NICK OF THE WOODS (1837)

Following several successful tragedies and a number of novels, *Nick of the Woods* was written with the avowed design of counteracting Cooper's heroic portrayals of the North American Indian. In his preface Dr. Bird says: "We look into the woods for the mighty warrior, the 'feather-cinctured chief,' rushing to meet his foe, and behold him retiring laden with the scalps of miserable squaws and their babes. Heroical?" He aimed also to show the generous if rough characteristics of the pioneers who redeemed the "dark and bloody ground" of Kentucky—farmers, hunters, and mountaineers—so that in 1792, sixteen years after the first block-house was built in the woods, the "wilderness" was admitted into the Federal Union, a free and sovereign state, with a population of 75,000. The characters of Bloody Nathan and Roaring Ralph Stackpole were drawn from traditionary tales of genuine persons.

 NE August afternoon in 1782, the sun was still blazing on the palisades and cabins of one of the principal stations, or forts of refuge, in Kentucky, when a train of emigrants from Virginia approached the chief gate. They were joyously received at Bruce's Station. At the rear of the column was a man about twenty-three years of age, although five years in the armies of the Revolution had given him an older look. With him were two negro slaves, mounted and armed, and a beautiful young woman.

Captain Roland Forrester and his cousin Edith were children of twin brothers, who had fallen in the Revolution, and were the wards of their uncle, Major Roland Forrester, a Virginian, of princely estates and wealth. He had been a royalist during the war, and never forgave his brothers for the part they took, even making a will in favor of an illegitimate daughter of his own lest they should inherit his wealth. The child, however, was accidentally killed; and when his brothers fell the Major brought up their two children as his heirs, although Roland also had taken arms with the Colonists. When the Major died, however, his confidential attorney, named Braxley, produced the original will in favor of the Major's own daughter, whom he declared to be still alive, and, as no second will was found, he took possession of the estate as executor. The war being then over, Roland had brought Edith to the West, where a relative at the Ohio Falls had invited her to live, intending to marry the girl eventually, between whom and himself existed a deep affection.

Colonel Bruce, commander of the station, a rough Virginian backwoodsman, was zealously hospitable, while his spouse tried to keep their three breezy daughters within the bounds of good manners, admonishing them to be as noiseless as Telie Doe—a slim, wild-looking, sensitive girl, who, on hearing the name of Captain Roland Forrester, had shrunk to her loom, and, looking almost terrified, worked in silence. The mother and girls took Edith Forrester into the house, and Telie was left on the long porch with her loom, when Captain Forrester opened his plans to Colonel Bruce, for proceeding the next morning, asking if there were any danger to be feared. The Colonel assured him that the path was broad and straight to the Upper Ford, and that no Indians had been heard of that year. Bruce suddenly noticed Telie looking with wild, sorrowful eyes at Roland, and ordered her into the house, explaining that she was the daughter of Abel Doe, a renegade rascal who had "turned Injun," and that out of compassion he had taken in the girl.

Suddenly entered Tom Bruce, the elder son, with a grin of awe and delight, announcing:

"The Jibbenainosay is up again, not in our limits, but nigh enough, on the north bank of the Kentuck, whar he's left a dead Injun with a split skull and the reggelar cross-cut two slashes on the breast."

It was explained to Roland that "Nick of the Woods," as the white men called him, or "The Jibbenainosay" (*Spirit-that-walks*), as the Indians named him, was accustomed to kill Indians and always marked them thus. He was said to be a ghost or devil, and the Indians—especially the

Shawnees, whom he most frequently killed,—dreaded him, and no one had seen an Indian in that neighborhood for a year past.

"Thar are men who have seen the critter—a great tall fellow, with horns and a hairy head, and a little devil that looks like a black b'ar, that points the way fer him. It's a sure sign, if he's about, that thar's Injuns at hand. Captain Ralph—Roaring Ralph Stackpole—brought the tale."

"Look out for the horses, Tom!" cried Bruce. "He has killed Injuns and stolen a many horses from them—but he does sometimes mistake a Christian's horse for an Injun's."

They went out among the cabins, and there was Captain Ralph—broad-shouldered, swaggering, performing frisky antics of dancing and leaping. As they approached he shouted: "Glad to see you, Cunnel; and you too, stranger. I'm Ralph Stackpole, and I'm a ring-tailed squealer! 'Tarnal death to me! I'm a gentleman, and my name's *Fight*. Foot and hand, tooth and nail, knife, gun, or tomahawk, I'm your man. Cock-a-doodle-doo!" and the gentleman jumped into the air and flapped his wings.

"If you're ralely ripe for a fight, Ralph," laughed Tom Bruce, "here's your man. Look, boys, here comes Bloody Nathan."

A tall, gaunt man approached, leading a lame horse and carrying a pack of skins; following him was a meek-looking little dog. The man's face was weather-worn, like his leather garments; his gun was old-fashioned and his knife was thin from long use.

The crowd egged Ralph on with laughter to challenge the newcomer, who was called Bloody Nathan, "because he's the only man in Kentucky that *won't* fight—he's only a poor Pennsylvany Quaker."

At last the meek Nathan agreed to "try a friendly fall;" but, to the general amazement, the bully was lifted in air and came down on his head. Good-naturedly agreeing that he had been "licked," Stackpole wanted to go, and Bruce lent him a horse, to be left at Logan's station. Nathan then told Bruce of a great gathering of Miami Indians, the probability being that they were already near. No one believed him, so he took the powder and lead for his skins, and stalked away with his little dog and his lame horse.

When Edith had retired to her room, Telie Doe came in and begged to be taken as her servant, urging that she could be of great use to her in the woods; but Edith said it was impossible, and the girl sadly withdrew. Roland slept with the other men in the porch. Near dawn he started up, having heard or dreamed of a low voice, saying, "Cross the river by the Lower Ford; there is danger at the Upper." Dismissing it as a visionary fantasy, he slept again until all awoke.

He was deeply moved when Colonel Bruce came indignantly in with the news that Ralph Stackpole had stolen the Captain's blooded horse, Brown Briareus, and a two-year old pony, and that the boys had started in pursuit. Unwilling to delay his party, Roland sent them on their road, while he, with his cousin and one of the negroes, would overtake them later. A storm delayed their departure, although the horse was soon returned by young Tom, having been found loose by the way, the party pushing on after Stackpole and the pony. But while they were getting ready to start, a horseman dashed up telling of a thousand Indians besieging Bryant's Station, and cried for help! Colonel Bruce despatched one son to Logan's for men, and mustered every fighting man to stand on the road, while Forrester, loath to take Edith without a guide, was furnished with one unwilling, surly fellow, who soon deserted them to join the fighters. But Telie Doe had galloped after them, evidently determined to be of the party. She asserted her familiarity with the trail, and at last was accepted. But when they reached the branch to the two Fords, Roland insisted on taking the trail to the Upper, as Bruce had said, while Telie besought them to go to the Lower. The road was dark and difficult and soon they heard an unearthly yelling. Fearing it to be Indians, they were relieved to find it the horse-stealer, Stackpole, sitting, bound, on a pony under a tree, a noose from an overhead branch about his neck: one step of the pony would hang him. At Edith's earnest request, Roland unwillingly cut the man free, and with his usual extravagance the Roarer declared he would devote his life to her service; but Roland sternly dismissed him and he rode away.

Presently a white man, known as Pardon Dodge, riding furiously, came at them with clubbed rifle, thinking them to be Indians, whom if he could not escape he would fight. But they calmed him, and he told of being followed by six Indians, one of whom he had shot; those he had left behind, but the Ford ahead was full of them. Reënforced by Dodge, they now started for the Lower Ford, but soon got confused and were riding in a circle, when they came upon a dead Indian, scalped and bearing two cross-cut gashes on his breast. "The Jibbe-nainosay!" exclaimed Telie. "Nick of the Woods is up again."

While vainly searching for some road, they saw a tall, shad-owy figure moving through the woods, preceded by a smaller, rolling object. As the stranger approached his apparently colossal height grew smaller and less impressive, until they discovered it to be only Nathan the Quaker, with his little dog, Peter. Roland begged him to guide them, but he objected that they might meet Indians, and he might be killed; yet, if they did meet them, and he might be excused from fighting, he would try to guide them. Roland scornfully assented; and Nathan, send-ing his wise little dog ahead, had the party follow at a distance. Peter discovered the tracks of the party and also of Dodge's five Indians, who had been quietly pursuing them. By a détour avoiding the five, Nathan brought the party to a ruined cabin on the steep bank of the river—swelled and roaring from the rains—and there they gladly entered. But hardly had they done so when Nathan came in, saying that Peter gave signs of danger. Instantly a shriek from Telie called their startled eyes to a tall, naked Indian at the door. Nathan rushed at him and threw him out, while Edith fainted; Roland shot at other Indians behind the leader, the old negro Emperor killed one with his rifle, and Pardon Dodge shot another. Roland was seized by an immense savage, and, despite gallant fighting, was in danger of a raised tomahawk, when a jet of hot blood gushed over his arm and the Indian fell dead.

"Up, and do according to thy conscience!" cried Nathan. But the Indians, dispirited by the fall of their leader, withdrew. All night the fight was kept up from a distance, when Nathan, seeing that morning would finish it, proposed to slip out for help. He went. Roland, as the moon was now rising with light for the Indians, withdrew his party to the river, when a small dug-out, rushing down the torrent, suddenly caught on the bank. He leaped forward to attack the man in it, who, however, proved to be their horse-stealing devotee, Stackpole. He had himself barely escaped at the ford, in the dug-out; and when he learned from Roland that his own stealing of the brown horse had brought the "anngeliferous madam" into her present plight, he proposed to Roland what they immediately undertook—the carrying of the two women down stream in the dug-out, while Roland, his negro, and Dodge should attempt it on their horses. The desperate effort succeeded, except for Dodge, whose horse came ashore without him, on the point where they all landed.

In the morning they started up the river-bank, but only, after an hour of riding, to encounter a crew of Indians, who captured them all, except Stackpole, who, roaring and swearing, rolled himself down the bank to the river. The negro was killed; Edith was borne away; and when Roland recovered his consciousness he was lying, bound, under the guard of an old Piankeshaw Indian, and suffering from wounds.

While lying there he heard the sound of approaching horses, and the young Kentuckians, headed by Tom Bruce, came dashing down. A fierce fight followed, and the white men were gaining, when Stackpole emerged from the river-bank and with a wild whoop leaped into the fight. Thinking him the ghost of the man they had hanged, the Kentuckians were confused and scattered in flight, pursued by the Indians. Stackpole, on one side, saw the brown horse "Briareus" dashing by, seized him, threw young Tom Bruce, severely wounded, across him, leaped on the horse, and sped away.

Roland was interested to see the savages now gathering and dividing the spoils, which, strangely enough, were not only arms but rolls of cloth and calico, heaps of hawks' bills, knives, pipes, and other trinkets dear to the Indian. These were distributed by a man of lighter color, seemingly a half-breed, who deferred to an old, malignant-looking Indian sitting apart. Roland's old Piankeshaw received a keg of whiskey, a horse, and Roland's person. But as he was about to depart Telie Doe ran up, seized Roland's cords, and cried to the supposed half-breed—"Oh, father! What are you doing? You promised you would not give him up to the murderers!" But he threatened her with his tomahawk and motioned to the Piankeshaws to go, holding her firmly till they had departed.

While lying bound, wondering what had become of Edith, Roland had noted in a neighboring grove a tall barbarian wrapped in a blanket from chin to foot, his head covered with the folds of a huge scarlet handkerchief, watching the savages and occasionally glaring malignantly at him. He felt that the captive girl was under that guard, but could see nothing of her.

It was a weary road that Roland took, with hands bound, and a rope dragging him after the old Piankeshaw on the horse and two young warriors, one on either side.

Arriving at their camping place, after supper they bound Roland firmly, and all went to sleep—except the agonized prisoner. It was an awful night; but just before dawn he was stunned by an explosion at his head, the crash of an ax upon one of the young Indians, the sound of running and pursuit, the huge old Piankeshaw, with his face shot away, climbing upon him, and expiring. Roland swooned, and when he awoke he was free from his bonds, Nathan was chafing his half-lifeless limbs, and little Peter stood wagging his tail. The Quaker apologized for having been guilty of violence, while Roland thanked him with tears. Nathan told of his escape at the cabin, his return with the Kentuckians, their pursuit of the party, his keeping out of the battle, and then taking little Peter's advice to follow the Piankeshaws and Roland. He questioned the captain about the chiefs, recognized the description of old Wenonga, the head, and told Roland how he had overheard Abe Doe and a big whi e man in a blanket talking of the price for capturing Roland and the young woman. When he heard of the cloths and trinkets distributed to the Indians, he understood the whole vile arrangement. Nathan tried to console him with the idea that Edith would not be killed, but Roland would rather see her die a thousand deaths than be in Braxley's hands.

"Thee is but a mad man," exclaimed Nathan severely. "Thee does not know what such a sight is—I do."

Then he detailed to Roland the massacre of his mother, his wife, and his children before his own eyes—he having given his gun and knife to the Shawnee chief to show his friendliness. His frantic looks increased with the horrid tale, till he fell in an epileptic fit. He soon recovered, and asked Roland what he would have done in like circumstances. The excited youth shouted that he would "wage eternal war upon them and their accursed race."

"Thee is right, friend," cried Nathan, "thee would kill, friend! thee would kill! Thee is a brave man. Thy enemies shall be pursued and the maid thee loves shall be restored. With little Peter for guide we will trust Providence, and find our friends."

Without waste of time, they set out for the Indian country.

When near Black Vulture's village they stopped for food, but soon discovered five Indians leaping about a white man bound to a tree. They approached silently, shot two of the Indians, and seizing their axes leaped at the others; while the white man, seeing rescue, furiously burst his bonds and threw himself upon the savage nearest him, rolled over and over with him down the hill, and there madly beat him to death with his fists, while Nathan and Roland finished the other two. The white man then sprang up and roared, "Arn't I licked him handsome! Hurrah for Kentucky and old Salt River! Cock-a-doodle-doo!" and stood revealed as the horse-thief, Stackpole.

According to Nathan's plan, the Quaker disguised himself in Indian garb, daubing himself with streaks of paint, and, with some jingling ornaments, was barbaric enough; Roland was left at the bottom of the hill with little Peter; Stackpole, nearer to the horse-pound of the Indians, to get animals for their escape; and Nathan stalked into the Indian village, when their drunken orgy was over and most of them lay about in drunken stupor. His aim was to find the place of Edith's confinement. Peeping into the log cabins, in one he saw two white men—one tall and athletic, but evil-looking, the other Abel Doe. He listened, and learned that Braxley had with him the second will of old Major Forrester, making Roland and Edith his heirs; Roland was now disposed of, and Edith he meant to force into a marriage legally giving him the estates. Doe was bargaining for his pay. Having heard enough, Nathan pursued his search.

He found a large cabin with two skin tents attached, and in one of these heard Edith's voice.

Crawling toward it, he came upon old Wenonga, dead drunk in the grass. He drew his knife and had almost used it, when he heard Edith's voice again, and with a sigh gave up his cherished vengeance.

Meantime Roland, wild with impatience, could wait no longer, but crept up the hill and, seeing Nathan, followed him.

When the Quaker got near to Edith's tent, he found with her the man Braxley vainly trying to compel the frightened girl's assent to marry him. But suddenly the villain was seized, thrown on his back, gagged and bound by Nathan, who tore from Braxley's bosom the stolen will, rolled him into a corner, threw over him a pile of skins, and caught Edith in his arms, saying, as he bore her out, "Thee is safe—thy friends are nigh."

The night was dark, and Nathan halted. But he had hardly stepped from the tent when he heard the stamping, galloping, neighing of a herd of frightened horses, making for the village. Stackpole, not content to run off three horses, was tempted to cut out a number of them, when the herd took fright and stampeded into the village, bearing him in the midst. A bundle of straw thrown on the dying fire lighted the region, as the Indians quickly awoke, and Nathan, skirting the village silently with Edith, hoped to escape, when Roland broke upon them rejoicingly. Edith, seeing him, gave a scream of joy, that attracted the Indians, who instantly pursued, caught, and bound them.

They were confined separately. Nathan was brought before old Wenonga, who, putting his two hands on Nathan's shoulders, glared at the prisoner fiercely. But Nathan responded with a face of such passion, eyes gleaming with such unearthly fire, that even the drunken chief drew back, while the prisoner fell foaming into convulsions. This, with Nathan's fantastic Indian dress, confirmed the Indian notion that he was a medicine-man.

The next day Doe, not coming to any satisfactory conclusion with Braxley, whom he of course distrusted, went to Roland, told him of Braxley's doings, and offered to rescue the captain and secure him the estate if he would marry Telie Doe. Roland would promise to care for her, but not to marry her; he would give Doe half of the estate to save his own life and the whole to save Edith from the Indians and from Braxley. Both being determined, Doe sullenly left.

That evening old Wenonga again summoned Nathan and offered him freedom and reward if by his medicine-power he would set before him the Jibbenainosay, killer of his people. He made a long speech, vaunting his deeds, and the scalps he had taken from the long knives.

Nathan accused him of scalping the son of Onas and murdering his wife and children, although the man was his friend.

"Yes, I killed them. I am not sorry. Their scalps hang to my fire-post," and he pointed to the shriveled scalps torn from childish heads, while Nathan sank to the floor and shivered.

"My brother shall show me the Jibbenainosay, or he shall die."

"The chief lies," cried Nathan with a taunting laugh, arising from the floor. "He can talk big to a prisoner, but he fears the Jibbenainosay."

"I will fight him!"

"Cut me loose from my bonds, then, and I will bring him before the chief."

The steel ax fell upon the thongs. Once free, the prisoner turned and, with a hyena-laugh shouted, "Look! thee has thy will. *Here* is the destroyer of thy race, and thy own—" and he leaped at the chief like a wolf, clutched his throat with a grip of iron, wrenched away his steel ax and buried it in the Indian's skull. Then, snatching up the chief's scalping-knife, he tore away his gray scalp-lock, gashed his breast with the Jibbenainosay's fearful cross, seized the scalps of his children from the post and, with a yell of triumph, fled into the night.

In the morning the village was in fury on discovering the work of the Jibbenainosay in the chief's own tent. Roland and Stackpole were chained to stakes, the fire-heap piled about them. Braxley seized Edith and bore her away, shrieking at that sight of horror. The fires were already flaming up when two hundred horsemen and footmen rushed into the square, kicked out the fire, and charged the astounded savages. The fight was brief but murderous; the village was destroyed.

While the conflict raged, the disguised Nathan leaped into it and with Wenonga's scalp at his girdle and those of his children in his left hand, with his right plied savagely Wenonga's steel ax. The sight of the Jibbenainosay completed the terror and defeat of the Indians and Nathan himself cut Roland's bonds.

"Hurrah for old Bloody Nathan!" cried one. "I'll never say Q to a Quaker agin, as long as I live!"

Just then in galloped Pardon Dodge on the horse that had lost him in the river. He had seen Braxley riding off on it with Edith in his arms and, believing him an Indian, had shot him and brought Edith back. Doe, mortally wounded, craved speech with Roland, who promised to care for Telie like a sister. Doe gave him the precious will, which he had taken from Nathan on his capture, and now Roland was free to return to Virginia with his bride and their faithful little friend.

Nathan bade them farewell, despite Roland's earnest beseeching that he would return to share their better fortunes, and they never saw him more.

BJÖRNSTJERNE BJÖRNSON

(Norway, 1832)

ARNE (1858)

This graceful tale was the second story of any length published by the famous Norwegian poet, novelist and politician. It is considered one of the best stories that he produced, and it has an added interest from the fact that for the many charming poems with which it is enriched special music has been written by eminent Norwegian composers. Chief among the musicians who thus gave wide popularity to these songs in *Arne*, making them favorites not only with the cultivated classes but also with the common people, was Björnson's brilliant cousin, Rikard Nordraak, who died in 1865 at the age of twenty-three, but who had already won a place as one of Norway's great composers.

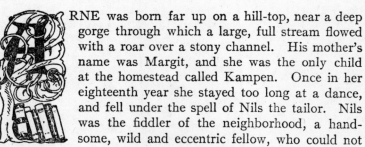

RNE was born far up on a hill-top, near a deep gorge through which a large, full stream flowed with a roar over a stony channel. His mother's name was Margit, and she was the only child at the homestead called Kampen. Once in her eighteenth year she stayed too long at a dance, and fell under the spell of Nils the tailor. Nils was the fiddler of the neighborhood, a handsome, wild and eccentric fellow, who could not endure to have anyone above him. He fluttered about all the girls, and they about him. When he went out as fiddler for a party, he would play at first quite steadily; but when drink had taken possession of him, he used to lay aside suddenly his fiddle, seize whatever girl took his fancy, move his foot with a grace that charmed every woman's eye, and with his boot-heel knock off the hat from the head of the tallest person present. Whenever he asked Margit Kampen to dance she could not resist him, though she hardly knew what she was about. So completely was she captivated by the fiddler that in the next winter she did not dance, but instead brought a babe to be baptized, who was christened Arne and whose reputed father was Nils the tailor.

Margit kept at home with the little boy. She heard about Nils, how he went from dance to dance and flirted with all the girls. She looked at the child and wept. She looked at him again and was happy. The first thing she taught him to say was "papa." Later, she taught him popular songs, among them a rough, wild song, reciting the exploits of tailor Nils and his barn-fights.

Meanwhile, Nils took to roving about the parish, neglected his business, and gave himself up more and more to fiddling, drinking and fighting. He had a special grudge against Baard, and a special admiration for Birgit Böen, with whom Baard was deeply in love. Nils took her from Baard at every dance and at every wedding party. Nils played fast and loose with Birgit, and yet she seemed to care more for him each time, and Baard was eager for revenge upon his rival.

One night there was a wedding at which Nils played. Two American visitors offered Nils a handsome sum to dance the Halling, a famous national dance. At first Nils refused, but when the request became unanimous he took the floor. The music struck up, Nils dashed forward along the floor, his body inclining to one side. Crouching down, balancing himself now on one foot, now on the other, he flung his legs crosswise under him, sprang up again; stood as if about to make a fling, and then moved on aslant as before. Farther and farther back Nils threw his head, and suddenly his boot-heel touched the beam above, sending the dust down from the ceiling in showers.

The people laughed and shouted. More and more fire was thrown into the tune; Nils hopped along in time with it, made ready for a fling, but only as a feint, and when he seemed least prepared for it, his boot-heel thundered against the beam again and again, and Nils turned somersaults forward and backward in the air, landing each time erect on his feet.

The American visitors were so delighted that they not only rewarded Nils most generously but proposed to take him with them out into the world.

In the popular dance that followed, Nils offered his hand

to Birgit Böen. But when she gave him hers, Nils rudely
turned away, and took out another girl. When Baard danced
off after him with the jilted Birgit, Nils contrived to run into
the other couple and knock them over. In the altercation that
followed, Baard struck Nils a blow with the fist so heavy
that the tailor fell across the sharp-edged hearth-stone, and
when he tried to rise it was found that his back was seriously
injured.

In this helpless condition, his health shattered for life, the
one who gave Nils shelter and nursed him and cared for him
was the one whom he had most wronged—Margit Kampen.
It was in the autumn when he was borne to her house on a litter.
Through the winter he improved a little, taught Arne to read,
and took in work in the house. In the spring the bans for
Nils and Margit were published, and soon afterward they
were quietly married.

At first Nils worked industriously, as much as he could,
and managed everything sensibly, and the couple were happy.
But one day when Arne and Nils had gone to walk on the road
leading past the church, they met a wedding procession. It
was that of Baard and Birgit Böen. After that Nils was quite
changed. He became habitually ill-tempered; often went away
from home, and always came back drunk. For everything he
blamed the innocent wife, and sometimes even struck her.

After he had slept himself sober the next day, he was
ashamed, and was especially kind to the boy. Soon he was
drunk again, and then he struck the mother. The boy cried
and lamented. Then he struck the boy. Having somewhat
regained his physical strength, he began to go about to the
merry-makings and to play the fiddle, and he took Arne with
him to carry the violin-case.

At the dances Arne learned many songs, and he sang them
at home to his father and next, at the father's command, sang
them at the dancing-parties to the people, amid laughter and
applause.

The father's ill-treatment of the mother increased with
years, as did also his fondness for drink. Arne now made new
songs of his own composing, and wove into them all that grieved
him most. When his heart became too gloomy, he sought

refuge in his books. One evening he sat up late reading. The mother had gone to bed.

Arne started up at the sound of a heavy fall in the passage way. It was his father, who had come home in a maudlin state of intoxication; Arne helped him in.

"Yes, look at me, you clever boy" penitently sobbed the tailor. "I am not handsome now. This I say to you—that you—never shall drink brandy; it is—the world and the flesh and the devil. Ah woe, woe is me!"

He flung himself down and sobbed convulsively, and repeated passages from the Bible that he had learned twenty years before.

The mother had awakened long since, but had not dared to raise her eyes, now that her husband was weeping like one who is saved. She leaned on her elbow and looked up.

But hardly had Nils descried her when he shrieked out: "Are you staring at me, you too? You want to see, I suppose, what you have brought me to."

He rose, and she hid herself under the bed-covers. ("No, do not hide, I will find you easily enough.")

"Tickle, tickle," said he, as he drew off the covers and placed his fingers on her throat.

"Father," cried Arne.

The mother convulsively seized Nils's murderous hand with both of hers, but could not free herself.

"Father!" again cried Arne.

"So life has come into you now," sneered Nils. "How she writhes, the fright! Tickle, tickle."

She let go his hand, and gave up. "Father!" shouted Arne again and again; and at length he sprang to a corner and seized the ax that stood there. But he remained standing as if nailed to the spot, for at that moment Nils drew himself up, gave a piercing cry, clutched at his breast, fell over, and lay quite still.

Arne knew not where he stood, nor what he stood over. He waited as it were for a strong light to break in somewhere.

The mother began to draw her breath heavily; finally she half rose, and saw the father lying stretched out on the floor, the son standing beside him with the ax.

"Merciful Lord, what have you done?" shrieked the mother. Then Arne felt as if his tongue were loosened.

"He fell down himself," said the boy.

"Arne, Arne, I do not believe you," cried the mother, and she flung herself over the body with piteous lamentation.

Now the boy came out of his stupor and, dropping on his knees, exclaimed; "As surely as I look for mercy from God, he fell as he stood there."

"Then our Lord himself has been here," said the mother, quietly, and sitting on the floor she fixed her eyes on the corpse.

It was a little after midnight, and they had to remain there with the dead until day dawned.

As the mother sat by the fire, it rushed through her mind how many evil days she had had with Nils; and then she thanked God for this providential release.

Then she recalled the good days, and wept for her recent thankfulness. It ended in her taking the greatest blame on herself, who, out of love to the departed one, had acted contrary to God's commandment.

Soon after this Arne passed his nineteenth birthday. He tended the cattle and read the priest's books and made songs, as he drove the sheep before him or the cattle around the wood.

Many of his songs got out among the people, where they were well-liked, and some of those who heard or read them wished to talk with him. But Arne was shy of all whom he did not know well.

One day Arne went to a wedding. Everybody stared at him, and two of the men told stories which seemed directed at Arne, and insinuated that wicked deeds would surely come to light. Arne in reply told another tale, illustrating the danger and wrong of stirring up the power of passion by imputing evil to others. To deaden the heart-ache, he drank brandy and was for the first time overcome by it. He felt ready to kill himself. His mother at last found him and comforted him, and Arne promised never to touch the perilous drink again.

From that day he lived closer to his mother, and his relations with other people also were changed. He looked on them more with his mother's mild eyes.

This companionship brought every day more comfort to the young man. He began to take a new interest in nursery stories, traditions and ancient ballads. He walked much alone, and many of the places round about, which formerly he had not noticed, seemed strangely beautiful, and he made musical songs about the sunny days and the pleasant rustic scenes and work of his farm life. One day he sat down by a large lake, near the Parsonage, called the Black Water.

As Arne was gazing at the charming scene, he overheard voices behind him in an animated conversation. It was Eli, the young daughter of Baard Böen, who had just left the house of the priest where she had been making a long stay and was going to her own home across the lake. It was the first glimpse Arne had had of the fair young girl, and it made such an impression on him that he kept his seat, watching the boat move across the water and then following the maiden with his eyes until she vanished in her father's home. Love and women were beginning to play a prominent part in his thoughts; and after that evening he found pleasure in singing about them. A two-fold longing, to have some one to love and to become something great, blended within his heart.

That winter Arne was at the parsonage for a time, doing carpenter work, and Eli also was there, visiting Mathilde, the priest's daughter, and there was no little talk back and forth and messages carried by the little brother between the young folks. Not long after this Baard Böen sent for him, much to the surprise both of his wife and Arne's mother, to do carpenter work in Baard's homestead across the lake. In the evenings, Arne sat with the family of the man who had given his father such a fatal blow, years before.

Birgit, the wife, sat upstairs, or if she was with the others she was silent with suppressed emotion, often dropping her sewing and staring fixedly at Arne. Arne and Eli did most of the talking, the father putting in an occasional word.

One day Eli asked, "How do you manage when you make songs?"

And Arne answered; "I hoard up the thoughts which others are in the habit of letting go."

Then Arne told Eli how he made a song after he had seen her the first time, and at her request he sang it to her:

"Fair Venevill bounded on lithesome feet
Her lover to meet."

Eli stood still long after he was through. At last she burst out: "Oh, how I pity her!"

The next day when Arne came into dinner he went over to the window. Outside it was gray and foggy. On the window-pane a finger had traced "Arne, Arne, Arne," and over again, "Arne." It was the window where Eli had stood the preceding evening.

A day later Eli heard that the priest's daughter Mathilde, her inseparable companion and intimate friend for so many years, had set out on a journey, to be gone a year or two. The shock of the surprise was too much for the delicate girl, and she fell fainting.

When she regained consciousness it was only to burst into hysterical sobs and weeping. It was the beginning of a pro-tracted illness, the seeds of which had been gathering for some time. Some days the poor girl would be delirious; then get a little better; then suffer a relapse. In the sad days that ensued the father and mother were much estranged. Baard confided to Arne the story of his life and the family discord, and a close bond of sympathy from this time existed between the two men.

When Eli had so far recovered from her illness that she could sit up, Arne, at the mother's invitation, went up into Eli's room and sang songs. Among other hymns and songs, he sang one of his favorite compositions, whose last stanza was as follows:

"The tree bore its fruit in the
Midsummer glow:
Said the girl 'May I gather
thy berries or no?'
'Yes, dear, all thou canst see;
Take them; all are for thee,'
Said the tree, while it bent
down its laden boughs low."

This song almost took away Eli's breath. Arne, too, sat silent for awhile, as if he had laid bare his heart. Their con-versation was very intimate and pleasant; and when Arne told her that he must leave her, she began to weep.

"Give me your hand," he whispered. And when she did not answer, he felt down on the coverlid, in the dusk of the room, and clasped a warm little hand that lay outside.

The next day Arne had to leave. But wherever he was working his thoughts turned to Eli. The young man was full of restless longings, so that his mother feared he would leave the country. So strong was her apprehension, so unbearable was the thought of his leaving home, that she even hid the letters and the money that his friend Kristian, who had gone across the Atlantic, had sent him. Her fault in this weighed so heavily on her heart that she had to confess it to the priest. But when he suggested that she should confess to her son what she had done, the fear that Arne would leave her was worse than continuing in her deceit.

Then the shrewd spiritual father made a suggestion: "If we only had a little girl who could lay hold of him, then you would see that he would stay."

The mother looked up quickly and exclaimed, "Eli Böen—What—"

Then she colored and looked down, until the kind priest offered to arrange it that the young couple should meet oftener at the parsonage.

The priest had begun to walk up and down. Now, he paused. "See here, Margit! When it comes to the point, perhaps this was your whole errand here to-day, eh?"

She bowed her head far down. "Well—yes—God help me! That was exactly what I wanted."

The priest burst out laughing, and rubbed his hands. Arne thought tenderly of Eli day and night; but so shy was he that even when he overheard her singing his own songs in the most melodious fashion, robed in the most bewitching costume, he was too embarrassed to speak to her, but instead contented himself with writing a fresh love-song in which he enshrined the beautiful memory of that precious forest walk.

One Sunday evening in midsummer, Arne's mother Margit overtook Eli as she was leaving the parsonage. Joining her, she asked the young girl to give her her company on the way homeward, and gradually Margit brought the pleasant conversation round to the subject of Arne and her own home, Kampen, which Arne would inherit.

When Margit proposed that Eli call and see the house, Eli at first declined, but when she was told that Arne was not at home she accepted.

Margit showed the young girl the cattle, and told her how much milk each cow gave, and had Eli smell the hay, "for such hay is not to be found everywhere." Then she let her try the garden seat, and gave her some of the flowers; then took her into the house and let her see what a cosy living-room there was, and took down Arne's guns and English fishing-rod and let her handle them. Then, in turn, Eli was taken through the kitchen, the store-house, the bake-house, and finally upstairs through the chambers. Margit kept up an unbroken stream of chatter. Eli walked as in a dream, touching very daintily what was held out for her inspection and occasionally uttering some word of admiration or putting some question about the things that most interested her.

Finally the mother took her into the son's own room and showed her the splendid view of the mountains from the window and the cheerful, artistic scene within, with the pretty cabinet, book-shelves and trinkets that Arne had collected; and Eli looked at them all, as happy as a child. Then patting her on the shoulder, Margit told her how fond of her she had already become; and taking her to a little red chest, she unlocked it and with motherly pride and artifice took out Arne's secret treasures—fine silk neckerchiefs, pretty silk ribbons, a beautiful black dress-pattern, and the daintiest little shoes. "He has bought something every time he has been to town," said the mother.

Eli longed to take her leave; but she dared not speak, nor dared she do anything to make the mother look up.

Margit, wholly occupied with her own thoughts, said to the blushing girl, "Does it not look just as if he had bought them, one by one, for some one to whom he had not the courage to give them?"

Then, opening a little box, she disclosed to Eli's astonished eyes a broad buckle, two gold rings, tied together, and a velvet hymn-book with silver clasps. Further Eli could not look;

for on the silver of the book was engraved in small letters her own name; and tear after tear trickled down on the silk kerchief.

Then the mother closed the little box, turned round, and clasped Eli in her arms.

While Eli was sitting in the corner by the clock, waiting for supper, a short, light step was heard in the passage, and the door was gently opened. The first object Arne's eyes lighted on was the young girl in the corner. Eli got up, embarrassed, and hurried toward the wall.

"Are you here?" said Arne softly. Eli shaded her eyes with one hand, as one does when the sun shines too full in the face. He advanced a step or two. Eli turned toward him, and then, bowing her head, she burst into tears.

"God bless you, Eli," said he, and drew his arm around her. She nestled close up to him. He whispered something in her ear. She made no reply, but clasped her hands about his neck.

By and by some one was heard weeping near the table. It was the mother. "Now I am sure you will not leave me, Arne," she said, approaching him.

When Arne and Eli walked home together in the bright summer evening, they did not talk much about their new-born happiness. They let Nature herself take the lead, so quiet, bright and grand she seemed. But a hymn of thanks echoed in his heart, which when it was finished became his daily song.

In the autumn there was a wedding in the church across Black Water. It was Baard Böen who gave his daughter Eli in marriage to Arne of Kampen, son of Nils. The house was full of neighbors bustling about in the preparations for the happy occasion. Baard had something very weighty to say to his wife; so he took her up into the attic, and when he had locked the door and offered her some wine, he said, breathing heavily: "Birgit, I dare say you are thinking of the same to-day that I am." Then he heard her move from one side of the window to the other.

"Oh, yes; you know whom I mean. He it was who parted us two. I thought it would not go beyond the wedding, but it has lasted much longer."

He heard her sigh. After a long conflict, he began again.

"To-day a son of his, well-educated and handsome, becomes one of us, and to him we have given our only daughter. Now, how would it be, Birgit, if we two were to have *our* wedding to-day?"

He heard her breathe, but he got no answer. She did not even turn her head.

But when the gentle knock at the door and the soft voice of Eli was heard saying: "Are you coming, mother?" then Birgit, in a broken voice replied "Yes, I am coming now," and crossing the floor she gave Baard her hand and burst into the most passionate weeping. The two hands met, both toil-worn now, and clasped as firmly as if they had been seeking each other for twenty years.

They still clung together as they went toward the door, and when, a while later, the bridal procession was passing down to the landing-place and Arne gave his hand to Eli, to take the lead, Baard, seeing it, took his wife by the hand, contrary to all custom, and followed them, smiling contentedly.

THE FISHER-MAIDEN (1868)

This story was published simultaneously in Norway and Germany, and has been so popular that it appeared not only in the author's native tongue but in several German and English translations. Björnson's aim in this book is, as Professor Rasmus B. Anderson states it, "to show how irresistible is the power of innate vocation and natural talent, and to vindicate the theater as a place not only of amusement but also of instruction against the unjust criticisms of the clergy."

ETRA, the fisher-maiden, was born in a little fishing town in the north of Norway. Her mother was Gunlaug, a fisher-woman, who kept an inn for sailors; her great energy of character and executive ability distinguished her as "the influential man of the town," and made her inn the favorite resort for the crews of every ship in the harbor.

Petra's father was Pedro Ohlsen, an eccentric recluse, whose strange ways made him the butt of the boys and girls and a mysterious character to the townfolk. Delighting to play the flute and to listen to Gunlaug's prattle, Pedro used to row with her about the waters of the fiord, and land on its rocky isles through the lovely summer evenings, until their mutual love swept them to the limit where only marriage could save Gunlaug's good name. But when Pedro, in his selfishness and cowardice, hesitated to deal honorably with her, Gunlaug, in her indignation, seized him in her vigorous grasp, thrashed him soundly, rowed back to town, and went home on foot across the mountains. Pedro, crushed by the terrible loss which his own folly had brought upon him, shut himself up in his old house and brooded over his own wretchedness. So little did he go about that he had never even seen his own daughter, after Gunlaug's return to the town, until the roguish Petra, at the head of a small army of boys and girls, one evening made an assault upon the large apple tree in his orchard. Pedro rushed

77

out with his club after the mischievous children, and when he
had caught the screaming leader of the attack, and looked at
her curly head and forced her to tell her name and parentage,
the disclosure so shocked Pedro that he fled into the house as
if he had encountered the Evil One.

As Petra was still crying from her alarm over this adventure, a young man of graceful build and noble countenance
accosted her and sought to comfort her. This was the priest's
son, Ödegaard, who thenceforth became a dominating factor
in Petra's life. Finding that, although Petra was more than
ten years of age, she could hardly read, he insisted that it was
her mother's duty to give the child an education. Gunlaug
maintained her right to do as she pleased with the child: but
Ödegaard insisted that the girl should cultivate the faculties
with which she had been endowed, and offered to teach Petra
till the time came for her to be confirmed, when she should pass
the boundary line that in Scandinavian countries marks the
transition from girlhood to womanhood.

Under the instructions of the young man the girl grew
rapidly in intelligence and knowledge; a great zeal for study
took possession of her; romantic longings filled her mind; face
and figure developed to a remarkable beauty; and the young
teacher found himself experiencing feelings for the charming
candidate for confirmation which were hardly to be described
in terms either of theology or of abstract scholarship.

But Ödegaard was not the only one whom her loveliness
bewitched. The ardor of her glance, the fascinating manner
in which the fisher-maiden laughed, blushed, sparkled, and
glowed, set aflame the hearts of all the young men of the town.
Her coquettish ways, her inexperience of the customs of courtship, her too ready acceptance of the gifts showered on her by
the young men, and, above all, her ignorance of the deeper
currents of her own heart, led more than one of her suitors to
believe himself her accepted lover.

But when she heard that Ödegaard had returned from a
sea-voyage, which he had taken immediately after her confirmation, Petra was irresistibly impelled to rush to him; and she
nestled up to him, among the trees where they met, "as a bird
beneath the wing that is uplifted for its shelter." He clasped

her hand and they embraced for the first time; and as they sat close together, bathed in the sunset glow, both felt "how sweet is Love's first meeting."

But the happiness of the lovers was brief. Yngve Vold, the rich young merchant whose fine gold chain had been accepted by Petra, had boasted to Ödegaard that he was going to marry the pretty gypsy, and in consequence the young merchant received an immediate thrashing. Then the indignant Öde-gaard bitterly reproached Petra for her fickleness and deceit, and, declaring that she had ruined his life, cast her off and fell into a dangerous illness.

Petra was overwhelmed with remorse and misery. The peaceful village was thrown into an uproar over the love-affairs of the young coquette. The town gossips fanned this tempest in a teapot into a veritable scandal, and a mob smashed the windows of the inn and tore up the garden palings. When the riot was over, the penitent Petra was about to flee secretly from the wrecked home, when her mother intercepted her, provided her with money and a suitable disguise, and by her father's aid put her on board of a ship for Bergen, where the unfortunate girl might begin life afresh.

Bergen was a larger town than Petra had ever been in before; and the grand mountain views, the novel scenes of city life, the bustling crowds, and the ease and cheerfulness of the people, soon restored her to happiness. She was taken to the theater, where she was absolutely dazed by scenes and performances of which before that moment she had not the faintest conception. Of actors and acting she never had heard, and at first took for reality all that passed on the stage. Her excitement over the romantic stage events set everyone about her laughing and star-ing; and when the bride in the drama swooned in a tragic episode of the play, Petra, too, rose to her feet and then fell to the floor with a piercing shriek. When at length she reached home, not knowing how she came there, and had it explained to her what a drama was, and what great actors had it in their power to do, Petra started up and said, "That is what I mean to be."

In the ignorance and impetuosity of youth, she went the very next day to the manager's door and insisted that he let her

become an actress at once. But when, after hearing her recite,
he assured her she could no more act than could a leathern
boot, Petra went sobbing down the stairs, and the same afternoon left Bergen for some place inland, she cared not where,
provided it was a place where she was not known.

Petra's journey took her through darkness and tempest
to a sheltered valley far away from the sea, until at last she was
brought, by what she deemed the guidance of the Almighty,
to the house of a kind priest and his daughter. Here were
more mountains; flowers outside and inside the house; everything was cheerful, pure, and bright; she had a sweet and gentle
girl of about her own age as companion; a faithful and earnest
pastor was the head of the household; and the memory of a
sainted mother, recently deceased, filled the whole house with
its gracious atmosphere. And Petra thought: "Ah! if I might
only abide within these blessed precincts." The prudent pastor
at first refused her request. But Petra's terrible distress and
forlorn situation, and the accidental discovery that she was a
friend of Ödegaard (an old acquaintance of the family), finally
led to her admission into the household circle.

In this quiet country parsonage Petra passed several happy
and helpful years. Her love for the gentle Signe became most
devoted. The father, the village priest, was a man of a scholarship and culture far above that of his neighbors. His nature was
ardent, and as a preacher he was endowed with native powers
of eloquence. As a young man he had been somewhat narrow
in his ideas, and the doctrines he had preached were characterized by an antique gloom and bigotry. But the sweet and
broader spirit of his Danish wife combined to broaden his mind
and mellow his heart. Not only did his theological ideas become
more cheerful and progressive, but a hitherto unknown interest
in national affairs, social improvements, and modern literature
awoke within him.

One of the household customs that most vitally influenced
Petra were the evening gatherings, when the priest and his
daughter read aloud from the works of European authors.
The famous scenes from the great English and German dramatists especially thrilled her, so that soon she knew them by
heart; and when this was discovered, Petra recited both tragic

and comic scenes with such faithfulness and good expression that Signe exclaimed, "I really wish the poor actresses had an eighth part as good faculties as you have."

But this chance suggestion that Petra might desire to become a play-actor greatly alarmed the priest; and when he happened to find an exercise-book of Petra's, to which she had confided her cherished aim to become an actress and invoked God's blessing on it, as a divine calling, he was so terribly shocked that he could not find words to express his wrath. His flaming countenance, however, was enough to make Petra feel guilty and long to throw herself at Signe's feet. But though she knocked many times at Signe's door, her friend would not answer nor open to her. In her wretched loneliness, Petra climbed up to Signe's window, then fell screaming to the ground among the brambles, and was so exhausted that on the Sunday morning following she was late to church. There another blow smote her sensitive heart; for the priest's sermon, on "Lead us not into temptation," seemed to be aimed straight at her and her chosen career. In sonorous tones, the preacher severely condemned those who endangered their Christian character by pursuing sinful vocations. At the family dinner that followed they were all naturally constrained; and Petra began to feel that she must bid farewell to this quiet home, much as she loved it and its dwellers. She could not endure to see the priest sad for her sake, and she could not bear to meet Signe daily if they could not resume the loving and intimate intercourse of former days.

Petra was about to take secret flight, when sleigh-bells were heard; Ödegaard was ushered in, and, with the addition of the new personal element into the family circle, the whole household atmosphere and situation seemed changed.

Hardly had Ödegaard been welcomed and informed of recent events, when significant discussion was curiously opened. Encouraged by the priest's strong sermon against the temptations of the world, five of his own parishioners, whose views concerning popular amusements were still narrower than their pastor's, had journeyed to his house to ask him to burn or to send away the piano to whose music the inmates of the parsonage sometimes sang and danced. It was, they claimed, a source of temptation to the young of the parish.

The priest defended the use of the piano, as affording wholesome recreation, and expressed the hope that his parishioners also might occasionally, in an innocent manner, divert their minds with singing, playing, and dancing.

The parishioners were terribly shocked by this, and contended that such amusements excited the flesh to sinful lusts and to the service of Satan. The only way to serve the Lord, they said, was by giving ourselves entirely to work.

But Ödegaard and the priest pointed out that labor also had its temptations, and that even faith and prayer might do harm. They said: "There is a kind of religion that is so gloomy that it turns the whole world into a penitentiary. The religion that does good is cheerful. It is only when we are happy that we are able to see and love what is good in others."

As singing, playing, and dancing are mentioned in the Bible as commonly practiced in ancient days to the glory of God, so they may be practiced today to the glory of God if they minister to health and innocent amusement. "They are an indirect way of praising Him who gave us health and loves to preserve in us the hearts of children," was the priest's argument.

These cases of conscience were vehemently debated, and the austere parishioners seemed to be getting the worst of it, when one of them made a masterly flank movement by suggesting that if the pastor's views were logically carried out they would justify also all sorts of fiction, poetry, and even the drama.

The priest warmly defended the reading of verses and tales, and the use of figures of speech and imaginative pictures in literature, inasmuch as they are authorized by their customary use in the Bible, and also by the great Protestant leader, Martin Luther.

But when confronted with the analogous question of the allowableness of the drama the priest was filled with apprehension, and his dialectic victory over his parishioners was by no means unqualified.

A train of thought had been awkened within him that he could not easily quiet. Soon another discussion, begun independently among his city guests at dinner one day, over the moral or immoral status of the theater, forced him to clear up his own convictions on this subject, which in the of case Petra now came home so close to him. In addition to Ödegaard and a narrow-minded chaplain, a sea-captain and several priests were present. The discussion in which they joined soon grew quite heated. The chaplain, while admitting that a good play might be performed by amateurs before a private company, held that the life of an actor was so full of temptation that it was everyone's duty to shun it. He said that the feigned scenes and actions of the stage awakened morbid appetites in the spectators; and that earnest Christians could find sin before the curtain as well as behind it.

Ödegaard, however, warmly defended the calling of the actor, asserting that all men were actors, every day of their lives; and that he in whom the dramatic talent predominated should not neglect a gift which the Creator had given, to the end that it be developed to the greatest possible perfection. He pointed out that, while the actor's life had many temptations, that the same was true of most callings, even that of the priests, saying that the danger of having the emotions excited, of acquiring a morbid appetite for hearing passionate and fanciful declamations, and of appropriating to oneself the character of models of virtue, was certainly present in the church no less than in the theater.

This bold statement caused a great clamor and confusion, which was further increased by his saying (as Petra and the other ladies opened the door) that, while he accorded no license to actors, he believed they had a great mission in the world. "Actors," he said with emphasis, "frequently become the instrument of some grand work in the hand of Providence."

As Ödegaard resumed his seat, several would-be speakers took the floor, and everyone began to speak at the same time; the uproar was quieted only by the sweet voice of Signe singing one of her beautiful ballads. When her auditors had been thus calmed and uplifted, Signe introduced Petra, who recited to the delight of all a long and beautiful poem, "The life of a Viking bold."

After Petra had electrified her audience with her unaffected and thrilling recitation, Signe led the merry voices of the whole company in a national song.

At the supper that followed the priest sat quiet, absorbed in thought. His perturbed mind was clearing up and he was beginning to see more clearly the leading of Providence, and to what his duty called him. At length, as the others were about to rise, he tapped his wine-glass and said:

"I have a betrothal to announce." Then he added: "I am free to confess that at first I was not in favor of it. To tell the truth, I did not think the bridegroom worthy of the bride."

Everybody was excessively embarrassed until the priest explained: "The bridegroom's name is Art, the great Histrionic Art; and his betrothed is Petra, my foster-daughter;" and he added to the announcement his blessing, and his hopes that the union might be happy.

Petra threw herself into the priest's arms, and then gratefully thanked Ödegaard, to whom, she declared, she owed it all.

"No, Petra," was Ödegaard's answer, "I have only acted the part of a good brother. It was wrong of me to wish to become more. For had that happened, your whole career would have been a failure."

From this time all the tangled threads and conflicting currents in the lives of the three were straightened; and the many mistakes and confused impulses of Petra's past were discerned in their proper bearing on the high mission to which she now found herself called.

As Petra had gradually become more and more absorbed in thoughts of the artistic career for which Nature had obviously intended her, so Ödegaard and Signe, through their interest in her dramatic ambitions and development, were gradually drawn together; and in Signe's constant sweetness and cordiality he found the peace of mind and of heart that Petra's restless impulsiveness and absorption in her dramatic work had failed to give him.

In the spring, Pedro Ohlsen passed away, leaving a considerable property to Petra, on the simple condition that her mother should confide to Petra his parental relation to her—a bequest most helpful and encouraging to her aspiration to appear on the stage.

Ödegaard found for himself congenial work by opening in

the parish a popular high-school; and Petra departed to the
Norwegian capital to begin her dramatic career.

One evening, just before Christmas, all the tickets were sold
for the performance at the theater in Christiania in which a new
actress, sprung from the people, but of unusual promise, was to
make her appearance. All Petra's friends, and the chief person-
ages who had in any way touched the course of her life, were
among the audience; Yngve Vold and Gunnar Ask, her early
suitors; Ödegaard and Signe, his bride, just back from a happy
wedding trip; the dark-haired priest, her loyal friend; and
Gunlaug, the snow-haired mother, with her tall figure and sun-
burnt countenance.

The audience were full of anticipation and sympathy.
Each felt as if he were the one that was to make his own début.
Many prayers rose to heaven, even from souls that seldom
prayed. Petra, with beating heart, sat behind the scenes and
listened to Oehlenschlaeger's overture to *Axel and Valborg*,
which was the tragedy Petra had heard on the first occasion
when she went to the theater.

"Peace pervaded the harmonies, and they gradually dissolved as into sunlight."

The overture closed. Anxious silence ensued. Then the
curtain rose; and Petra's life-bark was launched on its brilliant career.

WILLIAM BLACK

(Scotland, 1841-1898)

THE MONARCH OF MINCING LANE (1871)

This author was regarded as having no superior in depicting English life in the nineteenth century. The following tale of middle-class society is among his best known works.

HILIP DREM, only son of the greatest merchant in Mincing Lane, London, had just quarreled with his sweetheart, and was wondering whether he could ever love any other woman, when he read in the *Times* that a ship consigned to his father had gone down with all on board. The news pained him greatly, for Captain Seaford of the lost vessel was his father's cousin, and had endeared himself to Philip, when he was a boy, with many wonderful tales and songs of the sea.

The elder Drem had treated Seaford badly in past days, but Philip resolved that he would provide for the captain's family. Hurrying to his father's office, he learned that Mrs. Seaford, with her daughter, had come up from her Devonshire home to London to await her husband's return, and had gone out of the merchant's office after being informed of her bereavement. Although almost penniless, she had recalled Drem's cruelty to her husband and indignantly refused to accept assistance from the merchant.

Philip overtook the two women in the street and was recognized by the widow, who, like her husband, had loved him dearly as a boy. Mrs. Seaford had taken lodgings in London, but now she knew not where to go or what to do; so Philip, with a warm heart and full pocket, took her to Hampstead, the home of "Jims" Lawson, an honest, sturdy ex-weaver, with whom the young man had become acquainted while studying the so-called lower classes for the purpose of enlarging his views of political economy and perhaps fitting himself to enter Parliament.

Although he was very sorry for the widow, Philip could not help observing, on the way to Hampstead, that the daughter, who was hardly a woman as yet, had beautiful golden-brown hair framing a smooth white forehead, large violet-blue eyes with long lashes. and a lovely mouth, and that she was far prettier than the saucy-eyed, fascinating sweetheart with whom he had quarreled. But the latter was a woman in society; Lilian Seaford, although modest, was as frank and unconscious as a child.

Philip's interest in the Seafords became constant and practical. He saw that their every need was supplied, and his imagination busily devised sources from which Mrs. Seaford could not refuse to accept money. She and the Lawsons believed that he was as good as engaged to a lady in the city, so none of them imagined any other reason for his frequent visits to Lawson's cottage than friendly regard for the wife and child of his cheery old friend Tom Seaford. With Lilian he was masterful and almost blunt, though never unkind; it was that same masterful way of insisting on changes of manner that had caused his disagreement with his city sweetheart. He freely criticised Lilian's speech, her tastes, even her dress, and she listened as meekly as an obedient child; yet all the while he was studying her intently, until he came to know her almost as well as he knew his own soul, and found her nature wholly honest, admirable and charming.

Lilian in return admired him greatly; he was not only the first gentleman she had ever met, but her first frank and close friend. But one day she suddenly learned that she loved him; then she became so shy and reserved, so distant and strange that Philip discovered that the little maiden had taken full possession of his heart.

It was not long before the great merchant in Mincing Lane became very angry over what he heard of Philip's new attachment. Richard Drem had long wished that his son would marry Violet Kingscote, daughter of a baronet with more character and social distinction than money; and, as Violet and Philip were friends, the wish had become a belief, especially as Sir James Kingscote had been made to understand that in the event of such union of the families Mr. Drem would help the baronet out of some unfortunate business ventures. Now the old man, who was as autocratic in his home as in business circles, threatened to stop Philip's allowance and turn him out of the house.

The blow fell when Philip announced his intention to marry Tom Seaford's daughter. In Lilian's eyes, the only bar to their union had seemed to be Philip's wealth and social position; the young man quickly removed this by becoming, through necessity, a London cabman; for, like many another rich youth, he knew nothing practically of any business but the management of horses. Richard Drem was furious; he had already said to Philip's cousin Arthur, who aspired to heirship of the Mincing Lane millions, that he would give two thousand pounds to anyone who would thwart Philip by winning the girl away from him. Arthur persuaded one Hickes, an imaginative and bibulous playwright, to make the attempt, and the tool actually succeeded, by threat of shooting himself in her presence, in forcing the girl to marry him.

The couple separated immediately on leaving the church. Philip urged Lilian to disavow a marriage so brutally imposed upon her; but the girl's simple, straight-forward honesty—the first quality to impress her character on Philip's heart—was proof against all argument; she had given her word, and she must maintain it inviolate.

Philip was rescued from cab-driving and restored to his old social set by his friend Lord Cecil Sidmouth, who obtained for him the secretaryship of the Analytical Society at a salary that would support him comfortably. The elder Drem, who really loved his son, was so seriously affected by the first unyielding opposition he had ever encountered that he fell ill and believed himself at the point of death; his wife, Philip's stepmother, who had always loved her husband's son and humored him in every way, was wretched, so Philip became somewhat reconciled to his family, and also saw much of Violet Kingscote, who had been his confidante in his two love-affairs.

But serious trouble came quickly to Violet and Philip. The affairs of Sir James Kingscote had been going from bad to worse; his modest fortune had been invested in the shares of a railway company that not only paid no dividends but was so badly managed that the shares were almost valueless in the market; there seemed nothing for the baronet but to sell his home estate, which would be almost as humilitating an experience as could befall a self-respecting English gentleman; it would also greatly injure Violet's standing in society. Richard Drem, who had recovered his health and his determination to have his own way in everything, was willing and anxious to save Kingscote by assuming his obligations, but only on condition that Philip should wed Violet.

Philip gave the matter much serious thought, and discussed it with Violet. Evidently Lilian was lost to him, for although she unchangingly resisted the appeals of the man who had wedded her, who was so remorseful that he longed to make such reparation as he might, she remained true to her word and vow. Philip loved Violet as a friend, and she returned his regard; she was not plighted to any other man; could not two such friends marry, trusting that in time a closer affection might come of their union? With the fortunes of so fine a man as Sir James Kingscote in jeopardy, was not the experiment justifiable?

Philip satisfied himself that it was, although he still loved Lilian as dearly as ever. Violet almost consented, being deeply affected by Philip's devotion to her father; she and Philip were seen together so much that there was general rumor that they were engaged, and neither of them denied it. Philip had hoped that appearances would loosen his father's purse-strings for the baronet's relief, but Richard Drem remained obdurate and imperious; not a penny should leave his hands until after the wedding.

Philip's friend Lord Cecil Sidmouth, who, although not a rich man, had relinquished the secretaryship with which he rescued Philip from the cab-driver's box, had always leaned toward socialistic theories and experiments. Shortly after Philip's engagement to Violet was rumored Lord Cecil went to the United States, intending to spend ten years with a new socialistic community that had been established there. Philip was charged by Violet, greatly to his amazement, with having sent Lord Cecil away; slowly, and from Violet's own lips, he learned what no one had ever suspected: Violet loved Lord Cecil and was loved by him, although his comparative poverty had kept him from formally declaring himself. Philip denied the charge and proved his innocence; Violet relented, and now that her real lover seemed lost to her, she consented to become engaged to Philip. Yet he and she were as unhappy as people whose hearts were elsewhere could be.

One day the unexpected came handsomely to the relief of the Kingscotes and to Violet's far-away lover. An eccentric old bachelor member of the Analytical Society, of which Philip had been secretary, died, leaving to Philip his entire fortune of twenty-three thousand pounds in bank. The young man immediately insisted that Violet's father should accept the greater portion of this legacy, to relieve him from his financial embarrassments. Then he formally broke his engagement with Violet and sailed for the United States to bring Lord Cecil Sidmouth back to his own. Violet went alone to see him off, and kissed him with hearty friendship.

Lord Cecil was enduring his fate bravely, and he professed to be entirely satisfied with the socialistic enterprise and his duties therein; but when his mind had been disabused of some misunderstandings of affairs at home he was quite willing to drop everything and hurry back to England and Violet.

Meanwhile unhappy Lilian never had lost her love for Philip, and occasionally he went out to Hempstead to see her. But the miserable Hickes still lived. His ill-gotten money did not bring him the satisfaction he had expected; weak and vacillating, he became a drunkard, and was by turns remorseful, complaining, maudlin, and desperate, yet he continually longed for the unhappy woman, now doubly orphaned, whom he called his wife, and he made many appeals to her that brought him only the pity that Lilian would have felt for a worthless, yet suffering animal. Violet once found Philip's mind so far away while he should have been manifesting some interest in what she had been saying, that she asked him of what he was thinking so deeply, and he replied: "I am thinking that there is a man alive whom I may have to murder yet. I think it will come to that."

One day Arthur Drem sought out Hickes and informed him that Philip had learned of his father's share in the villainy of which Lilian had been the victim; that Philip was out of his father's house forever, and that Hickes would do well to keep out of his way. It was an inopportune time for Arthur's visit, for Hickes, who had been drinking heavily, had purchased a pistol and some ammunition, and was shooting so wildly in his own lodgings that Arthur barely escaped a bullet. He made haste to leave the house, but suddenly encountered his cousin Philip, who insisted that he should return and witness an act of justice. Arthur unwillingly complied, for Philip forced him into the house. There being no response to repeated knocks at Hickes's door, Philip broke it open. When the two men entered the room Hickes lay dead on the floor; beside him was a pistol, and on the table was an unfinished letter to Lilian, asking her forgiveness and saying he was about to do his best for her.

Philip left the house and the country, but after a few days of wandering he hurried to the Hampstead cottage and Lilian. No explanations were asked or needed by either; both recalled happy days they had passed together and talked much of Devonshire, where Lilian had lived with her mother until her fateful visit to London, where Philip had once taken her on a tour of scenes familiar and dear to her, and where, if she so desired, he would gladly take her again, or to any other part of the world in which she might prefer to live, so that it was some place in which he and she could never again be separated.

THE STRANGE ADVENTURES OF A PHAETON (1872)

The versatility of this author is nowhere better shown than in this story of English woods and fields, country lanes and winding rivers, sunsets and sunrises.

WELL-TO-DO English trio, consisting of the Lady Tita, her husband, and their dearly loved ward, Bell, began a winter's evening delightfully by devising a long, leisurely summer tour, by phaeton, of Wales and the North Country all the way to Scotland. They would use the old coaching roads, sometimes the by-roads, stop at the curious little inns, chat with the country folk, sit on the hillsides in the long evenings and sing ballads, sketch bits of landscape, and also fill the mind's eye with enough beautiful views to last almost a lifetime. They already had the phaeton, with the trusty horses Castor and Pollux; Bell had a guitar on which to play accompaniments for the ballads, and she could also be trusted for the sketches, for she was already an artist who had "exhibited." All that seemed needed was somebody to occupy the fourth seat of the phaeton and, incidentally, be a companion for Bell.

Suddenly the head of the family opened a hornet's nest by suggesting that Count Von Rosen, a young cavalry lieutenant, should be invited over from Germany to join the party and have a look at England. The two ladies disliked Germans in general and German officers in particular; for the Franco-Prussian war was still fresh in their minds, and their sympathies had been with France. Besides, they had met the Count some years before in his native land, and Bell said:

"I can remember him only as a very rude and greedy boy who showed a great row of white teeth when he laughed and made bad jokes about my mistakes in German. And now, I dare say, he is a tall fellow with a stiff neck, a brown face, perhaps a beard, a clanking sword and the air of a Bobadil."

But time can prepare the human mind to endure almost anything or anybody. When summer came and the trio was ready for the journey Von Rosen arrived, for he had been invited to join the party, after all. The ladies received him courteously yet in a half defiant way, as if to show that they were not to be overawed by any tall, browned, big-bearded young man. But insensibly and in a few minutes they became quite familiar with him, apparently won over by his careless laughter, by the honest stare of his blue eyes, and by a very boyish blush that sometimes overspread his handsome face when he stammered over an idiom or was asked some question about his own military exploits.

German officers are popularly supposed to regard the best of women as mere upper servants, but in the first day's drive the lieutenant made himself an unobtrusive yet effective squire. The trip ended at Twickenham, where Tita had two sons at school with Dr. Arburthnot, to whose son Arthur the gentle Bell was supposed to be "as good as engaged." Arthur, a young and as yet briefless barrister, with a nice face and a budding moustache, disliked the German at sight and became gloomily jealous. Von Rosen regarded him pityingly.

"He is not practical," he said. Arthur had declined to drink beer with him and knew nothing of the care of horses, to which task the lieutenant had addressed himself. "He has not seen much; he is moody and nervous and thinks much about trifles." As for Bell, the lieutenant pronounced her " a—what do you say?—a type of the pretty young Englishwoman; well formed, open-eyed, with good healthy color in her face, and very frank and gentle and independent all at the same time." When informed that Bell would probably marry Arthur, the German replied: "That will be very good for him, for she will look after him and give him some common sense. You know, all the best women marry stupid men."

Before the evening was over Bell was greatly mortified by Arthur's insulting manner to the German guest, and was grateful that the lieutenant received the young man's rude remarks with only mild-eyed surprise. When music was suggested as a diversion, Von Rosen sang an old German war ballad in a manner that delighted the ladies, but Arthur sat silent and stared; when Bell volunteered a German song Arthur's face became a study in grays and greens.

The next morning before breakfast the lieutenant had scoured the vicinity and brought back a Shetland pony which he gave to Tita's boys, an act which raised him greatly in the estimation of the ladies. Arthur had already hurried to London, to the relief of everybody, although later in the day, when the phaeton again took the road, Bell's eyes showed that she had been crying. The suggestion that probably within two or three days Arthur would drop down on the party, at an inn caused Bell to exclaim:

"I hope he will not do that! If he does, I know something dreadful will happen. You don't know what a temper he has at times."

Before the second day ended Tita and Bell ceased to fear that their guest might manifest some of the objectionable qualities supposedly inherent in German officers. He did not smoke continually, or smoke a pipe at all; he was uniformly cheerful, deferential, and adaptive; he knew much of music, fiction, poetry and history; English scenery delighted him greatly and so did English inns; he was a trusty whip and cared for the horses as faithfully as if they were his own. He had not fallen in love with Bell at sight, after the traditional manner of soldiers; as to that, his heart had been severely wounded within a few weeks by a bewitching German actress, but he confessed to Tita's husband: "When I look at your Miss Bell here, why, I see the difference."

On the third day of the journey the head of the family observed that any of the numerous small articles that had been confided to Bell's care were forthcoming at a moment's notice. It had not been so on other of the family's trips by phaeton, but now Bell did not trouble herself to look for them; she merely turned inadvertently toward the lieutenant. He was richly rewarded, for the girl found him an interesting talker, and she listened so well that at Oxford, where Tita and her husband took the oars of a boat, with Bell for coxswain, the girl was attending more to the young man's words than to her tiller-ropes—a fact which caused Tita's husband to say to himself:

"As for him, what man would not have looked contented

under these conditions?—to be strong, healthy, handsome, and only twenty-five; to have comfortable means and an assured future; to have come out of a long campaign with honor and sound limbs; to be off on a careless holiday through the most beautiful country, take it for all and all, in the world, and to be lying lazily in a boat on a summer's evening on a pretty English river, with a pretty English girl showing her friendly interest and attention in every glance of her blue eyes?"

Yet when Bell found at Oxford a letter from Arthur she could hardly keep her eyes dry at the dinner table. Von Rosen, who although not inquisitive was observant, was for kicking Arthur, if he could be found, and throwing him into the river. Arthur did appear in the evening; the next day would be Sunday, on which no well-bred English people would continue a pleasure-jaunt in a phaeton or any other kind of vehicle. The day passed miserably for every one; Bell had a headache and did not come down to dinner. The lieutenant, abetted by Tita, was for getting away early Monday morning, before Arthur could again inflict himself on the party, but just as the seats of the phaeton filled Arthur appeared from somewhere and said, as he handed a letter up to Bell:

"Bell, I—I have—there is something here I want you to see—only a moment, and you can give me an answer now—yes or no—"

At that instant the horse Pollux, casting his head about and longing to start, managed to fix his bit on the end of the phaeton's pole. A wild scene ensued; people flew in every direction; the lieutenant sprang to the horses' heads and was dragged along for some distance, with a little injury to himself; Arthur's answer was necessarily delayed, and the day passed as pleasantly as if the young barrister did not exist; so pleasantly, indeed, that the lieutenant expressed a wonder to Tita's husband whether, if a man were to change his country, he would not choose England out of all other countries to live in. He talked of coming back to England, be naturalized and remain, saying in self-defense:

"Patriotism? That is very good, but one need not make it a fetish. Perhaps I have more right to be patriotic in a country that I choose for my own than in a country where I am born without any choice of my own."

But, despite all its charms of scenery and companionship, England contained also Arthur. That unhappy youth appeared and reappeared as the phaeton's journey continued, and always served as a very wet blanket. What joy might have come to him had he, like the German, been unvaryingly more thoughtful of Bell than of himself is aside from the point, for in the course of one of his visits he sang an insulting parody of a ballad which Bell had often rendered most tenderly. Not long afterward he said, as he gave the girl a handful of forget-me-nots:

"They are typical of woman's constancy, are they not?—for they keep fresh about half a dozen hours." Bell took them without betraying vexation, but she said:

"Count Von Rosen, do you care to have one of these? You have very pretty songs about the forget-me-not in Germany." Von Rosen instantly became the most grateful man in all England. The journey continued day by day, week by week; two young people can become very well acquainted on such a trip if the man is unchangingly considerate, unselfish, reverent, and useful while the girl is being tormented by the remembrance of a man who displays none of these social virtues.

Early on the party's first morning in Scotland Tita and her husband saw a boy trudging to school; a moment later Bell, returning with the lieutenant from an ante-breakfast walk, dashed at the boy, chatted with him, and gave him two half crowns. It occurred to Tita that girls not blessed with super-abundant money do not habitually give coins so large to chance-met boys without profound emotional cause. Bell crossed the street, looking vastly pleased and proud, yet avoided Tita's eyes as she hurried into the inn.

"Madame," said the lieutenant, with a great apparent effort, while he kept his eyes on the pavement and an extra touch of color was visible on his brown cheeks, "Madame, I— I am asked—indeed, Mademoiselle, she was good enough— she is to be my wife—and she asked me if I would tell you—" He took Tita's hand in his, as if to thank her for a great gift.

Before the excursion ended the lieutenant had asked many questions as to the best part of England, near London, for a married man to live in if he had an income of about eight hundred pounds a year, and Bell, although an artist by profession, had consulted Tita regarding the best colors for a dining-room. Tita's husband, reviewing the affair, said later:

"As we drove on through the clear, warm day, careless and content, the two women had all the talking to themselves, and a strange use they made of their opportunities. If the guardian angels of these two creatures happen to have any sense of humor, they must have laughed as they looked down and overheard. You may remember that when it was first proposed to take this Prussian lieutenant with us on our summer tour both Bell and my lady professed the most deadly hatred of the German nation. That was about six months before. Now, thirty millions of people, either in the south or north of Europe, don't change their collective character, if such a thing exists, within the space of six months; but on this bright morning you would have fancied that the women were vying with each other to prove that all the domestic virtues and all the science and learning of civilization and all the arts that beautify life were the exclusive property of the Germans. My lady was a later convert; had she not made merry only the other day over Bell's naïve confession that she thought the German nation as good as the French nation? But now that she had gone over to the enemy she altogether distanced Bell in the production of theories, facts, quotations, and downright personal opinions. She had lived a little longer, you see, and perhaps she had a trifle more audacity in suppressing awkward facts. At all events, the lieutenant was partly abashed and partly amused by her warm advocacy of German character, literature, music and a thousand other things."

A PRINCESS OF THULE (1873)

This story became the greatest favorite of all the author's works, on both sides of the Atlantic, and tourists have for years visited the supposed haunts of the shy "Princess."

WO Englishmen — Edward Ingram — small, interesting, with brown hair streaked with gray; of the London Board of Trade—and Frank Lavender—much his junior—blond, talented and living on the generosity of a queer old rich aunt, arrived for a month's fishing and hunting on the Island of Lewis, in the Northern Hebrides. Ingram, having been there before, was warmly welcomed by the chief man in the town of Boeva, and his daughter Sheila.

Lavender was impressionable and romantic and promptly fell in love with Sheila, whom Lavender called "the Princess of Thule," because her father, a rough but amiable old man, named Mackenzie, was called the "King of Borva." The young girl, who had lost her mother in infancy, had become, under her father's instruction, proficient in all sorts of sports, such as boating and fishing, and also could sing the Highland ballads. She was tall, fine-looking, with clear complexion and dark hair, and was much interested in the welfare of the simple fisher folk, sympathizing with them in all their joys and sorrows. Lavender soon joined her in these expeditions, and not only learned to think the Island of Lewis the most enchanting place in the world, but the Gaelic dialect the sweetest English. At the end of the month, through the good offices of Ingram— his mentor and friend—he sailed away with Sheila's promise that he might return.

After six months of London, during which time he broke the news of his affair with Sheila to his queer old aunt, he returned to Borva, married Sheila and took her to London.

The bridal pair were welcomed in London by Ingram. He had been unable to attend the wedding in the Highlands, and first saw her as Mrs. Lavender in the pretty house her husband, through the generosity of his aunt, had arranged for her. Troubled by the new sights, sounds, and ways of a strange city, and by the efforts to become accustomed to the society in which her husband moved, how more than welcome to Sheila was the voice of the old friend who knew her father, his home, and the Island of Lewis!

Lavender took a studio near their house, but not being obliged to work he soon began to walk and drive in the park with the old friends of his bachelor days.

Sheila, being left alone, took her solitary walks with Bras, a dog she had brought from her island home; but later, after he had killed a deer in the public park, she remained at home, always supposing her husband to be working in his studio.

Lavender had among his acquaintances two charming Americans, both widows—Mrs. Kavanagh and her daughter, Mrs. Lorraine. Sheila had met them on her entrance into society but, her husband, not having much to do, got in the habit of calling on them alone, and making excuses for his wife's absence. One day, however, they all arranged to go to Brighton together. Sheila was delighted because she was to see the ocean again, but her happiness was short—this was not the wild shore like that of her island home and there were no simple fisher folk; brick buildings were stiff and built in rows, as in London itself, and she was greatly disappointed.

One morning her husband informed her he would ride with Mrs. Lorraine—a pastime he continued daily during their stay at Brighton—to Sheila's surprise and secret chagrin.

Ingram, who had run down to Brighton, found that all this thoughtless neglect had made Sheila very unhappy. He remonstrated with Lavender, who, in not very measured terms told him practically to mind his business, and later forbade Sheila to have anything more to do with him.

Ingram concluded, for Sheila's sake, to speak in remonstrance to Mrs. Lorraine herself. Disturbed, uncertain how to approach society ladies in their own drawing-room, without an introduction, he nevertheless took a hansom, drove to the house and sent up his card.

Instead of meeting a dashing widow, he was completely disarmed by the appearance of a slight young woman, with clear, pale complexion, light hair and large gray eyes, who received him graciously, as a friend of whom she had heard Mr. Lavender speak. After a few sentences, he broached the delicate subject of persuading them to get Mrs. Lavender to go out more, in fact, always when her husband was invited. This they seemed not only willing but anxious to do; indeed, to do them justice, they had frequently asked her to accompany them before, but now Frank Lavender was not left long in doubt as to their attitude. The next time he undertook to decline an invitation for his wife, without giving her the opportunity of accepting it, he was politely, but firmly, made aware that the invitation was considered declined unless Sheila could accompany him.

Sheila, all through these days of unhappiness, had kept one secret close within her heart; this was a coming visit from Mairi, her cousin, who in the democratic simplicity of life on the Island of Lewis, had acted as a serving-maid in Sheila's home. This little lassie was to bring with her as much of the island as she could put in her trunk—peat, heather, and shells, to make Lavender's smoking-room look like the old house in the Highlands, as a surprise, Sheila fondly hoping that it would turn his thoughts to the happy days on the Island, and that he might take her for a visit to her old home. But, just as all was ready, he came in and shattered her hopes with: "Sheila, what nonsense is this? Look here, I wish you'd give up this grotto-making until to-morrow. Mrs. Kavanagh, Mrs. Lorraine, and Lord Alfred Redmond are coming here to luncheon at two." When he heard that Mairi had arrived from Stornoway, he ejaculated, "Your cousin! don't be ridiculous, Sheila; you know very well that Mairi is nothing more or less than a scullery maid, and I suppose you mean to take her out of the kitchen and put her to sit down at the table with them. Is not that so? Surely I have some right to know what guests you invite, that I may be able, at least, to ask my friends not to come near the house while they are in it."

"That I did not tell you before—yes, that was a pity," said Sheila, sadly and calmly, "but it will be no trouble to you. When Mrs. Lorraine comes up at two o'clock, there will be luncheon for her friends. She will not have to sit down with any of my relatives or with me, for if they are not fit to meet her, I am not, and it is not any great matter that I do not meet her at two o'clock." Sheila then ordered luncheon for two o'clock; took Mairi and her luggage in a cab and a sum of money her father had given her, and went to her husband's aunt, Mrs. Lavender, to ask what to do and where to find lodgings.

The aunt, invalid though she was, was in a rage against her nephew. After indulging in some caustic remarks, and making her caller thoroughly uncomfortable, she insisted that Sheila and her cousin should remain in her house for a time, promising that her nephew should not be told of their presence there; and then she sent for Ingram.

Meanwhile Lavender had heard from the servants of Sheila's departure, and when she did not return to dinner, or during the evening, by twelve o'clock the truth burst upon him that she had left him, and he rushed to see Ingram. Ingram was thoroughly aroused, and gave Lavender a severe lecture, to which he listened meekly, overwhelmed by sorrow and remorse. Toward dawn the two men went to Lavender's home. They passed through the room that poor Sheila had so lovingly arranged like the one at Lewis; a bed was found for Ingram, and Lavender, exhausted, threw himself on a sofa. The next day he went to Glasgow and Greenock to see whether his wife had taken passage home on any vessel; but she had not been seen there.

When Ingram reached the house of Lavender's aunt, in obedience to her summons, he found her bolstered up in bed, but still energetic. She anathematized her nephew, and commented on his wife, and then informed Ingram that she had sent for him to inform nim that she intended to bequeath him all her money. He remonstrated, saying it should go to her nephew. But she would not agree to that; and when he suggested Sheila, she still insisted that she would leave it to Ingram, and that he should look after her and her property, in trust, if he wished. Then she sent for Sheila, who, to Ingram's amazement, immediately entered the room. This surprise made the withered, hickory-nut face of the old lady look like that of a joyful witch. Burdened with this secret, Ingram returned to Lavender with Sheila's message, that she was well and that he need not be anxious about her; and he also told him she was in London. But he was soon to be relieved of his burden, for Mosenberg, a young Jewish musician whom they both knew, rushed up to them with the news: "Oh, do you know, I have found out where Mrs. Lavender is, yes? She is at your aunt's house." Ingram was vexed, but Lavender said, "It does not matter in the least, I shall not seek to disturb her; I am about to leave London."

Sheila found lodgings in Pembroke Road, South Kensington, and when writing to her father she added the new address as a postscript. When the "King of Borva" read it far away in his island home, he took the next boat to London and to Sheila, and upon his breast she told her story. Though wounded and angry he professed to make light of it, and she was greatly relieved and comforted by his cheerful manner, and to feel that the dreaded disclosure was over, though her father would not be persuaded to take the separation seriously. While they were still talking, word came that the old aunt, who had summoned her relatives very often to her deathbed, had had another fit and really died. Shortly after, they reached the house with its dusty ivy and drawn shutters. A letter was put into Sheila's hands to read. It was from Lavender to his aunt, saying he thanked her for the liberal allowance she had made him for some time past, but that he was going to ask her to stop it, as he was about to go to the West Highlands to paint, to try to earn his own living, and asking her to take charge of the house and of everything that did not belong to Sheila. It ended: "Be as kind to Sheila as I have been cruel to her. In going away from her I feel as though I were exiled by man and forsaken by God." It was said that after receiving this letter his aunt had intended to leave everything to Sheila, but had died before the will could be altered, and all the property was still bequeathed to Mr. Ingram.

Lavender went to Tarbert, a little fishing town near Loch Tyne, and there painted assiduously sea views and landscapes, which sold well. At Tarbert he met Johnny Eyre—a youth fond of boating and shooting and with just enough money to permit him to live an idle life. Later Lavender went to Jura, lonely and sad, but always painting industriously. One day he was surprised by a visit from Johnny and young Mosenberg, the Jewish musician. He had learned of his aunt's death through an old newspaper, a fortnight after the funeral; but Mosenberg told him how she had disposed of her property; also that Ingram was going to marry Mrs. Lorraine, and that Sheila was still in Lewis.

When Johnny and Mosenberg went north Lavender joined them. The yacht Phœbe skirted the Island of Lewis, and ran up into Loch Raag to Borvabost. When Lavender saw once more the square dark house, with its scarlet copings, where Sheila lived, it seemed like coming home and he half expected to see her come out; then remembering he might be recognized, he went into the stateroom and sat alone, silent and miserable.

Seeing a yacht at anchor in the bay, old Mr. Mackenzie sent an invitation to the gentlemen on board of her to come up to his house; Lavender would not go, but Johnny dressed himself in his best blue jacket with brass buttons and went. He was so perturbed by having the secret of Lavender's presence on the yacht on his usually open heart, and at the idea of meeting the handsome Mrs. Lavender in her own home, that he was ready much too soon, and not having given the dwellers at the house sufficient time for preparation, he found no one to meet him.

Through a window he saw a bright light which showed him the great paintings on the walls of the dining room and illumined the white tablecloth and sparkling crystal. A beautiful young girl, in a light blue gown, was lighting two candles; then she knelt down beside a wonderful little bassinet of pink and white, and he heard the lullaby sung by the mother, Sheila, to her child. Mairi appeared and ushered him in, and in a moment he found himself speaking to Mrs. Lavender, who gave her little boy to Mairi to put to bed. During dinner Mr. Mackenzie inquired whether Johnny knew an artist named Lavender, who painted pictures. Johnny descanted enthusiastically on his works of art, and said he lived in Jura.

When Johnny returned to the yacht he hardly knew how to tell the great news; but finding Lavender alone in the cabin, waiting anxiously for him, he simply said, when asked whether he had seen Sheila, "Yes, I have, Lavender, and she was rocking a child in a cradle."

The next morning Mackenzie and his daughter visited the great yacht, neither being aware of Lavender's proximity. Johnny and Mosenberg were aghast at their appearance. The instant Mackenzie saw Mosenberg's face the truth flashed upon him, and expecting any moment to see Lavender appear, he sent Sheila ashore to prepare luncheon at the house for them all; but Lavender had gone on the island early in the morning, and when Sheila went home she found him with his head resting on the table and his face buried in his hands. He did not hear her come in until she knelt beside him and said, "I beg your forgiveness," Starting, as if she were a spirit, he said, "Sheila, it is I who ought to be there and you know it."

As soon as Sheila had left the yacht, Mosenberg told Mackenzie that Lavender was on the island, and the old man, anxious for the reconciliation which should make his child happy, was delighted when he saw Sheila on the shore with her hand over her husband's arm.

There was a joyful evening in the old room with its curiously painted walls, and Sheila sang her Highland songs. Lavender planned to build a house, which should contain a large studio, in Borvabost, from the profits of the sale of his paintings.

While all these events were happening Mr. Ingram had married Mrs. Lorraine, and after a time they made a delightful visit to their friends, the Lavenders, in their new home at Borvabost, on the Island of Lewis, in the Northern Hebrides.

MACLEOD OF DARE (1878)

The heroine of this story was drawn from real life—the model being a popular English actress, whose tragic end suggested the writing of her experience.

IR KEITH MACLEOD of Castle Dare, on the rocky island of Mull, was the youngest and last remaining of his mother's six sons, as well as the fourth brother to bear the family title. One by one the others had left their home, impelled by the martial instinct of their race, and all had died bravely in battle; so when Sir Keith bade his mother good-by for the first time Lady Macleod's heart was full of sad forebodings, although her boy was only going up to London for a few weeks.

Yet what was there to fear? Keith was a manly, cleanhearted youth; he had all the courage and daring of the Macleod's, but an only son would not desert his mother. He was devoted to his home, his mother, and his cousin Janet, who was his mother's companion. Although the family was poor and the castle meagerly furnished, the Macleod moors and forests never had been rented to wealthy sportsmen, so the lad had shooting that many noblemen coveted. His yacht *Umpire*, though old, was stanch and well-manned, and he was almost worshiped by his few retainers, especially by old Hamish, who had taught him fishing, shooting, sailing, and all other Highland sports. Surely the young Baronet would soon return to his own.

London contained some Highland families whom Keith had met at home during the hunting seasons, or who knew him by reputation for a handsome youth with fine spirits and a proud air; and Lieutenant Ogilvie, with whom he had shared a Highland tutor when both were boys, was glad to introduce him in society. Yet when Keith first found himself at luncheon in a fine London house his trepidation was so great that he was glad the room was semi-darkened. But the hostess was very gracious of manner, and Miss Gertrude White, the young lady beside him, had a voice so low and musical as to be delightfully soothing. Miss White had rippling golden-brown hair and heavy-lidded downcast eyes; the lids lifted when she spoke to him, and Keith saw eyes that startled him, so large, clear, and full of expression were they. When she rose from the table, Keith knew not which to admire the more, the careless simplicity of her manner or the singular symmetry of her tall slender figure, with its exquisitely shapely neck. He had met but few girls in his life, and he never had seen a statue or a picture in any book to be compared to this woman, who was so fine and rare and delicate that she seemed like a beautiful tall flower.

But greater was his wonder in the evening, when he accompanied his friend Ogilvie to the theater and saw Miss White appear as the principal actress in a society drama. It was his first night at a play, so everything appeared real, and the girl ran the gamut of emotion required by her part so skilfully and naturally that the young man was entranced. He met her afterward, for she was the newest favorite of the set in which he had been introduced; she was with some delightful people who took him to a yacht-race; she was the most admirable figure at a fancy-dress ball given for a fashionable charity; he met her, with her father and her sister, in her own home, which was almost as entrancing as its mistress; and in a few days she filled his thoughts to the exclusion of everything else. She in turn was an eager listener to his tales of old Highland feuds, although she shuddered at them; he was more manly, original, and reverent of womanhood than other young men she had met, and it was evident to everyone but himself that she liked him.

When he returned to Castle Dare he quickly learned that he had left his heart in London, and old Hamish learned it almost as soon as he. Lady Macleod and her niece Janet saw little or no difference in Keith's manner, but Hamish noticed that his master and pupil no longer cared for his favorite sports, and gave but little attention to the affairs of his estate. Highlanders of Macleod's type can think of but one thing at a time, and often they will be absorbed in one thing so long that never afterward do they seem able to think of anything else. When Ogilvie went up to Castle Dare for a few days' shooting Keith made a confidant of him, and talked of Miss White like a mono-maniac—almost like a madman. He assumed that she knew nothing of his regard for her and probably had forgotten him, but Ogilvie added fuel to the fire by saying:

"Do you know this, Macleod? A man never yet was in love with a woman without the woman being instantly aware of it."

Meanwhile Miss White was not entirely happy, and one day, in the course of a long talk about her profession to her father, a reputable man of some attainments but little heart, she said:

"It isn't the life of a real human being at all. It is cutting oneself off from everything that makes life worth living. It is a continual degradation—an exhibition of feelings that ought to be a woman's most sacred and secret possession. Already I begin to think I don't know what I am. I have to sympathize with so many characters, I have to be so many different people, that I don't know what my own character is, or whether I have any at all!"

But her spirits were suddenly lifted by the receipt of a package of handsome otter-skins from Sir Keith Macleod, accompanied by a respectful note expressing the hope that they might be found worthy to be made into some article of attire. A few days later Keith was startled and delighted by a letter in which Miss White called him "My dear friend," and spoke gratefully of not having been forgotten the day after good-by had been said, as actresses were accustomed to have newly-made friendships vanish. She continued at great length, with some confidences about her life on the stage.

To Macleod these confidences were a revelation that she was not banished forever into the region of art in which her father would fain keep her. The victim might be reclaimed from the altar and restored to the sphere of simple human affections, natural duties and joy. And if he—? Herself and him! The conjunction set his heart throbbing quickly. Again he read the letter. The very frankness of it made him fear. There was none of the shyness of a girl writing to one who might be her lover. If only he could see her again he could tell by her eyes what she meant, whatever her words might be.

The change in his manner was now so visible to his mother and his cousin Janet that he was compelled to admit, with a forced laugh, that London and its associations had taken possession of his mind. A business pretext for revisiting London was devised for him by the faithful Janet; but he must soon return to his home, for the Highland winter was near.

Arrived in London, he hurried to the theater, and when Gertrude White came upon the stage he almost uttered a cry of delight, for there was the real woman, a thousand times more interesting and beautiful and lovable than all his dreams of her. Yet as the play proceeded his soul raged within him, for Gertrude played the part of a gay and thoughtless wife who, before that theater full of people, listened to a villain's advances which in her innocence she was supposed not to understand.

He called on her the next day, and she received him with outstretched hand, smiling lips, and eyes full of gladness. They chatted for a few moments, as friends might, but suddenly Keith lost self-control and startled the girl by exclaiming: "A drowning man will cry out! How can you help his crying out?" With a torrent of words he told his love, but when he reproached himself for inflicting the story upon her the girl sprang to her feet, placed her hands on his shoulders, and the eyes that met his were tearful and piteous. She admitted that sometimes she had thought of giving up her profession, with all the wishes and dreams she had cherished, and living the simple life of an ordinary woman; under whose guidance would she rather do it than his? But she could not be sure of herself; for her to say "Yes" might only bring him further pain.

Keith persisted; Gertrude begged for time, at least until the end of the week. When Keith went for his answer a vision in white came to him timidly and did not speak at all, but buried her head in his bosom, and he held her hands tight. He longed to marry her at once and take her away from the stage forever—take her to Castle Dare, or anywhere she might prefer, but most of all to himself. But again the girl insisted on asking for time, and much of it, but she promised to visit Castle Dare in the summer.

So Keith returned to the Highlands and began discreetly to tell his mother and Janet about Miss White, from whom he brought a little present to Lady Macleod. He showed them so many photographs of the lady, taken in various cities, that he was obliged to explain that she was an actress, but also a favorite in good society. She and her father would visit Mull in the summer; would not his mother write Miss White and invite them to Castle Dare?

"You must be mad, Keith," said Lady Macleod, "to write in the middle of winter and send an invitation for the summer! And, really, the whole thing is so extraordinary; a present coming to me from an absolute stranger, and that stranger an actress who is unknown to anyone I know."

"Mother! mother!" Keith cried, "don't say any more. She has promised to be my wife."

Days passed before Lady Macleod could be persuaded to yield to the inevitable. Keith had many gloomy hours of wondering whether his promised bride would be able to endure the somberness of winter in the Highlands, which even in summer could offer but a rude exchange for the life and scenes to which she was accustomed. Yet frequent letters from the girl brought him many hours of sunshine; and when spring began to banish winter he did all in his power to make his old yacht and grim castle as sightly and comfortable as possible for the gentle guest that was coming.

When she arrived, Lady Macleod found much to admire in the fair lady from the South; but old Hamish, who had the Highlander's faculty for looking a stranger through and through, muttered to his wife:

"A fool would he be, who would burn his heart to warm her."

In truth, it seemed difficult for Keith to please his sweetheart. She detested the sound of the bagpipe, although Castle Dare's own piper ranked high in his profession; she exhibited little interest in traditions of the family, and shuddered when taken to the grave of Macleod of Macleod, and the little excursions that Keith had planned for her proved tiresome. She

was distant, almost cold, to her lover, though he chivalrously
refrained from unburdening his heart while she was his guest.
She was almost afraid of Keith, and wished that her father would
take her away; when she tried to imagine herself young Lady
Macleod, forgotten by the world from which she had come,
the prospect terrified her. There were other men; the distinguished artist, Mr. Lemuel, who had painted her portrait,
admired her greatly; besides, she had signed a contract for a
new engagement at the theater. Keith made no scene when
he learned that she would continue to act, but he said sadly:
"You are going forward to a triumph, Gerty, and the first
step you take will be on my heart."

On her return to London she wrote him kindly, but still
begged for more time; he answered in person, to her great
annoyance; they quarreled, for the first time, and he went
back to Castle Dare, where never again did he seem his old
self to anyone. Soon came from Ogilvie a London rumor that
Miss White was to marry Mr. Lemuel, the artist; then the
rumor was confirmed, and Keith, whose reason seemed to have
left him, laughingly repeated the news to old Hamish, who
raged at the woman who would trifle with the heart of a Macleod.
Hamish said he would tame her, could he have his way; he
would sail Keith's yacht down the coast, up the Thames, and
abduct the faithless creature!

This mad project intertwisted itself with Keith's passionate
longings and troubled dreams, and soon he adopted it as his
own. The lady was persuaded to visit the yacht, for was not
the master ill, and had she not a heart, although her mind
was changeable? No sooner was she on board than the yacht
slipped moorings and made for the Highlands. When she
found herself a prisoner, Gertrude White did the most superb
acting of her life, though not a line or gesture of it had been
rehearsed. But it had no effect on Keith; he was not violent,
but still talked of his love and of his duty to rescue her from
her surroundings, and make life simple and happy for her.

The wind went down when they were not far from Mull and
Castle Dare, so the yacht had to be anchored in open water.
The sea was smooth, yet the weather was so uncertain that
Keith sent his crew ashore for shelter in case of danger. Old

Hamish had almost to be forced to accompany his men. Before long a thunderstorm burst suddenly; from the east came a stirring of wind, the sea began to moan, and soon a furious gale swept down upon the yacht. Through the darkness the crew peered at the lights of the stout little craft, but when these became changeable and intermittent and finally disappeared, old Hamish, who knew the ways of storms and seas, wailed wildly for his lost master, the last of the Macleods of Dare.

RICHARD DODDRIDGE BLACKMORE

(England, 1825-1900)

LORNA DOONE: A ROMANCE OF EXMOOR (1869)

This is the author's best known work. It has been said of it that to a Devonshire man "it is as good as clotted cream." Blackmore was especially proud of the fact that as a native he had "satisfied natives with their home scenery, people, life, and language." It is not, however, to the natives alone that this story has appealed; it has made Exmoor, "England's most beautiful country," known over many lands. The grim duel toward the end between John Ridd and Carver Doone is said to be founded on reality; and that in the actual fight it was the heart which the mighty Exmoor man tore out of his opponent's body instead of the muscle of the arm, as the book gives it.

 JOHN RIDD, of the parish of Oare, in the county of Somerset, yeoman and church-warden, am the son of John Ridd, the elder, who was seized for many generations past, since the time of good King Alfred, of the best and largest of the three farms into which the parish is divided. And he, being a great admirer of learning, and well able to write his name, sent me, his only son, to be schooled at Tiverton in the County of Devon. Here, by the time I was twelve years old, I had risen into the upper school, and could make bold with Eutropius and Cæsar by the aid of an English version. And said school was founded and endowed in 1604 by Master Peter Blundell, of that same place, clothier.

Now the very day that I was twelve, who should appear at the school but John Fry, our head man on the farm, with two horses, the one he rode on and a pony. It was cause of wonder to me, for it lacked yet two weeks to the holidays. Something must be wrong at home, but I could get nothing out of him except reasons which, young as I was, I could still perceive must be mere excuses to keep the truth from me. But he

Insisted that before setting out for home I should fight out to a finish a quarrel forced on me by a larger boy. When I had won, although I groaned all over with bruises, we mounted and made for Plover's Barrows, our farmstead, across the dreary waste of Exmoor.

When we reached home I soon learned why my mother had sent for me. My good father, a man of large size and great courage, but a courage not without heat and rashness, had imprudently rushed into a fight with one of the ruthless Doones who had affronted him in a certain high and mighty way they had. The troop of seven or eight crowded around him and laid him dead on the moor.

A word is in season here about this noted band of outlaws, with whom my fate and fortune came to be so closely interwoven. Sir Ensor Doone, the father and head of the clan, was of a noble family in Scotland, with a dash of English blood. He lost his estates in a lawsuit with another branch of the family, and, crossing the border with his sons, sworn to wrest his rights by booty and outlawry, if not by law, proceeded south until he came to a wild, deep valley in Somerset County, which, in their hands, became a haunt for all manner of cruelty and crime, a den, as it were, of wild beasts. The sides of the valley were steep, and at the bottom, on each side of a roaring stream called the Bagworthy, their huts were clustered. One way to reach the valley was to follow the stream, wading up its steep, winding bed. But this was very dangerous, even if haply one could do it without meeting any of the Doones, for in places it was very narrow and the banks were like straight walls of hewn stone, almost meeting overhead. The other entrance was very broken and steep, and at the top it was protected by culverins and the trunk of a great tree suspended by chains, ever ready to be dropped with crushing force on whosoever should penetrate so far without permission, and two of the Doones were always on guard there, from sunset to dawn.

Sir Ensor Doone was the grand- and great-grandfather of all the Doones of Glen Doone, and blended with his ruthless, cold-blooded rule a certain courtesy inherited with his rank. His oldest son, the counselor, as he was called, was no less wicked than the others, but he fought against mankind not by violence and arms so much as by a craft the devil might envy. Carver, his brother, was the most truculent of all the clan, and in stature and strength beyond all his comrades. Besides the spoil which they gathered from the whole countryside, the Doones had increased greatly in number by carrying off the women, both wives and maids, from the neighborhood, sometimes slaying children in mere wantonness. Thus, of men alone, there were now more than forty in the valley; all of mighty strength and stature, although there was but one among them, Carver Doone, who in those respects could match with me, for I stood on my bare feet six feet and seven inches high and two feet across the shoulders. They had a door in the Glen exactly six feet and one inch high and one foot and ten inches wide. If any man-child was born of the Doones who at twenty-one could not measure up to this door he was driven out and told to seek his living elsewhere. An advantage which I had beyond them all was my skill in the art of wrestling. This, too, was not always a gain to me, for it led me sometimes to trust in it too rashly, without other arms than a stout staff, being also skilled at single stick; and thus I placed my life and the security of those who naturally looked to me for defense in serious jeopardy more than once without sufficient reason.

As if the loss of my father had not been enough trouble for us at the hands of the murderous Doones, I came into most dangerous relations with them in the following year, although with no deliberate intent at first. My dear mother being sick at heart for the loss of her husband, and of slackening appetite, I thought some loaches would do her good, being very pleasing to her taste. For this purpose I sought the stream of the Glen Doone, and waded in the nooks under the stones; but finding the fish scarce, I kept wading farther up the stream, the water being cold and myself growing chilled. Then, hardly knowing what I did in my eagerness, I entered on the dark channel where it was more easy to proceed than to return, and then, when my strength was just giving out, an opening appeared in the steep bank, and I stepped out of the water exhausted and threw myself on the sod. And then, as if two stars peeped suddenly out of a cloud, I gazed into two bright, black eyes looking into mine with interest, wonder, and sympathy, for their owner saw that I was weary. I was fourteen and she was eight. As was fitting, I explained to the little lass why I happened to be there, and she told me that her name was Lorna Doone; that Sir Ensor Doone was her grandfather and her guardian, for her father and mother were dead. And then the dear creature, young enough to be simple still and old enough to understand the terror of life in that den of violence, told me she was glad to see me, but that it was very dangerous for us to be there, and urged me to go, saying that some other time the chance might come to meet again. Then she led me to a secret path, with a dark cave at one side which she had found, and into which I might hide if anyone should haply pass.

More than seven years passed before I visited Glen Doone again. The care of the farm and the sports in which a healthy growing youth delights had taken my thought; and then it happened that someone in joke asked me whether I had ever been to Glen Doone and seen its fairy queen, as she was called, Lorna Doone. Then it all came back to me, as it were, with a sudden fever and longing to see her again, as if a divine spark of love had been smoldering all those years in my bosom. Saying naught of my purpose to a living soul, I set out one afternoon to brave the terrors of that robber stronghold, and not least, perhaps, the cold looks and scant welcome of Lorna herself; for who but myself would so wildly dream that a child of eight would carry in her mind and heart until she was nigh sixteen the memory of an awkward stranger lad she had seen only once?

But, wonder of wonders, when I waded the burn, finding it shallow now since I had grown so tall, I met her standing there on the bank as if she were expecting me. We had both grown tall, I to a height near to that of a giant, yet each recognized the other and called each other by name. Situated as we were, we had not time nor opportunity to wait and fall to a liking, not to say love, such as comes to those who gradually grow to unity of heart and soul. Without saying this in so many words, we both seemed to see the condition of affairs instinctively. And thus it was agreed that we should meet every few weeks, not less than a month, owing to the danger; and that, if any serious emergency made it expedient that I should hasten to her aid, she or her small but faithful attendant Gwen should throw a dark mantle or cloth over a large white rock on the brow of the hill near the outer entrance to her retreat, but not visible except from the high moorland near our farmstead. To show me how important for us was extreme caution, she told me of a handsome young Scot, Lord Allan Brandir, who had found his way up there to see her and inform her that by Scotch law he was her guardian on the mother's side, when his father, old and feeble, should die. He seemed to know no danger and laughed at her warning to depart ere the Doones should spy him out. At that very moment Carver Doone appeared, put his arm about him and carried him off like a young babe, slew him almost in her sight, and tossed the corpse into the stream. Lorna wept bitter tears as she told this tale of blood and woe. But she had barely told me this gruesome story ere she heard the voices of a troop of the Doones approaching. Knowing every thicket and turn, she hastened to hide me in her cave until they had passed.

Notwithstanding the extreme peril of visiting Glen Doone, such was my ardor by this time, that in a few days I thought of visiting her again, especially as I began to enter into the second stage of love, to wit, jealousy, which gave me some pangs lest some young popinjay, like poor Lord Brandir, should steal her away from me. But ere I could realize my intention a messenger from court, Jeremy Stickles by name, rode up to our gate, and standing in his stirrups, shouted to me, "Service of the King! Service of our lord, the King! Come hither, thou great yokel, at the risk of fine and imprisonment."

Not quite pleased at this, I went up to him as a loyal man, but quite at my leisure, and he gave me a parchment tied up with strings and seals and various superscriptions, and on the top I saw, "Ride, Ride, Ride! On His Gracious Majesty's business; spur and spare not."

Jeremy Stickles explained that the matter concerned the giving of evidence, so far as I was able, before the judges of his Majesty's court as to the existence of disaffection and threatened risings in the country wherein I lived. It was in vain that, for reasons of my own, I urged Master Stickles to wait until Monday. Saturday was the extreme limit that he would allow, perhaps, and thus I was taken away without hope of seeing my Lorna for months, as indeed it proved.

At last, after many a delay in London, I was summoned into the dread presence of Judge Jeffreys who, ere long, was to earn eternal infamy for the cruelties he practised after the Monmouth Rebellion. I had little information to give, and in due course was dismissed.

By this time I had used up my money, and how was I to get home? But at this point Jeremy Stickles came to my aid most heartily and lent me five pounds without security. On this I walked one hundred and seventy miles through the mud to Dunster; and there I found mother's cousin, the tanner, who had some excellent daughters, who darned my stockings and made good pie; and he would not listen but that I should ride his stunted nag; and so, in due time, I got home.

Above all things I now longed to see my Lorna. I knew that my first Monday on the farm I should be carefully watched by everyone to see how I took hold after so long an absence in London. I inclined, too, to tell the whole story of Lorna to mother, and then, likewise, how did I know whether Lorna was there, or would welcome me, I having been a month more than the specified month away from her, and no word or sign from me? But reason as I would, Love's arguments were paramount. So I strode away over the moor to find Lorna, if haply she were still there, and learn my fate before another sun should set.

I went the way that led me to the white stone on which her signal would be set in case of need. And lo! there it was, and I knew not how long it had been there. I circled this way and that, in desperation, to find her, and last of all, and daring all, I crossed over to the place where I first had had access to the cliffs which made a rampart for the men of the robber den. And there she was indeed, but in manner timid and constrained, as if my more than two months' absence had destroyed her faith in me. Then, bethinking herself, she led me quickly to her bower, lest the Doones should spy us. Of all that we said and looked at that blessed interview, it suffices to record here that we reached a complete understanding before we parted as to the sentiments that drew us together and the sweetness that destiny promised. I knew quite well, while all my heart was burning hot within me, and mine eyes were shy of hers, and her eyes were shy of mine; for certain and forever I knew—as in a glory —that Lorna Doone had now begun and would go on to love me. This was the supreme hour of our existence. Extraordinary and various doings of Providence with us were manifest as the year went by, but they all turned and proceeded from what passed on this afternoon. But fate has a way of playing with us, and when the sun shines brightest draws over it a threatening cloud. Only a day or two passed, and in my joy and impatience I sought her again. But neither was she there nor was there sign of her, while I waited with growing impatience and anxiety. But Carver Doone came, and I, grown careless, permitted the great, handsome, cruel man to catch a glimpse of me. Straightway he fired, shooting my hat into the stream. I dived under the water, and seeing only the hat he judged that I was both shot and drowned and so gave over hunting for me at that time. After this I daily sought in vain for Lorna's signal, growing sick at heart, until a very secret, faithful messenger brought me word to go in the morning, for she could not come out after midday, being suspected and watched.

After a time my mother and sisters gradually received the news about Lorna, and little by little agreed to open their arms and accept her in our family, but with much curiosity and misgiving and jealousy at first. One day Gwenny Carfax, Lorna's little maid, was sent to fetch me to the very midst of the perilous Glen Doone, and I was permitted by the great Doones to pass in and enter the dwelling of Sir Ensor Doone, the head of them all, for Sir Ensor lay dying. Lorna had told him all, so far as related to me, and as her grandfather, the strong master feared by all the Doones, he had at last given consent to our union, should he find me worthy to be allied to the clan of the Doones.

The old man was wonderful to behold, propped up to receive me, with his long white beard flowing to his bosom and his voice dwindling to a whisper. With a certain majesty, he gave a grudging, half scornful, cynical command that we be left to choose our own destiny, and from under the coverlid drew out secretly a necklace of diamonds of enormous value which had belonged to Lorna's mother and which he had long kept sacred for Lorna, a treasure greatly sought and desired by his elder son, the Counselor. And so the great, wicked, venerable Sir Ensor Doone passed in his account to the Judge of the universe.

After his death the great winter set in with such snow and cold as had been unknown for generations. It was against us in one way and in our favor in another. The Doones kept themselves close in their den, for little booty could be got and no enemy was feared in such a storm. But I was able thereby to creep up under the window where Lorna and Gwenny were imprisoned, as it were. Her cousin Carver was bent on keeping Lorna safely enclosed until she would consent to marry him. She was permitted neither to go forth nor to receive food in her house, and what with cold and with hunger she was on the verge of despair and death. As soon as the election of a successor to Sir Ensor should be settled a woful crisis would befall her. Now or never was the time for action. When the election was decided great carousing would and did follow; and while they were all sunk in a drunken slumber, I sped over the moor to Glen Doone on snow-shoes I had made, of which I had read in books, drawing after me a sledge. Glen Doone was all asleep when I knocked at Lorna's window. She stole out with Gwenny; I tucked them on the sledge with warm furs, and with my great strength and length of limb sped them in two hours to Plover's Barrows, where mother and my sisters received them with a kind welcome that did my heart good.

Thus matters stood when the rebellion of Monmouth broke out in the West. I took no part in it, but went toward the meeting of the rebels and the King's army to look after Tom Faggus, my dear sister Annie's husband, who foolishly trained with the rebels and was like to meet with a short shrift if captured, and poor surgery if wounded. As a man of peace, I took no arms but my stout stick. But this availed me little; for when the rebels were beaten and the royal troops espied me, I was seized and my arms were bound. Feversham then ordered me to stand up and be shot. The file that was to do this leveled their arms and Feversham began to count the seconds, when Jeremy Stickler rode up shouting for a halt. He took Feversham aside and mentioned that I was one whom Judge Jeffreys had favored, and to slay me without trial might make trouble; and that he, Jeremy, would be responsible for me. With manifest reluctance Feversham turned me over to Jeremy, who lost no time in setting out with me for London. There I lingered for months, my case being apparently shelved and forgotten. Sir Ensor being dead, Lorna's next guardian by appointment in the Court of Chancery, Earl Brandir, her maternal uncle, sent for her to come up to London. And the dear girl, although living there in attendance on the Queen until all formalities were satisfied, received me with a welcome that showed plainly how enduring was the troth she had plighted to me. The unexpected way in which events that shape our destiny often come was shown by the luck I had in saving the life of Earl Brandir, who was attacked by robbers, who had burst into his mansion in London when he was asleep in bed. When his gracious Majesty heard of it he ordered me to kneel down and then bade me rise as Sir John Ridd. I cared not for the title, but I knew it would mightily please mother, and, what was more, it removed all danger of being summoned for trial and whatever opposition Earl Blandir might have raised to our marriage on the ground of disparity of rank.

Soon after my return home the yeomen of Exmoor neighborhood planned an expedition finally to disperse or destroy the robbers of Glen Doone, who had at last become outrageous beyond further forbearance. By means of a stratagem and cool courage the Doones—that is, the men, not the women and children—were exterminated, being more than forty stalwart ruffians, all except the Chancellor, who never was seen again, alive or dead, and Carver Doone, who remained in hiding.

And now, there being nothing further to hinder, and all being ready, my precious Lorna and I went to our parish church to be made one. All the countryside was there to witness the happy event. The service had been read, we had plighted our vows, and I was bending to kiss my bride, when the crash of a carbine rang through the church, and Lorna dropped, as one dead, in my arms. As I turned to look, I saw Carver Doone darting out of the door. I gave Lorna to my mother, and sped after him on my horse. Already the ruffian on his great black steed had gained a quarter of a mile when I started in chase.

But my horse, as if knowing what was at stake, the life of a man, perhaps two, delayed not, but gained in the pursuit. I wore the silk embroidered bridal vest spotted with the blood from Lorna's wound, but had no weapons. As I drew near him, Carver turned and fired a glancing shot which happily did no more harm than to break a rib. I stopped only to tear a small branch from an oak tree. This was all the armor I had, when Carver turned and fired at me and then drew his sword, having come suddenly on a bottomless bog that stopped his way. With the limb of the oak I struck the horse, who fell with his rider. When Carver rose, I scorned, with my too frequent foolishness, to seize the advantage, but allowed him to make the first attack, saving that when he was down I removed his weapons. With a fearful scowl he came toward me, and I led him to a scant, grassy sward by the slough and there the death-struggle was fought. The first grapple of his arm around my body crushed in the wounded rib. In my agony I took such a grip that I actually tore out the large muscle of his arm from the roots. Little recking of the quagmire, we pressed down into it. Fortunately for me, he was on the near side to the bog. With one tremendous final effort I sprang from his awful grasp to solid ground, while Carver was swallowed up inch by inch before my eyes and disappeared forever. I had barely strength to climb to the saddle and with loose rein crept home. For weeks my life hung by a thread. When my kind nurses thought nothing else would do, they ventured, as a last resort, to tell me that Lorna, my darling wife, who I thought was dead, still lived, and then brought her in to see me. Then, at last, my cure began.

GIOVANNI BOCCACCIO

(Italy, 1313-1375)

THE DECAMERON (1350)

This collection of stories of the "ten days" (the meaning of the Greek word *Decameron*) is not only the most famous book of its author and his age, but also and unquestionably the most influential work of fiction in the entire history of literature. Several of the *Canterbury Tales* of Chaucer are amplifications of Boccaccio's stories; Shakespeare and his fellow dramatists resorted to the same prolific source for situations and even entire plots; and in more recent times, Dryden, Keats, Tennyson, Longfellow, Swinburne, and George Eliot have made poetic use of the immortal hundred tales.

INTRODUCTION

In the year of our Lord 1348, in Florence, the finest city in all Italy, a most terrible plague broke forth. Such was its contagion that it spread from the sick to the hale as a forest fire leaps from dry leaves and decaying limbs to enfold in its flaming embrace the green and growing boles and branches; and such was its virulence that few persons seized by it escaped its mortal effect nearly all dying the third day after the first symptoms appeared. Between March and July more than a hundred thousand persons perished in Florence, whereas before the calamity it was not supposed that the city contained so many inhabitants. There were barely enough left to conduct the forms of political and religious life, with few to act as subjects of their administration.

NE Tuesday morning, seven ladies, all in deep mourning, composed the entire congregation in the church of Santa Maria Novella. They were all young, discreet, nobly descended, and perfectly accomplished both in person and in behavior. Nevertheless, lest what I am about to relate of them may give a pretext to ill-natured persons who are wont to carp at unconventional conduct without taking into account the unusual circumstances which may warrant and even compel it, I shall mention the ladies only by fictitious names, though these shall bear in each case a suggestion of the character and quality of the person. From eldest to youngest, then, let me present to you, dear reader, Pampinea, Fiammetta, Filomena, Emilia, Lauretta, Neifile, and Eliza.

These seven ladies, made bosom friends by a community of misfortune, drifted together into a corner of the church, and there, seated in a ring, neglected their *pater nosters* and began to talk of the one inevitable subject. Pampinea, seeing that they augmented their terror by dwelling upon it, cast about in her mind for a diversion. Finally she began:

"My dear girls, let us not increase these horrors by inconsiderately dilating upon them, but instead let us use our reason in calmly discussing our personal situation. We stay here in church for no other purpose that I can see but to observe what numbers come to be buried; we go hence either to see the sick borne through the streets, or to behold vice and crime flaunting in open bravado; we go home to chambers empty save for haunting suggestions of the departed; not the comforting images of them in smiling health, but the terrifying aspects of their tortured end. And to what benefit do we rack our souls by such a routine? When the most skilful physicians are of none avail, what service can we distracted women render the doomed? We can, however, aid ourselves, and that without incurring the charge of selfishness, which is the gratifying of our own interests at the expense of our fellows.

"Let us, then, quit the town for some one of our country seats, where we may make ourselves innocently merry without offering the least violence to the dictates of reason and our own consciences. As no blame can ensue from following this course, and as sickness and death may do so from not pursuing it, I would have us take our maids, and such conveniences as we may require, and divert ourselves with various pleasures until we see what end Providence designs for this visitation."

The ladies heartily approved of Pampinea's proposal, and at once began to lay all sorts of conflicting plans for its execution, when Filomena, who was most discreet, remarked: "There is no occasion to rush headlong, or rather, headless, into this matter. Since no men are present, we women may frankly confess to ourselves that we shall never be able to conduct such an affair except under the leadership of the sterner sex. I move, therefore, that we set about supplying this deficiency."

As Eliza, the youngest of the party, was seconding the suggestion, its execution was providentially arranged for by the

entrance into the church of three gentlemen, who, in truth, were
in quest of their lady-loves, these being, indeed, three of the
party. Neifile, who proclaimed by her blushes that she was one
of the beloved ladies, remarked to Filomena:

"While these gentlemen are of the best breeding and highest
character, and so are admirably fitted to manage our enterprise,
yet I happen to know that they are the gallants of three of our
company, and I fear that we all may be drawn into some scandal
without our fault or theirs."

Filomena replied: "I care not what others may think and
say, so long as I know myself to be virtuous. If the gentlemen
are willing to accompany us, let us thank heaven, I say, and not
distrust it, for this most apposite fortune."

The rest of the ladies approving these sentiments, Pampinea,
who was related to one of the gentlemen, approached them and,
telling of the proposed expedition, announced that they had
been drafted as its managers. The gentlemen (whom I shall
call Panfilo, Filostrato, and Dioneo, though these are not their
names) at first supposed Pampinea was jesting, and answered
in kind, disclaiming their ability to manage each a woman, not
to speak of two and a third members of that fractious sex. Persuaded, at length, that the ladies were in earnest, they yielded,
and agreed to arrange their affairs with dispatch, so as to set out
on the expedition on the morrow.

At break of day, accordingly, the ladies with their maids,
and the gentlemen with every one his servant, set out from the
city, and shortly came to the place appointed, which was the
country seat of Pampinea. It was a little eminence, remote from
any great road, green with umbrageous trees and gay with
flowering shrubs. On the top was a stately palace, builded
around a beautiful court, in the center of which a fountain
dispersed its grateful coolness. This palace they found set
in order for their reception, the chamber assigned to each lady
being decked with her favorite flowers, and those of the gentlemen, which were in another quarter of the house, with what were
presumably their favorites also—the same kind of blooms that
decorated the rooms of their sweethearts.

The company being seated upon the lawn, Pampinea arose
and said: "There are ten of us in this pleasant party, and I

propose that each in turn bear the dignity and the labor of presiding over it for the space of a day, and directing our diversions."

These words were received with a clapping of hands, while Filomena, running to a laurel-tree, broke off one of its branches, and, entwining it into a garland, approached Pampinea and encircled her head with the symbol of authority.

After her coronation the new queen first disposed of the economy of her realm by assigning to the servants their several household duties. To the royal line of her fellows and successors she then gave the stern edict: "I will and command you all, on pain of my displeasure, that wherever you go, or whatever you hear and see, you bring no news hither but what is pleasant. Here are gardens and meadows in which you may disport yourselves until a more imperative summons than mine shall call you to our morning repast."

The company broke up into little groups of two and three, and walked through the gardens, chatting merrily, singing love songs, and weaving chaplets of flowers. It was not long, however, before their wanderings by gradual approaches, as through some strange attraction, brought them all together to the palace, where in the saloon opening on the portico they found a long table set forth with snowy linen and gleaming glass and silver. The dishes were served in the most elegant manner by the accomplished servants, and the gentlemen and ladies feasted, like the kings and queens they were all shortly to be, in a truly royal way. When dinner was over, the queen ordered a viol and a lute to be brought. A dance was struck up, which was followed by song, while the servants were sent to dinner. Then all retired for the siesta, Pampinea ordering them to meet again at three in the afternoon upon a certain glade open to the eastern breeze and shaded upon the west by a grove of lofty trees.

When they had reassembled at this place, they found tables set with chess and backgammon. Pampinea said:

"If you will be advised by me, I suggest, instead of these selfish games which wear out the day for the participants at the expense of the patience of the looker-on, that we employ ourselves at story-telling, whereby the pleasure of all is served."

This motion being approved by all, the queen continued: "Let everyone for this day take what subject he fancies most."

THE THREE RINGS

The brief silence that followed the words of Pampinea was broken by Filomena. "Since our gracious queen," she began, "has given us liberty to choose what subjects we will, I will tell a story showing how a good understanding may secure a man in the midst of utmost danger, and, indeed, bring him to honor and dignity.

"Saladin, Sultan of Babylon, though successful in his wars, had incurred by them extraordinary expenses, and was in dire need of money. In his extremity he called to mind a rich Jew of Alexandria, Melchizedeck by name, who let out money at interest. Wishing to have an occasion against this man, the Sultan summoned him to court, and receiving him graciously, put to him the ensnaring question: 'Worthy man, since thou art known to be wise in religious matters, tell me which faith thou judgest to be the true one—the Jewish, the Mahometan, or the Christian.' The Jew at once surmised that Saladin had a mind to trap him, and would gain his end should the answer exalt one of the religions above the other, and so he craftily replied with the following parable:

"'Once upon a time, O most gracious Sultan, there was a great and rich man whose choicest possession was a ring of rare value and extraordinary beauty. Desiring that this should continue forever in his family, he made a will designating that one of his sons to whom upon his death he should leave the ring, as his successor in the headship of the house. The son to whom the ring thus fell in turn made the same law with reference to his children; and so the ring passed in long succession from one favorite son to another until it came to a man who had three sons, all dutiful to their father and equally beloved by him. Now the young men, knowing the significance of possession of the ring, and being ambitious of superiority, began to entreat the father, as he neared the end of his days, every one for himself, that the ring be given to him. So the good man, wishing to satisfy all, and in the end to reprove them for their selfish emulation, privately got a jeweler to fashion two other rings, which were so like the first that he himself could not distinguish the original. When at last he lay upon the bed from which he knew he would never arise, he secretly called his sons to him, one by one, and gave each a ring. So after his death each son proclaimed himself the heir, showing the ring that had been given him as authority. To settle the contention which naturally arose, recourse was had to the law.

"'Your Majesty, the case is still in the courts.'

"Saladin perceived that the Jew had cleverly escaped the net which was spread for him; he therefore resolved to discover his necessity to him, and see whether he would lend the sorely needed money, frankly confessing his original design to entrap him. Melchizedeck freely supplied the monarch with what he wanted; and Saladin afterwards repaid him in full, made him large presents, and took him into his court to act as his counselor and friend."*

At the close of the first day's story-telling, Pampinea, taking the laurel crown from her own head, placed it upon Filomena's, and humbly saluted her, in which obeisance all the company followed. Gently blushing at the honor, the new queen made her coronation address:

"I shall continue the admirable domestic order instituted by my predecessor, our beloved Pampinea, and confirm her wise law regarding the conduct of yourselves, the nobility of the realm. Yet to this service of perfect freedom I would make one exception. Owing to the impossibility of granting time for consideration of subject, our queen gracefully, if not graciously, allowed us to talk upon whatever theme we would. Now there is afforded at least a day for warning, and I propose, therefore, to keep you within the bounds of some particular subject, which all your stories of the morrow must illustrate. This, if you please, shall be: Triumph through vicissitude."

To this order all agreed except Dioneo, who asked that he be allowed to come last in every day's story-telling and to talk upon any theme he chose, in order to relieve any weariness that

---

* This novel supplied Gotthold Ephraim Lessing [Germany, 1729-1781] with the central situation of his poetic masterpiece, *Nathan the Wise*. Undoubtedly it also suggested to Shakespeare the test of the three caskets devised by Portia's father for the selection of her husband, in *The Merchant of Venice*.

might be occasioned by the similarity of the preceding tales. As the queen knew him to be a merry fellow, and surmised that his purpose was to send the company away each day in gay spirits by telling a humorous story, she granted his request.

On the morrow, after all the others but Dioneo had related their stories, Queen Filomena began what we shall call

THE WIFE'S REVENGE

THE STORY OF GINEVRA, WIFE OF BERNARD OF GENOA

"It is a common saying that the deceiver lies at the mercy of the deceived. This I propose to show you in the following narrative.

"Some Italian merchants sojourning in Paris met at supper one night, and, beginning by questioning each other's fidelity to his wife under stress of the allurements of that gay city, they ended by discussing the revenge which was probably being perpetrated upon them by the wives they had left behind.

"Only one man of them all, Bernard Lomellin, of Genoa, resented the insinuation. He warmly insisted on one exception at least, that of his young wife, Ginevra. He dilated upon her beauty and accomplishments, the crowning glory of which, he declared, was her virtue and chastity. He firmly believed, he concluded, that, were he to be absent from her ten years, she would have to do with no other person.

"As he finished his eulogy, one of the company, Ambrose of Venice, who had been smiling cynically at the speaker's earnestness, dryly asked him whether the Emperor had given him this privilege exclusive of the rest of mankind. Bernard hotly retorted: 'Not the Emperor, but God Almighty, who was something more powerful than the Emperor, had bestowed this favor.' In reply Ambrose took a cold, philosophical attitude toward the subject. 'I have always understood,' he said, 'that man is the most noble of God's creatures, and that woman is in the next degree to him. If a man, therefore, cannot resist the attractions unwittingly exerted by a member of the other sex, what can a woman, weaker by nature, do against the entreaties, flatteries, gifts, and a thousand other means, which an artful lover knows how to employ? Take it from me as a rule: that woman only is chaste who has never been asked; or who herself has asked and been refused. I should not speak as I do if I had not tried the affections of many different women. Let me also tell you that if I were in company with your most virtuous wife I should still be confident that I would not receive my first rebuff.'

"'And I am so confident,' Bernard hotly interjected, 'that, shameless as you are, you would be driven from her presence confounded and abashed, that I invite you to attempt her conquest, and will wager you five thousand florins to one thousand you will not succeed.'

"'Done!' said Ambrose. 'I will at once set out for Genoa, and in less than three months return to this company assembled in this place with such tokens as you yourself will admit shall prove that I have won the wager.'

"The other merchants attempted to calm the excited men, and dissuade them from their purpose, but to no avail. These at once drew up and signed articles binding and conditioning the wager, Bernard agreeing to remain at Paris and not to interfere in any way with the execution of Ambrose's purpose. Ambrose set out for Genoa, where he lay quiet for a few days informing himself cautiously the situation of Bernard's house and the possibilities of secretly entering it. He was much cast down when he heard that the place was as impenetrable as a fortress, and that Ginevra kept herself so closely immured therein that there was little hope he would get the chance of exerting upon her his irresistible physical attractions. And, to cap his despair, he heard that all Bernard had asserted of his wife's virtue was true. Her modest conduct during her husband's long absences had even been memorialized in a proverb: 'As chaste as Ginevra.'

"However, Ambrose found another woman who was not so unapproachable, a poor widow, recently bereaved, who was about to remove with her scanty possessions to her mother's home in the country, and to whom Ginevra had charitably offered temporary harborage both for herself and a great chest which contained all her belongings. Telling this woman that he had an *amour* with one of the maids, Ambrose bribed her to have him conveyed in the chest into Ginevra's house, upon the pretext that it was to remain there for safe-keeping over night, awaiting the call of the carrier for it next morning. For its greater security Ginevra proposed that it be taken into her own bedchamber, at which the conscience-stricken widow was fain to have confessed her wickedness, but did not dare to make protest, since her suborner within the chest, who had threatened her with death if she betrayed him, was hearing— with great exultation you may be sure—the kindly offer.

"About midnight Ambrose lifted up the lid of the chest, which was fastened from within, peered out, and, seeing by the dim light of a night lamp that Ginevra was soundly sleeping, stepped quietly from his cramped hiding place. Tiptoeing softly around the room, he observed carefully, even minutely, the furniture, pictures and ornaments in order to keep them in his memory. Finally he approached the lady in the bed, who, the night being warm, lay with her bosom exposed. Holding the night-lamp as close to her as he dared, Ambrose scrutinized her carefuly for some unusual mark, and at last found it in a little mole under the left breast. After this he took from the lady's dressing-table a purse, a ring, and a girdle, trusting that the theft would not be discovered until the carrier, who would undoubtedly be blamed for it, was at a safe distance in the country. Secreting these on his person, Ambrose crept back into the chest again, and, leaving the lid unfastened, awaited the lady's first movements in bed quietly to close and fasten it. Early in the morning the carrier came and removed the chest with its unsuspected contents to a house in the country, as Ambrose had previously planned.

"Ambrose hastened to Paris and summoned Bernard and the other merchants who were witnesses of the wager to the appointed place. When they were all assembled he declared that he had accomplished his purpose, and gave as evidence a detailed description of Ginevra's bedchamber and the furniture within it. To this as proof Bernard objected, saying that Ambrose could have learned of these things from some servant of the house. Then Ambrose showed the purse, the ring, and the girdle. Bernard's faith in his wife was still unshaken, and he declared that these, too, could have been procured by tampering with a chambermaid. Then Ambrose remarked: 'You are indeed hard to convince. But what would you say if I told you of the sweet little mole, that undoubtedly you, too, have often kissed, which lies under your wife's left breast, and is the only mark upon her perfect bosom?'

"When Bernard heard this he was struck to the heart, and, unable to say a word, he called for pen and paper, and, writing an order upon his Paris banker for five thousand florins, gave it to Ambrose.

"The next day Bernard set out post-haste for Genoa, most cruelly incensed against his wife. He stopped within twenty miles of the city at his country house, and sent the man in charge of it, an old and faithful servant of his family, to Genoa with a letter instructing Ginevra to return with the attendant to meet him. Privately he charged the servant that, as soon as they came to a fit place, he should put his companion to death.

"The sad-hearted old servitor was hard put to it to retain his tears when Ginevra received the message with manifestations of joy, kissing the letter and placing it in her bosom. He had resolution enough, however, when on the way to the country home they came to a solitary vale surrounded with trees, to draw his knife and say: 'Madam, commend your soul to God, for here you must die.'

"Ginevra, in utmost astonishment, asked him how she had injured him that he proposed such a cruel deed. 'Madam,' he replied, 'you have never injured me; on the contrary you have been goodness itself to me and mine. Know that it is your husband who has ordered this, and as his faithful servant I must obey his commands, the more particularly because he holds not only myself but my family in his power. Ask me not what reason he has for this action, for I know it not. So forgive me if you can, dear lady, but whether you forgive or not, prepare to die.'

"The lady wept piteously, and said: 'Alas, do not murder me, who have never injured you, for the sake of another person. God is my witness that I have done nothing to deserve this from my husband. But, setting this aside, you may, if you please, serve God, save me, protect yourself and family, and satisfy your master, in this manner: Do you put up that knife, and, taking my clothes, save only my shift that for decency's sake you would leave with my body did you murder me, carry them to my cruel lord as token that you have obeyed his commands; and I swear, by the life for which I shall be indebted to you, that I will go where you, he, or any person in this country will never hear more concerning me.'

"The servant, whose resolution was fast ebbing, readily seized upon this way of escape from the tragic predicament. Prevailing upon her to accept his cloak, and his purse, which contained a little money, he returned with the lady's clothing to Bernard, and told him that he had performed his duty and left the body to be devoured by wolves.

"Ginevra hid in a thicket until dusk, when she made her way back to the hut of a purblind old woman she had noted by the roadside, and, representing herself as a neighbor, procured from her shears and needle and thread. She returned with these implements to her covert, and spent the next day cutting her hair and fashioning the cloak and shift into doublet and hose. At night she returned the shears and needle to the old woman, and set out for the nearest seaport. Here she bought a sailor's outfit, and calling herself Sicurano da Finale, sought for a place as steward on a vessel that had just come into port. The brightness and deftness of the lad that she appeared to be commended him to the captain, who was also the owner of the ship, and he gladly engaged him as his personal servant. The vessel was bound to Alexandria, on arriving at which port the ship-owner paid his respects to the Sultan, taking a present of several trained falcons in charge of Sicurano. The Sultan viewed the handsome lad with even more favor than the hawks, beholding which the quick-witted trader begged that his Majesty accept the servant also.

"In a very short time Sicurano became the Sultan's chief favorite, and, because of his skill in languages, was advanced from the care of the royal falcons to the position of court interpreter. In this capacity he met many Italian merchants who came with presents to the Sultan. One day a Venetian presented himself, on whose finger Sicurano noticed the ring that in the old days of happy wifehood had been taken from her dressing table—by a carrier, she had supposed. Curious to learn how the merchant had come by its possession, and wishing to regain it by purchase, Sicurano visited on the morrow that quarter of the bazaar where the foreign merchants displayed samples of their wares, and asked to be directed to the shop of Ambrose, the name by which the Venetian had announced himself. Here the former Ginevra saw to her delight the girdle and the purse that had been stolen with the ring. On inquiring their price, however, she was laughingly informed that they were not for sale. With quick suspicion, due to her ever-present consciousness that she was a woman in man's disguise, Sicurano asked resentfully the cause of the merchant's merriment. 'Is it because I as a man appear interested in womanish toys?'

"'Sir,' replied Ambrose, 'I do not laugh at that, but at the thought of how I acquired them.' And, being pressed by Sicurano, he told the story of his wager with Bernard, and the trick by which had he won it. 'So,' he concluded, 'I laugh at Bernard's folly, who lost five thousand florins because he must needs test the virtue of his wife, and then lost his wife, for I understand that he put her to death. And I can testify that the florins were good coin, for I spent them, and that his wife was a good woman, as women go, for of all wives I have attempted, she only I did not enjoy.'

"Trembling with rage against the wicked man before her, the injured wife nevertheless dissembled her animosity. Indeed, she laughed immoderately at the story, and told Ambrose that its relation would greatly please the Sultan, and that he might shortly expect an invitation from his Majesty to appear before him and repeat it.

"Sicurano then inquired among the Genoese merchants in the bazaar concerning her husband, and, to her amazement, found that he was in prison in the city as a captive of war, awaiting a ransom that was not likely to be forthcoming, as a few years before that he had suddenly abandoned his business and departed to the Holy Land to take part in an insurrection against the Turks, the failure of which had resulted in his captivity.

"The Sultan, when Sicurano had laid bare to him the whole story, summoned Ambrose and Bernard before him. Not with the smiling countenance which the Venetian merchant expected, but with the stern visage of an accusing judge, his Majesty commanded Ambrose to tell the story of his wager and the subterfuge whereby he won it. Expecting from the form of the question that he had at the worst but to lose the five thousand florins, he narrated the tale as he had told it to Sicurano. Turning to the Genoese, the Sultan then asked: 'What, then, did you do to your wife on account of the lie?'

"Bernard, weakened by imprisonment and racked with sorrow, answered in a broken voice: 'Woe is me! I had my servant kill her and leave her body to the wolves.'

At this Ginevra could not restrain herself. Abandoning her manly voice and demeanor, she cast herself at the Sultan's feet, begging the release of Bernard; at the same time confessing to all assembled that she was the wife who was thought to have been murdered. The Sultan granted her request on condition that Bernard humbly kneel and beg her pardon. But, seeking to do this, he was prevented by Ginevra throwing her arms about his neck and fainting for joy in his arms.

"As for Ambrose, the Sultan ordered that he be fastened to a stake in the most eminent part of the city, with his naked body smeared over with honey to attract the stinging insects with which that country abounds, and that he should hang there till his corpse dropped in pieces, in testimony of his villainy, and the truth of the proverb: The deceiver lies at the mercy of the deceived."*

After Dioneo's closing tale, which made the company laugh till their sides ached, the queen, taking the garland from her own head, placed it upon Neifile's saying: "To you, sweet sister, belongs henceforth the government of our little kingdom." Neifile, blushing like an April rose, accepted the honor, and said: "When we shall next assemble let our next argument be the mutability of fortune as exemplified by those who, enjoying great prosperity, have lost their all and then have won it back through their diligence or cleverness, or, if you will, by unexpected favor of the blind goddess, Chance."

---

*The story of the wager was used by Shakespeare as the central situation of *Cymbeline*.

THE MISTRESS REGAINED

The Story of Tedaldo and Monna Ermellina, Wife of Aldobrandino

Emilia, who had been designated by Queen Neifile as the next speaker, thus began:

"Since the subject for the day is the recovery of precious things that had been lost I shall tell you the story of a Florentine who, having been deprived through no fault of his own of what is a man's dearest possession, to wit, his mistress, regained it by his cleverness, and secured it beyond all hazard of future misadventure.

"Tedaldo Ele was the eldest of five brothers of a noble family in Florence which had been reduced to poverty by the unfortunate mercantile ventures of the father, who died, broken-hearted over his great losses, just as Tedaldo was entering manhood. This young man, on whom fell the burden of his brothers' support, had been educated in the fine arts, especially music, rather than in business, and so was forced to adopt the poorly paid profession of music-master. In this, however, he speedily secured the patronage of the best people of the city by the ability he displayed, not only as a teacher of music but also as a composer of tender love songs.

"The chief of his patrons was a wealthy merchant, Aldobrandino Palermini, who engaged him as the music-master of his young wife, Monna Ermellina. Although she was as fair as Saint Cecilia, and had a voice that could draw down the angels from heaven, she was neglected by her husband for other men's wives, for Aldobrandino was a coarse-minded person, attracted only by the grossest of feminine charms.

"It was inevitable that Tedaldo and Ermellina, young, handsome, and of the same cultivated tastes and emotional temperament, should fall violently in love. It was Tedaldo who first declared his passion in a song wherein he vowed eternal constancy to his beloved, however hopelessly separated from her he might be by fate and fortune, even by the coldness of her he adored. To this appeal the lady responded with a warmth that promised he should never be put to the latter test, and

135

Tedaldo trod on air, in the seventh heaven of bliss. From this, however, he was suddenly dashed to the inferno of despair by the lady's withdrawal of all her favors. She refused him even a sight of her face, and made no answer to his many imploring messages. Her action could not be accounted for by considerations of discretion, for the amour had been conducted so secretly that the husband still continued to be Tedaldo's bosom friend, making him a confidant in all his intrigues.

"Life in Florence became unendurable to Tedaldo under these conditions, and, though he had four brothers to whom he was bound by the strongest ties of fraternal affection and mutual dependence, without saying a word to anyone he stole away to Ancona and hired himself as a supercargo to a merchant about to sail to Cyprus. In time Tedaldo (who took the name of Philippo di Sanlodeccio, by which we shall for a time call him) by his industry and ability so commended himself to his employer that the merchant made him his partner, and gave him entire charge of their business in the Levant, with headquarters in Cyprus. So well did Signor Sanlodeccio manage his office that in a few years he became very wealthy and famous. In his good fortune he did not forget his brothers, but, as they severally arrived at manhood, established them in business in their native city, intimating that their benefactor was an old friend and debtor of their father. Engrossed with business, he thought less and less of Ermellina, until his love had faded into but a sad memory. Then suddenly, at the end of six years, it awoke in his heart with all its original poignancy, with this difference, that whereas before it had forced him to flee from her vicinity, now it drew him toward her with irresistible power. The occasion of this resurrection of passion was the chance hearing of a song sung by a pilgrim returning from the Holy Land which he recognized as that in which he had declared his love and vowed his constancy to his mistress.

"Purchasing the habit of the pilgrim, Sanlodeccio set out forthwith for Florence in the character of a poor palmer. Arriving in the city he went at once to the house of Aldobrandino, which he found with windows closed and barred. Fearing that his love was dead and not daring to assure himself by inquiry, he sadly turned toward his old home, which he saw marked with signs of recent death. At this moment, however, he was assured that his brothers were all living by their emergence from the house, dressed in mourning. This surprised him very much, and, knowing that his disguise was impenetrable, he asked a neighboring shoemaker the reason for these indications of bereavement. The artisan replied:

"'The case is a peculiarly sad one. Six years ago the brother of these men, Tedaldo by name and a music-teacher by profession, disappeared for no reason that was then known. Now it has transpired that he was in love with one of his pupils, the wife of Aldobrandino Palermini, and fearing, probably, that the husband had detected the intrigue, he fled the country. Fifteen days ago he returned, and, before visiting even his brothers between whom and himself a deep fraternal love existed as shown by secret aid which it is reported he had been giving them, he went privately to the house of his mistress, where he was killed by Aldobrandino. At least this is what I understand has been proved in the courts. And it is said that the brothers of Tedaldo have sworn, in case his murderer is acquitted, each in turn to challenge Aldobrandino in mortal combat, till he or they are all slain.'

"Though greatly mystified, Sanlodeccio was wonderfully relieved by these disclosures. Now that he knew his mistress was alive, his chief concern was for her husband, the innocent man whom in some hidden fashion he seemed to have so greatly injured and endangered. Pondering upon these matters he returned to his hotel, and wearied with travel lay down to rest. His bewilderment, however, would not let him sleep, and, lying close against the wall, he heard his own name spoken in a low voice within the next chamber. Listening intently he pieced out a conversation between a man and a woman, which revealed that they were accomplices in the plot that had put Aldobrandino in jeopardy of his life. The woman, it appeared, was a discarded mistress of the imprisoned merchant and the man a former friar who had been unfrocked through charges made against him by Ermellina. They were congratulating themselves upon their cleverness in avenging themselves by implicating the husband in a murder and the wife in a scandal without danger of their own detection. 'Tedaldo,' said the man, 'or rather his double, whose dead body I carried to Aldobrandino's door to involve him in trouble, is now safely buried by those who suppose themselves his brothers. The stupid merchant is certain of death at their hands, if not by sentence of law; and his proud wife, whom six years ago I frightened into dismissing the true Tedaldo, will go mourning to her grave over a false one. We are avenged, and, save for some indiscretion on our part, our acts will never be discovered.'

"Sanlodeccio was at first about to raise an outcry and apprehend the conspirators, but a sudden thought came into his mind of how he could turn his secret knowledge of the situation to account in his relations with Ermellina, and he kept silent. In the morning, still disguised in his palmer's weeds, he went to the home of Aldobrandino, knocked, and, to the servant who unbarred the door, announced that he had a message for the lady of the house. On being admitted to her presence he found her seated on the floor of her darkened boudoir, sobbing as if her heart would break. 'Madam,' said he, 'dry your tears; your peace is at hand. I am a messenger sent by God from Jerusalem to save your husband's life.' To her astonishment he related the story of the recent tragedy, with many details about the private life of herself and her husband which she supposed to be known to no other living person. Believing him to be a prophet, she fell upon her knees and prayed him, if he would save Aldobrandino, to make haste, as the time was short.

"'First, madam,' said Sanlodeccio, assuming the aspect of a very holy personage, 'you must confess your sin on account of which you suffer this tribulation!' 'Alas, sir!' she said, 'my sins are many, and I know not which one it is to which you refer. Shall I confess the mall?' 'Madam,' replied the false pilgrim, 'I know which sin it is; I do not ask for information, but that you may the more easily gain absolution by free confession. Had you ever a lover?'

"At this pointed question the lady was in great amaze. 'I perceive that Heaven,' she said, sighing deeply, 'has revealed to you my secret. I did love, I confess, that unfortunate young man whose death is laid at my husband's door. And my heart is stricken beyond remedy by the remembrance that I was harsh to him when he was blameless, and that I left him in utter ignorance of the cause. And I will further confess that neither his long absence, nor his miserable death, has been able to drive him from my heart.'

"'The poor man who is dead,' said the pilgrim, 'never loved you, though Tedaldo did. But you have not confessed the cause of your breaking with your lover.'

"'It was all due to a wicked friar, to whom I confessed my love for the young man, and who thereupon threatened me with all the pains of hell if I did not cease all intimacy with him. I was so frightened that I would no longer see him or receive his messages, though I was on the point of relenting, when he went away, as it resulted, to return only to his death. And afterward, when the friar revealed his true devilish character by attempting to substitute himself for the lover he had contrived to send into exile (although for that I punished him by securing his expulsion from his order), I compassed earth and sea to recall Tedaldo, among other things teaching a song he had composed to pilgrims about to set out for the Holy Land, and hiring them to sing it on their journey, in the hope that my exiled lover might hear it and interpret it as a message of love from his repentant mistress.'

"'Madam,' said the disguised lover, summoning up an undue severity to disguise his feelings, for his heart was overflowing with this evidence of her fidelity, so strikingly corroborated by his own experience, 'by your own confession your lover deserved no such usage as he received at your hands. This, therefore, is the sin for which you are now being punished. All that you can do, then, to expiate your guilt is to pledge yourself, if Tedaldo returns from exile, to reinstate him in the favor he enjoyed before you were terrorized into dismissing him by that wicked friar.'

"'Gladly,' cried Ermellina, 'would I do as you say. But how is it possible? He is dead; and of what value to him is a pledge?'

"The stranger made answer: 'Madam, I know that he is alive, and that all is well with him—provided he has your favor:

"'But I saw him lying with a knife in his breast before my very door,' cried the lady.

"Raising his hood the pilgrim looked into her face. 'Do you not know your Tedaldo?'

"Telling his mistress not to reveal his secret, Sanlodeccio resumed his disguise and went to the prison of Aldobrandino, who lay sullen in the straw, expecting nothing but death.

"Standing above him the pilgrim said: 'Aldobrandino, I am a messenger sent from God (who has regard to your innocence) to bring you tidings of deliverance. Before to-morrow night you will receive not only a pardon from the judge but the forgiveness of your enemies, the brothers of Tedaldo Ele. In return for this favor I ask but one pledge from you.'

"'On the word of an innocent man, such as you recognize me to be,' answered the prisoner, 'I swear to grant the condition.'

"'It is,' said the pilgrim, 'that you forgive in return the brothers of Tedaldo for their mistaken pursuit of you (for I declare that the murdered man was not Tedaldo Ele), and that, if he himself should return, you will receive him as of old at your home with no suspicion against him.'

"Right joyfully Aldobrandino gave this pledge, and Sanlodeccio went straight to the judge and laid bare to him, under pledge of secrecy, the whole story. The unfrocked friar and his accomplice were at once arrested. Under threat of torture they confessed their conspiracy, telling how a citizen of Lunigiana, Fativolo by name, had come to Florence, and, because of his striking likeness to Tedaldo Ele, had been taken for that person by the ex-friar and slain by him in jealous rage. It was only after he had stabbed the stranger that, in rifling his pockets, the assassin discovered his error from papers found therein, whereupon he had conceived the plan of fitting the misadventure to his vengeful purpose by fabricating letters addressed to Tedaldo, which he substituted for the papers of the dead man, and by procuring from Aldobrandino's cast-off mistress, now his own drab, a knife belonging to the merchant which, after conveying the corpse by night to Aldobrandino's door, he had placed within the wound made by his own weapon.

"The judge at once released Aldobrandino who, in gratitude to the pilgrim, invited him to a banquet at his house. Reminding the merchant of his promise, Sanlodeccio requested that he also invite his four brothers, who, though they were informed that Aldobrandino had been exonerated by the confession of the real assassin, were not enlightened as to the identity of the victim. The brothers came to the banquet still in garments of black, and, laying down their arms in the presence of the guests, they humbly asked pardon of their host, which he gladly accorded. The brothers, in their sorrow for Tedaldo, could not forgive, however, what they considered the unfitting and unseasonable merriment of a pilgrim present, whom the host evidently regarded as his chief guest. They sat in gloomy silence throughout the feast until the dessert was served, when, feeling free to depart, they arose to make their excuses. Seeing this, Sanlodeccio started up, crying: 'Nothing is wanting to this merry meeting but the presence of Tedaldo. Let the holy man from Jerusalem, then, gloriously end his career by miraculously summoning him before you. Tedaldo, come forth!' And, throwing off his pilgrim's robe, he stood before his brothers clad in the rich garments of a merchant prince, but the same dear fellow they had last beheld in the shabby robes of a poor music-master."

Queen Neifile, knowing her sovereignty to be at an end, placed the crown on Filostrato's head, saying: "We shall now see whether our masters shall govern us better than we have hitherto governed them." At this Filostrato replied: "For my part I have ever been under the domination of the ladies. Yet it has availed me nothing that I have been humble and obedient to their wishes, for I am constantly being discarded for some other lover, and expect no better fortune to the end. Therefore, that my misery may have the consolation of company, I appoint as our next subject: Misfortune in love."

THE LOVER'S HEART

THE STORY OF GHISMOND, DAUGHTER OF PRINCE TANCRED, AND GUISCARD

When the company had assembled on the morrow, the king commanded Fiammetta to lead in the story-telling. In a soft and tender voice, befitting the subject, she began:

"Prince Tancred of Salerno had an only daughter, Ghismond by name, whom he loved so fondly that he was loath to be separated from her, and, indeed, did not give his consent to her marriage until long after she had arrived at womanhood. When soon thereafter she returned a widow to his home, he took no care to secure another husband for her, whereupon the lady sought out a lover of her own. Her choice fell upon a person of noble qualities but of low birth, whose name was Guiscard. To keep their intrigue from Tancred, Ghismond prepared an underground grotto reached from her chamber by a secret staircase, and from a corner of the palace garden by a ladder let down an old, disused well covered with a growth of brambles. Here she used to meet her lover with no danger of discovery. Growing bolder, in time the lady brought her gallant into her chamber, and thereafter it became their place of assignation. This led to their undoing, for one day Tancred entered the room in his daughter's absence, and seating himself in a great chair in a corner fell to dozing. While he was fast asleep, Ghismond entered the room, and, perceiving no one there, descended the secret staircase, and brought back her lover. Hereupon Tancred awoke, and was a witness of all that passed between the lovers, for he stifled his first impulse to cry out at the shame they were bringing on his house, resolving to take a great and unforeseen vengeance upon them. When it came time for the lovers to part, Ghismond accompanied Guiscard down the staircase, and Tancred seized the opportunity to escape unseen from the chamber through the window.

"The next day he apprehended Guiscard as he was emerging from the well. To the old man, bitterly reviling him for his presumption, the young lover made no other answer than: 'Sir, love has greater power than you or I.'

"Placing Guiscard in custody, Tancred sought his daughter, and told her that her amour had been discovered and her paramour taken. She, having no doubt that the fierce old man would slay her lover whatsoever she might say, answered him with calmness and dignity:

"'It is true that I love Guiscard, and whilst I live I shall continue to love him, and if love continue after death, I shall never cease to love him. While I might plead female frailty and the little care you took to marry me again as my excuses, I do not do so. I loved Guiscard for his superior worth. You bitterly reproach me with condescending to a man of low condition. I tell you, he is the only noble man of all your court. How often have you yourself commended him! If I was deceived, it was by following your opinion. And I tell you that if you put this good man to death, as is evidently your intention, unless you do the same to me, my own hands shall do it for you.'

"The stern old man, who should have considered that his daughter had inherited his determined disposition, believed that she was only making but an idle threat, and he persisted in his resolution to kill Guiscard. By his orders the prisoner was strangled and the heart removed from his body. Placing this in a golden cup, Tancred sent it to his daughter with this taunting message: 'Your father sends this present to comfort you with what was most dear to you, even as you comforted him in what he held most dear.'

"Taking the cup in her hands she replied: 'Tell him that sent you I have much to thank him for. He has given this heart of gold a fitting sepulchre. So benumbed was my own heart by grief that I could not weep, as was due him, over the fate of my dear one, and the giver of this chalice has opened the floodgates of my sorrow so that his present will not be able to contain my tears.'

"When she had done speaking, she fell to weeping and kissing the heart, as if she would never leave off. At length, however, she desisted, and, taking a potion of poisonous herbs that she had distilled, and pouring it into the cup, she drank the draught mingled as it was with her own tears and her lover's blood. Then she lay down on her couch and calmly awaited death.

Her maid sent at once for Tancred, who, when he arrived and saw, too late, the result of his hardness of heart, began to lament most grievously. Ghismond, with her dying words, bade him save his tears for himself when he should need them. 'I want them not. But if any love for me remain in you, grant that my lover and myself, whom you would not suffer to be happy together while living, share one grave in death.'

"The repentant father obeyed the request, and buried them in one stately tomb in the most public manner, amid the general grief of all the people of Salerno."*

---

* This tale is the most popular of all of Boccaccio's. Five Italian tragedies have been founded on the theme, and the story has been told by poets of many lands, Dryden among them (in his poem entitled *Sigismunda and Guiscardo*). It has also formed the subject of many paintings, chief of which is one attributed to Correggio.

LA FIAMMETTA (1341)

While Boccaccio was a student at the University of Naples he fell in love with the Lady Maria, a natural daughter of King Robert of Naples and the youthful wife of a nobleman of that city. In 1340 his father summoned him home to Florence, and soon thereafter, probably the next year, he poured out his soul to his absent love in this work, to which he gave the name by which he always called her. John Addington Symonds says of *La Fiammetta*, "it is the first attempt in any literature to portray subjective emotion exterior to the writer * * * The author of this extraordinary work proved himself a profound anatomist of feeling by the subtlety with which he dissected a woman's heart." The story has furnished to succeeding writers the motives of many tales. The only English translation extant is that made for, and published by, The National Alumni, in 1906, in their sixteen-volume edition of *The Literature of Italy*.

EGINNETH the Elegy of Madonna Fiammetta, sent by her to Ladies in Love. For, so far as lies in my power, I would withhold my complaints from men, on account of the bitterness of soul toward them which the cruelty of one man hath stirred within me.

Born and reared amid boundless affluence, I learned whatever manners and refinements it beseems a demoiselle of high rank to know. As a child I heard my beauty acclaimed by many, and I gloried therein, cultivating it by ingenious care and art. When I attained a riper age, being taught by nature how love can be quickened in young men by lovely ladies, I exercised my charms upon the noble youths who were attracted by my beauty— ill-fated gift for one who desires to live virtuously! By many of these young men was I sought in marriage with most passionate entreaty. From them I chose a husband who was in every respect congenial, and, the others ceasing to trouble me with their attentions, with him I lived most happily, so long as passionate love, lighted by flame hitherto unfelt, found no entrance into my young soul. It was with the peaceful regard of married partnership that I looked upon my mate. Woe is me that this sweet love was ever supplanted!

For my ensuing misfortunes I alone am to blame. The gods gave me sufficient warnings. On the very night that preceded the day of my woe's beginning, I dreamed that while I was lying in a flowery meadow a viper stung me under the left breast. I thought I clasped the cold serpent to my warm bosom, feeling that thus I should render it more kindly disposed. But the ungrateful worm was made all the bolder by the favor, and laying his hideous mouth on the wound, he began drinking my heart's blood. Finally from me, who resisted—but ever more faintly with my diminishing strength—he drew forth, methought, my very soul, and glided away with it.

The morrow was the day of the August festival, and I arrayed myself for it in glittering cloth-of-gold and adorned my head with flowers. While I was lost in admiration of myself, just as a peacock is of his plumage, a blossom from my wreath fell to the ground. But I, careless of the occult signs of divine warning, restored it to its place, and passed out from my abode to the sacred temple. There my rank had reserved for me the central seat among the noble ladies. No sooner was I seated than (even while the sacred office was going on) the men, and the women, too, fixed their eyes upon me, as if Venus had descended from the sky and would never be seen by them again. Oh, how often I took glory unto myself because of such things, as if in truth I were a goddess!

At the close of the ceremony I was encircled by noble youths who vied with each other in praise of my beauty. But, while I kept my ears attentive to their discourse, and received therefrom much delectable sweetness, I turned my eyes away that I might appear unaffected by it. And, looking aside, I saw, apart from the others, a young man leaning against a marble column. Meseemed he was the most beautiful in form and graceful in bearing of all men whom I had ever seen. Soft and silky locks falling in curls about bloomy cheeks gave proof of his youthfulness. The look wherewith he eyed me seemed to beg for pity; yet it was marked by a wariness with which, while it is usual between man and man, I had never before met in men's attentions to myself. Dominated by the new experience of a power greater than my own, I could not help gazing at him with unconcealed interest, and even admiration.

Methought I could read in his eyes a challenge: "Lady, of all women in the world, thou belongest to me."

"And thou to me," my heart made answer, for I found myself enmeshed in the snares of sudden and unforeseen love in a manner beyond all my powers of telling, and so I remain unto this very hour.

When I returned to my chamber I thought that if I could not banish this new passion from my breast I might at least be able to keep cautious control of it therein. So I formed my plans to bring him to my side without revealing to any other than himself the passion that inflamed me. When next I saw him I showed my purpose in my eyes, and he responded with ready comprehension. He used every subtle art to win the friendship of all about me, beginning with my friends and relatives and ending with my husband. When at last he was come into open converse with me, he taught me how to conceal our love from the world by symbolic acts and words. Thus he named me Fiammetta, and himself Panfilo. Woe is me! How often, when warmed with love and wine, did we tell tales, in the presence of our dearest friends, of Fiammetta and Panfilo, feigning that they were Greeks in the days of old—and the tales were all of ourselves!

Although by this public declaration of our love, in cryptic language though it was, we were inviting discovery, nevertheless, it was by a distant hap that Fate interrupted our stolen intercourse. The father of Panfilo, who lived in a distant city, falling sick, called him home to his side. Ladies, who have parted from your beloved ones and have been wracked with apprehension for them on their journey and spent with longing for their dear presence, I will not recall these pangs by recounting my sorrows of the self-same kind. But perchance the gods have been kind and have never visited you with the torments of jealousy. These, too, fell to my lot. Be patient while I shall relate them.

One day, while I was visiting certain ladies, a merchant of jewels brought in his wares to exhibit them. While chaffering with him, one of the ladies questioned him from what city he came, and on his giving the name of Panfilo's birthplace she asked him concerning the welfare of the one absent from our circle. Oh, how pertinently this question comported with my heart's dearest desire. I listened hungrily.

"Oh, he is the happiest of men," replied the merchant. "His father, if he were, as you say, sick, has certainly recovered from his illness. This was probably a rusé of the young man to elude the toils you fair ladies were laying for him here and to return home to a bride his father had selected for him—the daughter of a wealthy noble of the city. On the very day I was leaving I saw your friend entering his father's house with a beautiful young lady on his arm. There was great merry-making going on within. From all I heard the couple had just been married."

Although I had been listening in the bitterest anguish, yet did I keep my eyes fixed on the face of the young lady who was asking these questions. I perceived that as soon as the news of Panfilo's wedding reached her ears, her cheeks flushed, her eyelids fell and her eyes brimmed with tears which she could barely refrain from shedding. Although crushed to the very earth by what I had heard, I could hardly hold myself from falling foul of her with rancorous abuse, being jealous that she should show forth her love by such open signs. But yet I did restrain myself and did not let the anguish of my heart appear on my face, even masking my grief with a burst of laughter at Panfilo's ruse for escaping from the snares of the ladies of our city.

When I returned home and entered my chamber, I burst into violent weeping. "And this is the man," I cried, "for whose grief for his dying father I was shedding tears of sympathy, for whose dangers by land and sea I was in constant anguish. O ye gods, visit him with all those perils that I dreaded he might encounter! Slay him by whatever death ye will, that I may not alone bear the penalty of our sin, and that he may not remain, after laughing at both you and me, to enjoy himself with his new spouse."

Then in my abject humiliation I bethought myself of the anguish of the young lady whose inquiry the merchant had answered.

"Oh, Panfilo! thou devil in angel's guise, wilt thou tell me into how many portions thy love was divided, or capable of division? I presume thou wert in love with numberless other ladies at the very time when I thought thee to belong to myself alone. Would that I could gain comfort from believing that I am not alone in my misery! But oh, unreasoning creature that I am, how I hate those other women who love him!"

My good husband perceived that I was wasting away, but he had no idea that it was from secret grief. To restore my failing health he sent me to charming Baiæ on the sea-coast. But my anguish was thereby increased, because every rock, every islet of the beautiful place recalled Panfilo who had been with me when I had visited Baiæ in happier days. When I saw blissful lovers wandering together on the shore my torments became so exquisite that, like the bereaved nightingale that presses her breast against the thorn, I was seized with mad desire to cherish them. "O Love," I prayed, "since thou hast denied me preëminence in felicity, give me, as thou gavest Dido, eternal fame of dolorous betrayal."

At last my husband divined that my sickness was of the mind rather than of the body and he pressed me to disclose the cause of my grief. Whereunto I, with my sex's duplicity, answered by a lie, although lying is an art that was once foreign to me. I told him that I grieved for the death of my brother (who had been slain some years before while engaged in a disgraceful intrigue), mourning not the fact of his murder, but the shame to him and his family that accompanied it.

With what tenderness did my noble husband seek to assuage my sorrow, which, indeed, had once existed but had been long allayed! I felt myself the falsest, most despicable of wives. After my husband had left me, I besought Hell to draw me down to the torments I deserved.

"Let no mercy be shown me," I cried, "who have preferred the faith of a stranger to the sanctity of the marriage tie. Is not my husband as handsome as Panfilo? In virtue and nobility, and every other distinguished quality, is he not far superior to my betrayer? Certainly he is. Fool that I was to cast away a true love, because it was mine without asking, for a false one, because it seemed hard to attract and hazardous to enjoy."

In my self-abasement I determined to kill myself. "Thus,"

I argued to myself, "I shall atone for my guilt, and make reparation to my betrayed husband in a manner befitting my dignity."
My real desire, however, was that perchance, in the spirit, I
could join Panfilo, which I could not in the flesh. Then I
bethought myself that he, being in the flesh, would be ignorant
of my presence. "Live," cried Hope, "and he may return to
thee. Whether he come as lover or enemy, thou shalt see him.
If he be not overcome with pity when he beholds thy wretched
condition, then will it be time for thee to die."

As if to prove the wisdom of my resolution, I heard shortly
after I had come to it that Panfilo was to return to our city.
At once all my doubts of his fidelity vanished.

"Oh, what shameful things I have hitherto thought of my
true lover," I said, "and how unreasonably have I condemned
him for his delay! Accursed be the liars who told me he belonged
to another woman! He is true, true, and he is coming back to
me, of all the women of the world his one dear love! How
shameful it was of me to distrust him! Yet he will not know
all the foolish things I have thought, and if he ever learns them,
he will say: 'She must have loved me very ardently to do such
things.'"

From the heaven of these expectations I was cast into the
depths of bottomless despair by the discovery that the Panfilo
whose coming had been announced proved on arrival to be
another of the same name.

You may perceive now, O ladies, to what misery I have
been brought by the immemorial deceptions of Fortune. I do
not dare to die, lest in truth Panfilo return. I do not care to live
tormented now by my sense of infidelity to my husband, now
by remorse for my distrust of my lover. My only consolation
is the writing of this book, which shall make my grief immortal.
*Endeth the Elegy of Madonna Fiammetta, sent by her to Ladies
in Love.*

GEORGE HENRY BORROW

(England, 1803-1881)

LAVENGRO: THE SCHOLAR—THE GIPSY—THE PRIEST (1851)

This romance is in part, with no attempt at concealment, an autobiographical record of the eccentric author, though it is embroidered freely with fictional characters and events. Borrow was a well-born and educated Englishman, but he chose rather to consort with gipsies and men and women of the road than with his own class. These associations gave him an opportunity to add to his very unusual knowledge of many languages by the mastery of the gypsy tongue—the "Rommany"—derived from the ancient Roman speech, according to the gipsies' firm belief. *Lavengro* is one of a series of books on the same subject; it was followed by *Zincali, or Gypsies of Spain*, *The Romany Rye*, and *Wild Wales*—all of which form a unique and valuable record of the manners, customs, and language of the mysterious nomadic people. Jasper Petulengro represents a real gipsy, well known throughout Lancashire as Ambrose Smith.

 WAS the son of an army-officer of small patrimony, and my early childhood was spent in the vicissitudes of garrison life in various parts of England, Scotland, Wales, and Ireland. I was passionately fond of nature and solitude and cared but little for books; and it was not till I read *Robinson Crusoe*, at the age of seven, that my mind and imagination were really awakened. The passion for wandering and adventure thus inspired was destined to dominate my life. Among the things that stood out most saliently in those days was my acquaintance with a rustic naturalist, and what came of it. He taught me to catch and train vipers, and one of these, having been made fangless, I carried in my bosom. One day, rambling in the outskirts of a small garrison town, I happened on two gipsies—my first contact with the Rommany clan, with whom I was destined to become so intimate. Man and woman were bending over a small cooking-pot, and near by were ramshackle carts and grazing horses. The sight of my small self inspired them with distrust, whereon the man advanced with an oath, as

if to strike me. I showed them in my bosom the hissing viper, which reared its crest angrily. The gipsies at once put on an air of fear and reverence, for they thought me a "devilkin," and did not much remit their servility when I told them about my snake-hunting skill. They dubbed me *Sap-engro*, which means a snake-tamer in their tongue. A boy came running up, the son of the pair, Jasper Petulengro, who seemed disposed to despise me as I looked too puny to box; but when told I was a snake-master, he said he would be my "gentle brother." Three years later—within which time I had learned Lilly's Latin grammar by heart—my father was ordered to Edinburgh and I was placed at the celebrated High School there. Here I became a doughty champion in the bickers between the "Auld Town" and the "New Town," an adept in stone-throwing, a proficient in wrestling and fist-fighting, and a daring dragoman, for my health and stature had greatly improved in our two years of sojourn.

The billet of the regiment was changed to Ireland, where I studied Latin and Greek in a seminary at Clonmel; but I was much more interested in the Irish language, the rudiments and much of the vocabulary of which I learned from a papist *gossoon*, one of my schoolmates. The taste for language was stirring, which by and by was to change my gipsy sobriquet from *Sap-engro* to *Lav-engro* ("language-master"). Here, too, I learned to ride, as a fractious cob, the despair of the regimental grooms, took a great affection for me and I could do anything with him.

With the passing years the great war came to an end, and my father retired from the army on a very moderate competence to spend his declining years in a quaint old English city. My love of learning languages was gratified by the study of French, Italian, and Spanish under an exiled priest; but I found other diversion in more active pursuits, in which I rubbed against all sorts and conditions; but most of all I loved the sights and sounds of nature in the amusements of shooting and angling.

One day at a horse-fair three dark men with shining eyes and elf-locks were riding in a ring showing off their beasts. They looked at me, stopped, and rode away, but a few minutes later a voice sounded to the snap of a whip: "What, the *Sap-engro!* Lor! the *Sap-engro* upon the hill!" I followed them to their gipsy camp, and my "pal," Jasper, inquired about me and told me of himself. Jasper Petulengro had become Rommany Kral or gipsy king, the Pharaoh of his tribe, champion horse-shoer, pugilist, jockey, and soothsayer. Many a meeting and visit followed this. There was much talk about the Rommany tongue, in which I found many strange analogies with other languages of which I knew something, but this, I thought, contained the wreck of an older speech than any of them. Jasper began to teach me the Rommany tongue, at which his mother-in-law, old Mrs. Hearne, a fierce and malignant crone, protested with much objurgation as a theft of their language.

"I hates the *gorgio,*" said she, "and would like, speaking Rommanly, to poison his waters. I goes broken-hearted. I can't keep you company. Ye are no longer Rommany. To gain a bad brother, you have lost a good mother." So she deserted the camp for another gipsy home, and Jasper, with his following, migrated Londonward.

My next phase of experience was in a solicitor's office, to which I was condemned as a last resort since I appeared to be otherwise useless. Here, if I neglected Blackstone and spoiled many a legal document, I found consolation in the mother British tongue, Welsh, which I studied with great assiduity when no eye was on me. In the "Comydds" and odes of a famous wild bard, Ab Gwilym, a copy of which I stumbled on, I found delightful companionship. With Ab Gwilym in my hand I was on enchanted ground, where I experienced sensations akin to those I had felt of yore whilst spelling my way through the wonderful *Robinson Crusoe*—the delight of my childhood. It was not very long before another linguistic adventure befell. An elderly yeoman, for whom I had done a trifling favor, gave into my hands an uncouth book bound in wood with iron clasps, printed on vellum in black-letter Gothic. This had been washed ashore many years before in a shipwreck. It was a Danish book. The question was how to unlock this treasure. I didn't know where to find a grammar and a dictionary, but I did succeed in finding a Danish Bible. By incessant work in comparing the English Bible with this, word for word, I found myself able in a month to master the contents of this flotsam of the shipwreck, although it was in a more ancient dialect. I found it a book of ballads about the deeds of knights and champions and men of huge stature, immemorial ballads of the North, collected two centuries before by one Anders Redel, who had lived as assistant with a certain Tycho Brahe, famous in star-lore. Indeed, to one praising German literature, who had been helping me to learn German, I took occasion to say, "there is more genuine poetry in the old Danish book, which I came so strangely by, than has been produced in Germany from the period of the Nibelungen lay to the present time."

But it ill befits one to carry all his eggs of pleasure in one basket. One day, in wandering on the heath, I happened on a little conventicle where an earnest field-preacher was exhorting, and the simple hymn-singing impressed my imagination more than the most gorgeous rites of religious pomp. As I wandered along the heath a man appeared through the thick furze, who proved to be Jasper Petulengro, who had come to see a great prize-fight to be held thereabouts; and we discussed issues of life and death.

"A Rommany chal would wish to live forever," said Jasper. "There's wind on the heath; if I could only feel that I would gladly live forever. Dosta we'll now go to the tents and put on the gloves; and I'll try to make you feel what a sweet thing it is to be alive, brother."

I met Mr. Petulengro again at the prize-fight, where all the great bruisers of England, when the glorious art of pugilism was in its prime, were assembled. At its close, amid a terrible rage of thunder, lightning, and rain, as one of the exultant victors drove away, the gipsy pointed to a strange kind of cloud in the sky, and said: "That cloud foreshoweth a bloody dukkeripen." "A bloody fortune!" said I, "and whom may it betide?" "Him," said Jasper, pointing to the companion and backer of the bruiser, a prophecy which was surely fulfilled.

My father's death, with the cessation of his half-pay, left barely enough for my mother's support, so perforce I must go to London to earn a living. I betook me thence with but little store of money, but with my precious manuscripts—translations into English verse of Ab Gwilym and of the Danish ballads of the "Kaempe Viser" with which I hoped to lay the foundation of fame. If it should not be akin to that of Sir Walter Scott or Lord Byron, the overture would at least give me usable foothold. But publishers scoffed at these offerings, and at last I became a mere publishers' hack spurred by need. My employer was an unscrupulous and pompous ass, himself a pretender to philosophical distinction. I was glad to compile for him the chronicles of Newgate and do such-like work, and undertook to translate the publisher's lucubrations for the German market, as well as to write sugared reviews of books, that nobody would ever read, for my employer's new review. All this on starvation wages, and it was only the episode of human life that ran athwart mine with keen smack of interest that saved me from a dive from London Bridge. At last I was lucky enough to find a publisher who printed an adventure story for living rates; and, with twenty pounds in pocket, I was fain to shake London dust from off my feet, for my health had begun to pine and my heart was thirsty for the sweet air and green fields.

The adventures of the road—for I was on the tramp with slender luggage—were diverse, and as diverting as those of the town. One related, indeed, to London, with a touch of pathos. A sailor, or a man so dressed, with frank, honest face, accosted me with inquiry for the London road. He had once fallen into evil ways and been transported to Botany Bay. There, good behavior had earned his ticket-of-leave, and he was now on his way to see and care for his old mother, whom he had left an applewoman with a fruit-stand on London Bridge. He mourned over the thought that she might be dead, for she was the only one who cared for him. Then I bethought me of the old fruit-seller with whom I had been wont to collogue, and who had given me an ancient copy of *Moll Flanders* to exchange for a Bible for her, which I persuaded her would be more for her soul's good. So I wagered him five shillings to five pence that he would within a week find her alive, and he departed, after a mug of ale at a public, much heartened. But what was destined to affect me most was my adventure with an unhappy tinker whom I met on the road, with his ragged wife and children. I ordered ale for them and filled their bellies with good cheer, while the tinman, whose name was Slingsby, rehearsed his story. He had got a good living on the road from the rural folk till he had been driven off his beat by the biggest rogue in England and the cruellest one, called the Flaming Tinman. That big ruffian, who called himself the king of all tinkers, with his brawny wife, Gray Moll, had beaten the poor fellow and his woman savagely, and compelled him to swear on the Bible to quit the roads, had this lusty gipsy villain with flaming red bandanna.

Myself: "I'm half inclined to buy your cart and pony and your beat, too."

Tinker: "Why, you would get your head knocked off. Suppose you were to meet *him?*"

Myself: "Pooh! don't be afraid on my account. If I should meet him I could easily manage him one way or another. I know all kinds of strange words and names, and, as I told you, I sometimes hit people when they put me out."

So, after some further palaver, we struck a bargain. I gave him five pounds ten for all his belongings, and, buying some provisions from the landlady, I began my new life, the most independent in the world.

One brilliant morning I was mending pots and pans when I heard a voice singing an old Rommany song of predatory meaning. A young girl about thirteen appeared, and after some talk, in which she was very curious, I answered her wicked lilt with another *gillie.* She started, stared, and said to herself, "Gray, tall, and talks Rommany," with an expression compounded of fear, curiosity, and deepest hate. That evening I thought I saw a shaggy, unkempt face peering through the bushes, and the girl came back next day with two rich cakes as a present in return for a little gift I had made her. I ate a little piece of one of the cakes, and that night I was seized with dreadful qualms and deadly pains torturing my whole frame. As I lay half-unconscious the next morning, the gipsy girl and an old crone—in whom I recognized my old enemy Mrs. Hearne as they pattered in Rommany—sat at the tent door. Then I found that the ancient witch, who harbored an undying hate for the *gorgio* who had stolen her language, had poisoned me. But even as she talked, the spirit of soothsaying, the

dukkeripen, possessed her, and she recited her weird canticle.
She dreamed she was in York to see a hanging and lo! it was
the tinker (myself). Anon there was a change: she was in a
big church, and it was the tinker and not the dean that preached.
Presto! she was at the scaffold again as the drop fell, "and I
looked and saw not the tinker but my own self hanging in the
air." Then she cursed me and stabbed at me with her metal-
pointed stick. But a sound of wheels frightened the pair and
they scuttled through the furze. It was a Welsh preacher and
his wife on their peregrinations, and 'twas their ministrations
that saved me. He himself was half-crazed in certain moods
with an obsession that he had sinned the sin against the Holy
Ghost, but of this I succeeded in curing him by wholesome
suggestions during our sojourn in company. When I told him
I knew Welsh, and had translated the odes of mighty Dafgdd
Ab Gwilym, he would have me cross the Severn with him into
Wales to receive the homage of the people. But no! there were
other things a-doing, for I met Mr. Petulengro at the ford, who
was returning from Mrs. Hearne's funeral, as that ancient
dame had hanged herself.

I turned back with him and we had much pleasant converse,
in which he said his mother-in-law had acted in conviction
that the time had come for her long journey, on account of her
dream of the hanging. The child Leonora's story of the poison-
ing and my own narration filled up all the gaps. Jasper shook
his head in disapproval of his relative's doings—for he said she
had poisoned other *gorgios* and even gipsies—yet he looked
at me with a sober and questioning eye, and suggested that
there was a beautiful place under the trees. There was a point
of honor to be settled between us, he explained. He couldn't
have a pal going about with him who had caused his mother-
in-law's death without some satisfaction given. After an half-
hour of tussle, in which my face got brilliantly smudged with
much red, Mr. Petulengro said, "I am satisfied; blood has
been shed, which is all that can be reasonably expected for an
old woman who carried so much brimstone about her as Mrs.
Hearne."

As I declined just then to dwell with him in the tents of the
Rommany Chal, because I hankered after solitude varied with

the diversions of blacksmithing and the tinker's craft, he told
me of a fine retreat for such pursuit of ideals, and we parted
with hearty hand-grip.

Two days later, after settling down in a charming and lonely
dingle, I was about caparisoning Ambrol, my pony, for a forag-
ing trip, when I heard the grating of wheels among gravel, and
then a distant shout. Soon a ruffianly and athletic-looking
fellow, with a red cap and a Barcelona kerchief on his bull-
neck, appeared, accompanied by two females, one an exceedingly tall girl with a handsome but determined face, the other a
coarse virago. I accosted the man comradely and bade him welcome. "I am a *Rome chabo* by matriculation," said I. The fellow snorted with a "H'm," and, while I was discoursing with the
tall girl, who was half-inclined to be friendly, he cast his eyes on
the pony among the trees. "The horse of that mumping villain,
Slingsby," he shouted. "I swore I would seize it the next time
I found it on my beat, ay, and beat the master, too."

We squared for battle, and though I had by no means
recovered my strength, I had no difficulty in marking eye,
nose, and mouth with bloody left-handers. But he cared for
these as little as would a wild bull, and rushed in, throwing
me by sheer strength. In a second his huge hands closed on
my windpipe, and he would soon have throttled me had it not
been for the tall girl. She twisted the handkerchief on his
neck with so shrewd a wrench as released his grip, till I could
jump to my feet. We went at it again, Belle, the tall girl, acting
as my second, while Gray Moll served the Flaming Tinman.
In ten minutes I received six knock-down blows, though,
striking six blows to his one. I was cutting his face into mince-
meat. Belle adjured me, gasping for breath, to use "Long
Melford"—"you'll never beat the Flaming Tinman in the way
you fight—it's no use flipping at the Flaming Tinman with
your left; why don't you use your right?"

The giant came at me almost as fresh as ever in wind and
spirit—though his eyes were swollen and his lower lip was cut
in half—striking right and left with windmill strokes. He aimed
one terrific blow which might have annihilated me, but it only
grazed my shoulder and smashed into a tree-bole. At the same
moment, gathering every ounce of strength, I let him have it

under the ear with a right-hander, and the Flaming Tinman toppled senseless to grass. That ended the Homeric bout that was to make me unwittingly famous throughout the country-side, for the Flaming Tinman was a much-dreaded champion. It was like what my father, good Christian gentleman that he was, had done in his youth, for he had pounded one of the great bruisers of his time to a standstill.

When the discomfited pair departed, as they did right speedily, with looks of the deepest malignity, Isopel Berners—for that was her name—remained behind with her belongings. The girl told me her story over our tea that night; she had been born in a great house, where there were only two other noble names beside her own—Bohun and Devereux. It was the workhouse, for her father, a sailor officer, had deserted her gipsy mother, and was killed in sea-fight on the way home to do right by his victim. The girl had had many experiences, had learned to take care of herself by her strength, size, and courage; indeed, had once knocked down a rich farmer on whose estate she worked, because he made her an insulting suggestion. Finally, through melancholy and want of company, she had joined the little caravan of Blazing Bosville. That worthy had wished to marry her instead of Gray Moll, but she had sternly quelled his aspiration.

I went to a neighboring public one night, and the landlord, noticing my swollen fist, looked at me admiringly, with the whisper that Gray Moll had told him all. So, when certain tavern blusterers would be pugnacious, he proposed a ring in the yard with ten pounds on my head, and referred to the Flaming Tinman episode. Whereat there was respectful dropping of jaws with change of tune.

Belle was a little sad and even shy, in spite of her bigness, any allusion to which she resented. So to cheer her I determined to teach her Armenian, which Oriental tongue I had picked up in London. We passed the time, each in our own way, with tents side by side in that beautiful dingle. She was very entertaining and intelligent in recountal of her wandering life, and all things betokened the dauntless heart of this maid. I told her of my experiences; how I had tamed savage horses, wrestled with Satan, had dealings with ferocious publishers

and swallowed strange tongues. She would weep and blush
over it all, and when she was too curious I would punish the
contrite girl by making her conjugate Haïk verbs and repeat
the numerals up to a hundred. One night Belle had returned
home after a long day's absence, and, after removing all signs of
dust and fatigue, with a changed dress on, she sat down by
the crackling wood blaze. It was green ash, emitting an
aromatic fragrance.

"That makes good the old rhyme," said Belle, "which I
have heard sung by the old women in the great house:

> 'Ash when green
> Is fire for a queen.'"

"And on fairer form of queen ash-fire never shone," said
I, "than on thine, O beauteous queen of the dingle!"

"I am half-disposed to be angry with you, young man,"
said Belle.

"And why not entirely?" said I.

Belle made no reply.

"Shall I tell you?" I demanded. "You had no objection
to the first part of the speech, but you did not like being called
queen of the dingle. Well! if I had the power I would make
you queen of something better than the dingle—Queen of
China. Come, let us have tea."

"Something else would content me," said Belle, sighing
as she rose to prepare our evening meal.

PAUL BOURGET

(France, 1852)

COSMOPOLIS (1892)

In his own letter of introduction to *Cosmopolis*, Paul Bourget called the story "a romance of international life," and justly characterized it as "a drama of passion." He was at pains to explain that the placing of the action in Rome was accidental and without significance. His purpose was neither historical nor in any sense geographical. It was altogether artistic, dramatic and psychological. The author wished to present a study of race characteristics and race impulses under conditions that exist in every great cosmopolitan city. As a stage for the setting of his tragedy, Rome served his purpose as might have any other of the world's great capitals. The story was crowned by the French Academy as the most notable work of fiction produced in France in the year of its publication.

THE Marquis de Montfanon, one-armed and rather shabbily dressed, entered the littered bookshop of Ribalta to purchase a rare breviary.

Ribalta was a chronic revolutionist and destructionist by nature, and by long habit. He had fought with Garibaldi and helped in the overthrow of the papal power in Rome. He was ready now to revolt against the Piedmontese government for what he deemed its weakness and cowardice in leaving even the Vatican to the Pope's control. In the absence of opportunity for physical revolt, he vented his rancor in epigrams and versicles.

The Marquis de Montfanon was a French nobleman, partly of Germanic blood. In his youth he had been dandy, duelist, gambler, lover, and soldier. His empty sleeve bore witness to the courage with which he had fought as a Pontifical Zouave at Patay. He was now a devotee who lived meagerly in order that he might give his income to charity and his toil to the literary exaltation of a past that had gone forever. In his own person and manner he still preserved much of the arrogant intolerance of his unregenerate days, but it was directed now to the service of religion and the preservation of conservatism rather than to any more personal purposes. In behalf of religion and conservatism he was a fanatic and a radical of extreme intolerance.

Ribalta showed him the prayerbook he desired to buy, one which had belonged to the celebrated Montluc. Ribalta lied about it and, when caught by the superior knowledge of Montfanon, insisted upon selling the book for four hundred francs, though Montfanon had offered a hundred more.

Soon after leaving the shop Montfanon saw a carriage pass in which rode the beautiful Fanny Hafner, and while he was looking at her, he was accosted by Julien Dorsenne, the brilliant young French novelist, whose praises were in everyone's mouth. Fanny was the daughter of Baron Hafner, world citizen, financier, swindler, and colossal thief, who had escaped the penalty of his crimes by a technical verdict which left him with his vast, ill-gotten wealth, and a name that was saved from universal execration only by the modern world's slavish deference to money, tainted though it be.

Fanny Hafner was the catechist of a great cardinal, preparing for baptism, notwithstanding her Jewish blood, and intending to be baptized when her father should have completed his arrangements to sell her and his millions for the title of Roman princess by making her the bride of Prince D'Ardea, the ruined heir of the Castagnas. Fanny Hafner was sincere in her religious fervor; but the wily old trader, her father, had no mind to let the Church have her as a convert until it should pay his price. He had himself helped mightily in the financial ruin of D'Ardea and in forcing the sale now about to be made of the treasures in the palace of the young Prince's ancestors. He was in negotiation with D'Ardea for a marriage which should give him social place in spite of his scandalous financial misdeeds and rehabilitate D'Ardea financially. Montfanon intensely hated Hafner, and he had bought the Montluc prayerbook just in time to prevent Fanny Hafner, who was on her way to purchase it for her confessor, from making it play a part in the drama of her conversion and marriage—a matter upon which the ill-tempered old soldier discoursed bitterly with Julien Dorsenne after Fanny had passed on her way to the bookseller's shop.

Dorsenne was on his way to D'Ardea's palace to inspect the art treasures that were presently to be sold. There he was to meet a number of the people whose social position in the Eternal City justified him in calling Rome a "cosmopolis." Baron Hafner—nabob and notorious swindler—was to be there, and Madame Steno, the fascinating Venetian, whose daughter Alba, a marvelous beauty, and a young woman as charming as she was beautiful, was known to everybody but herself to be the offspring, not of Madame Steno's dead husband, but of Werekiew, a noted diplomatist, who had been one of the lady's long succession of lovers. Lincoln Maitland and his wife were expected. Maitland was an American painter whose fame filled Europe at that time, and he was just then the lover of Madame Steno, in whose favor he had supplanted Boleslas Gorka during that person's absence in Poland.

Maitland's wife, Lydia, and her brother, Florent Chapron, were descendants on the one hand of Napoleon's old Colonel Chapron and on the other of a negress of Alabama. With only a trace of negro blood to darken her complexion, Lydia had the subtleties and the meannesses of her slave ancestry fully developed in her nature, while her brother, Florent, was marked in his character by a positively slavish and dog-like devotion to his brother-in-law, Maitland, who had been his bosom friend during school-days in England. Maitland cared nothing for his wife, whom he had married solely for her money, and Florent Chapron stood ready in every way to sacrifice his sister to the advantage of Lincoln Maitland.

Finally, there was Madame Gorka, the English Catholic wife of Boleslas Gorka, the Pole. Madame Gorka knew nothing of her husband's *liaison* with Madame Steno, which had continued during two years, and, in spite of that *liaison*, Gorka, with strange inconsistency, loved and honored his wife.

In the course of the conversation between the novelist Dorsenne and the Marquis Montfanon, the Marquis incidentally said that Gorka had returned from Poland and that he had caught sight of him in a cab that morning. When Dorsenne discovered later that neither Madame Gorka nor Madame Steno was aware of his return, he thought it best to forestall a tragedy by casually mentioning the fact of Gorka's presence in Rome to Florent Chapron.

A little later Dorsenne was summoned to his own apartments

by a peremptory message from Gorka, whom he found there in a condition bordering upon frenzy. Gorka had received twelve anonymous letters telling him of the Countess Steno's transfer of her affections from himself to Maitland, and giving such details as left him no room for doubt.

His impulse was that of a murderous madman, but he shrank from any conduct that might apprise his loyal wife of the facts; and Dorsenne, anxious to avert a tragedy, urged him to remember the inherent infamy of anonymous letter-writing. Under stress of his anxiety, Dorsenne falsely gave Gorka his word of honor that he had neither seen nor heard anything to suggest the alleged *liaison* between the Countess Steno and Maitland.

Troubled in his mind on all accounts, Dorsenne attended Madame Steno's next salon, determined to talk of the infamy of anonymous letter-writing, hoping that perhaps in that way he might surprise the secret of the authorship of the letters to Gorka, whose presence in Rome was even yet unknown.

He there found the Countess Steno in suspiciously friendly and secret converse with Maitland on the darkened terrace. After a discreetly circumspect approach, he paid his respects to his hostess and retired to the salon, where he fell into converse with Alba Steno, for whom he entertained as much of affection as was possible to his artistic, analytical, psychological nature; and presently he learned, without a word of direct information from her, that she too had received anonymous letters concerning her mother and Maitland. She was too loyal and too sincere to distrust her mother upon such evidence, but she was sorely troubled nevertheless.

After a time—and to the amazement of the guests—Boleslas Gorka entered the salon, accompanied by his entirely unsuspicious English wife, Maud, who explained his sudden return to Rome by repeating the fiction of a miscarried letter which he had invented for the purpose. He could not avoid catching sight of the Countess Steno entertaining Maitland on the terrace, but that gifted intriguer carried the matter off in a way that deceived her daughter Alba, and well-nigh raised doubts in the mind of Dorsenne himself.

So completely mistress of herself was the Countess that she slept well that night, and at seven in the morning was clearheadedly directing her intendant as to complex business affairs, such as those by the adroit management of which she had many times multiplied the fortune left to her by Count Steno.

Then came Prince D'Ardea to her, and, in spite of his procrastinating habit of mind, she fairly forced him to a decision to let her propose the marriage between him and Fanny Hafner. She had not finished this part of her work when Gorka's card was brought to her, but she was in no wise disconcerted by its coming. She knew the storm that impended, but she calmly went on with the negotiation until it was finished.

Then she received Gorka. She made no attempt to deceive him. She frankly told him she had ceased to care for him, and when he raved in a fashion that threatened her life itself, she rang for a servant and coolly sent for her daughter to drive with her to Maitland's studio, where Alba was to give the painter a sitting.

Gorka followed in a cab, merely by way of gratifying an absurd desire to prove to himself the repulsive truth of which he was already certain. He saw the Countess and her daughter dismiss their carriage and enter the painter's house. He started to drive away. Then he turned and went back to the painter's door, meaning in his blind jealousy to provoke a controversy, in temporary forgetfulness of the fact that any outbreak must reveal his own misdeeds to his wife, whose confidence in him was more precious to him than all else in life.

The serving-man at the painter's door refused him entrance. Gorka falsely asserted that he had an appointment to meet the Countess and her daughter there. While the serving-man hesitated, Florent Chapron descended the steps and took the matter into his own hands. A quarrel ensued, of that kind that could mean nothing less than a duel, and Florent rejoiced that he had himself alone to think of in the matter, his brother-in-law knowing nothing whatever of the quarrel.

Chapron went at once to Julien Dorsenne and asked him to be his second. Julian consented, with no other intention than that of bringing about a peaceful adjustment of the affair. To that end he besought Montfanon to serve with him in the duel, and the old soldier put aside his devotions in order that he might help to prevent the encounter, with all the scandalous consequences that must ensue if the duel should occur. Meanwhile, Boleslas had engaged the Baron de Hafner and the Prince D'Ardea as his sponsors in the affair, and they were as earnest as Montfanon himself in their desire to reach a peaceful settlement. But in his disgust at finding himself in negotiation with Hafner and D'Ardea, both of whom he loathed, Montfanon forgot his peace-making purpose. Devotee as he was, the old Adam revived in him, and he chaffered over technicalities of the *code duello* so insistently as to defeat the only end he had sought in suffering himself to be drawn into the affair. His remorse was great, but it had come too late. A hostile meeting was arranged to take place the next morning in the courtyard of an obscure inn.

Hafner and D'Ardea, who had also gone into the affair with the sole purpose of settling the quarrel by negotiation, decided to withdraw. In excuse they pleaded D'Ardea's engagement with Fanny Hafner, which two hundred telegrams, sent out by the Baron, had announced to all Rome.

Gorka at once secured two other seconds in their stead, two young men as eager as he for the fray.

On the day before that appointed for the duel, Chapron prepared his will, giving all his wealth to his brother-in-law, Maitland. He locked the document in his desk, together with certain unsealed letters, which were to be read only in the event of his death.

Lydia Maitland had begun to suspect something of what was going on. It was she who had sent the anonymous letters, and it had been her malignant purpose to bring about a tragedy. But she had meant that her husband, whom she hated intensely, should be the sacrifice, and not her brother, who was in fact the only human being she loved.

She was well used to spying, and it was her habit to have master keys with which to open locks that stood in the way of her insatiate curiosity. She opened Florent's desk and read all that he had written. Instantly she fell into panic, and set about preventing the duel. She decided to go at once to Boleslas Gorka, remind him that his real grievance was against Maitland and not at all against Florent, and entreat him either to end the controversy without a duel or fire in the air, or do some other of those things, of which she had heard and which she had vaguely misunderstood, by way of sparing her brother.

Gorka's wife, Maud, was Lydia's most intimate friend. The Englishwoman loved her without understanding her—perhaps she loved her because she did not understand her meanly malignant nature, hidden as it was behind a mask of demure false pretense. Lydia asked herself whether Maud might not assist in preventing this duel, should she hear of it.

With a confused but desperately determined mind, Lydia drove to Gorka's house. He had gone out, nobody knew whither, but Maud was there, having returned upon some errand after setting out for a drive.

Maud Gorka was quick to discover that her friend was agitated, ill—she knew not what. She insisted upon accompanying her home.

Madame Gorka was the only woman of society in all Rome who knew nothing of her husband's long-continued relations with the Countess Steno, and she was utterly unsuspecting. During that drive homeward Lydia Maitland, supposing that the wronged wife knew all, revealed the terrible secret.

Maud refused to believe it, but Lydia, desperate now in her determination to make Madame Gorka the enemy of the Countess Steno, shamelessly revealed her own infamy of espionage and placed before the Englishwoman the singularly unreserved love-letters written by Madame Steno to Maitland, in which she had frankly spoken of her former relations with Gorka—in the past tense it is true, but without a word of disguise or apology.

In a frenzy of anger and shame at the discovery of Gorka's perfidy, mingled with disgust and loathing for the infamous methods of the woman who had revealed the truth to her, Maud Gorka returned to her home.

Lydia thought her a coward, and foresaw that she would forgive her husband; but she rejoiced in the conviction that at any rate Maud Gorka would be henceforth and forever the relentless enemy of Madame Steno.

On her return to her home Madame Gorka was informed that the Countess Steno and Alba were awaiting her. Her first impulse was to go to the Countess and drive her out of the

house with insult. But Alba was innocent, and Alba was her
devoted friend. In order to spare the girl she sent Madame
Steno a note telling her that she knew all and ordering her to
quit the house instantly. As she finished the note Gorka
entered. She handed him the sheet and bade him read what
she had written. When he had done so, she enveloped the
paper and sent it by a servant.

Then Boleslas Gorka made complete confession. To do
him justice, he was far less concerned for himself than for his
noble wife, whom he admired and honored, and for whom,
in spite of his unfaithfulness, he still cherished an abiding love.

Maud received the confession implacably, unforgivingly.
The spirit of the high-bred Englishwoman was dominant
in her mind and soul. To her, and to her ancestors in a long
line of descent, loyalty, honor and truth had been a religion, nay,
more than a religion, a faith that knew neither question nor
qualifying condition. To such a woman it was as idle to talk
of forgiveness for disloyalty and unfaith as to suggest the
repeal of the law of gravitation itself. Her mind was made up.
She was determined to leave for England on the morrow with
her little boy Luc.

In their discussion of the matter, she revealed the fact that
Lydia Maitland was her informant, and that it was she who
had written the anonymous letters. Gorka's soul was instantly
moved to revenge. He resolved to kill Lydia Maitland's
brother first and then her husband.

Baffled in her effort to see Gorka, Lydia Maitland determined to prevent the duel by notifying the police. But the
police missed their man, and the adversaries met at the time
·and place appointed. At the first fire Florent Chapron was
shot through the thigh. Apparently the affair was over, with
no great harm done, but just as the seconds were about to
retire to prepare their official report, Gorka advanced and
with insulting words struck Julien Dorsenne in the face with
his glove. His grievance was that Dorsenne had falsely given
him his word of honor concerning the relations between Maitland and Madame Steno.

In order to gain time, and perhaps prevent a second duel,
Montfanon refused to act in the new affair, thinking that it

would be impossible for the combatants to find seconds at so short a notice. But two huntsmen who had been breakfasting at the inn were pressed into service, and the new duel was fought upon a plan which seemed to promise the certain death of one or the other of the combatants. It ended, in fact, in the wounding of Gorka in the pistol hand.

As he lay suffering with his shattered hand, Gorka was surprised by the entrance of Maud. The wife remembered what he had told her years before of the saddening of his own childhood and the perversion of his character by the estrangement of his father and mother, both of whom he loved, as little Luc now loved both Boleslas and Maud Gorka. For the child's sake, therefore, and abating no jot or tittle of her abhorrence for her husband's disloyalty, Maud Gorka had decided not to separate from him, provided he would consent to certain conditions. These were that they should leave Rome at once and forever, and that Gorka should renounce Madame Steno and have no communication with her so long as he should live.

Gorka, who really loved his wife, was eager in his consent and sincere in his determination to win Maud's love again and make of the unhappy past a thing as unreal as if it had never been. A few days later Boleslas Gorka and his wife quitted Rome and set out anew upon the pilgrimage of life together, with little Luc, whom they both devotedly loved.

The saddest victim of the drama was innocent little Alba Steno. Knowing less than all that was evil round about her, she knew enough to blight her life, and in her shame and horror she was alone. She had lost Lydia, and her still dearer friend Maud had gone, without a word of farewell. She still had Fanny Hafner, and she planned to make much of her at the coming wedding time. News reached her that in some fit of remorse old Montfanon had returned the Montluc prayer-book to Ribalta. She would take Fanny with her, go to the bookshop, buy the precious relic, and give it to Fanny as a wedding gift.

The old rascal Ribalta demanded two thousand francs for the volume and when Alba reminded him that he had sold it for one-fifth of that sum to Montfanon, he flew into a vindictive rage and produced a pamphlet which he offered for the smaller sum. It was a copy of a scathing history of Baron Hafner's crimes, a work that Hafner had pretty effectually suppressed by buying every copy he could anywhere find.

Alba saw its title and hurried Fanny out of the shop, denouncing Ribalta as she went for having dared exhibit the book. Fanny replied with a fervent eulogy of her father for his scrupulousness and honor, in all of which she devoutly believed. But her curiosity was aroused. She went back to the shop in secret, bought the pamphlet, read it and learned what a monster her adored father really was, and in what repute he was held by honest men everywhere.

About the same time the agent whom Hafner had employed to ruin D'Ardea and compel his marriage to Fanny demanded higher pay, and, being refused, exposed the infamous scheme.

In shame and heartbreak, Fanny canceled her marriage engagement and went into retirement.

Disappointed of her vengeance in one way, Lydia Maitland diligently planned to secure it in another. She would expose Madame Steno's relations with Maitland to Madame Steno's daughter Alba. With devilish ingenuity she prepared the way. There was a passage leading out of the studio which was screened off with opaque, stained glass. With a diamond ring Lydia cut a round hole in one of the panes. When Madame Steno and Alba came to give the painter another of the many sittings for Alba's portrait, Lydia, after a long time, urged that mercy from the painter's long posing be shown the girl, and that she be allowed to rest awhile. To give effect to this, she asked Alba to go with her to another part of the house and view a new costume. The two left the studio, Maitland and Madame Steno remaining to indulge in those caresses which Lydia was sure would follow. In passing through the glass-screened gallery, she pretended to discover the hole she had herself cut in the glass. Upon pretense of discovering what it might mean, she asked Alba to examine it. What Alba saw Lydia discovered by the tremor of the hand she was holding, but when she tried to look for herself Alba struck the glass and shattered it, giving warning to those behind and painfully lacerating her own hand.

The exposure of her mother's infamy had been averted, but Alba Steno now knew certainly what she had tried to avoid believing—that her mother was, "not a good woman."

In the desolation of her soul, but one hope or care was left to poor Alba Steno. She knew now that she had long loved Dorsenne, and he had in many ways manifested a tender interest in her—as tender at least as a cold-blooded student of human emotion for purposes of literary art could be expected to manifest in one of the subjects that lay upon the dissecting-table of his mind.

Alba's mother had left her to await the return of the carriage which she had promised to send back for the girl after it should have delivered her at some pretended place of social or business appointment. Alba knew in her soul that her mother had in fact gone to keep evil tryst with Maitland.

She was strongly impelled to commit suicide, but Dorsenne came in time to prevent. He had come, not to make the declaration of love for which she had hoped, but to bid her good-by. He had taken his sleeping-car ticket for Paris.

In her despair, Alba so far put aside convention as to declare her love and beg him for his in return.

His response was such as only a man of his nature could make. He had been deeply interested in her as a subject of sociological and psychological study, but no impulse of a warmer kind had ever been kindled in his acutely critical soul.

When he had left her the girl was strongly tempted to hurl herself over the parapet by which she stood and dash out her life on the pavement below. The coming of the carriage suggested a less brutal way of exit. She drove to a little lake on the outskirts of Rome, and there, taking a boat, rowed out upon the still water. It was her thought to drown herself, but remembering that this was the most pestilential spot in all the region round about Rome, and that the most pestilential time of year was upon her, she adopted another plan. She rowed with heavy oars till the relaxation of exhaustion came upon her. Then, stripped of her wraps and with bared chest she invited the chill.

When Alba Steno died of "Roman fever," Julien Dorsenne was still in Rome. He had forfeited his sleeping-car ticket and postponed his journey, thinking to see her once more.

When all was over with the poor child, Montfanon manifested his sympathy with Dorsenne by a pressure of the arm. Neither attempted utterance in words.

HJALMAR HJORTH BOYESEN

(Norway, 1848-1895)

GUNNAR (1874)

Boyesen, like Björnson, found poetry and romance in Norwegian peasant life, at which Ibsen sneered as a field for literary exploitation. Though born in Norway, and taking Norwegian subjects for his writing, he composed his works in English, in the use of which language his facility was marvelous.

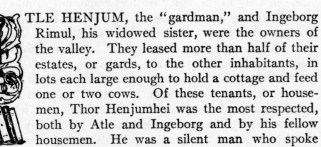TLE HENJUM, the "gardman," and Ingeborg Rimul, his widowed sister, were the owners of the valley. They leased more than half of their estates, or gards, to the other inhabitants, in lots each large enough to hold a cottage and feed one or two cows. Of these tenants, or housemen, Thor Henjumhei was the most respected, both by Atle and Ingeborg and by his fellow housemen. He was a silent man who spoke only words of wisdom. Seldom was any new land broken, or a lumber bargain settled in the valley, before his opinion was obtained. He was a widower, and lived with his mother Gunhild, an old woman wise in the mythical lore of Norway, which she taught to Thor's only child, Gunnar, a boy of such vivid imagination that he was not able to distinguish between the worlds of reality and fancy.

Atle Henjum had two children. Lars, the boy, was of the same age as Gunnar, and Gudrun, the daughter, was two years younger than they. Both realized the importance of their father's position, but this had a differing effect on their characters. It made Lars forward, insolent, and, as the case usually is with bullies, cowardly. Gudrun was frank without being bold, and of a most friendly disposition, taking the lead among her fellows out of consideration for their diffidence rather than to satisfy her vanity.

Ragnhild, their cousin, the daughter of Ingeborg Rimul, was entirely unaffected by her mother's superior position. Had she been born in a little cottage instead of the fine large homestead of Rimul, she would have been the same sweet, tender-hearted girl, the sunshine of the home. There was a peculiar fitness, however, in the fact that she had opened her bright, merry eyes in Rimul, for there the sun came first and lingered longest. There was sunshine without and within.

Ingeborg Rimul, the grave, sad-hearted widow, saw in her fair and happy daughter a picture of her own youth. As a maiden she had been the flower of the valley, whose beauty the rude peasant lads looked upon abashed. Her hand had been sought by the parents of almost every one of them in turn, but none had ever presumed to play the part of a lover, and their suits were all courteously dismissed. While this did not offend the young men, their mothers and sisters could not forgive the girl, that in their phrase, "considered herself above her neighbors"; and, afterwards, when she became a woman, she had few friends remaining among her own sex, although she commanded the respect of all the men, chiefly of Thor Henjumhei.

One day there came to the maiden a lover from the outer world, named Vogt, a student for the ministry in the University of Christiania, who was spending a vacation at the parsonage. On his first day at church he was attracted by a girl with long golden hair and a pair of sunny eyes. Although he was betrothed to a young woman of Christiania, well-born, well-to-do, devout, who loved him sincerely and for whom he had an admiration which, until he met Ingeborg Henjum, he thought was love, he could not resist his infatuation for the country maiden, and wooed her with an ardent passion which she as fervently returned.

Soon every woman on the countryside was talking of the lovers. One had noted a golden head reclining on a black-coated breast under the great birch by the river; another had noted the trim figure of a man with the ministerial tassel, and the form of a woman taller and more graceful than any houseman's daughter, strolling with arms around each other's waists upon the shore late one dreamy summer evening.

At last Atle heard these tales, and called upon the young

divinity student at the parsonage. None but these two men
and the pastor ever knew what there occurred. Mr. Vogt left
for Christiania that very night, and Ingeborg did not appear
at church or elsewhere in public for several weeks; and when
she did appear, it was noted that she looked pale and carried
her head defiantly high.

A week thereafter Ingeborg married Sigurd, the heir of the
Rimul estate, which, with Henjum gard, comprised the valley.
A daughter was born to them before the close of the year.
Shortly after this, Sigurd died from a blow on the head received
in a fight at a wedding with a half-drunken man who had
slurred the chastity of his wife. The widow remained with
her child upon the estate, in the management of which she displayed an ability even superior to her brother Atle's, the gardman of Henjum. She made Thor Henjumhei, the silent wise
man of the valley, her chief adviser.

When Thor's son, Gunnar, reached the age of eleven, his
father thought that it was time he was learning something
more practical than his grandmother's fairy tales; so he sent
him with the colony of herdsmen, who, with their women,
and children, watch the cattle in the mountain pastures (*saeters*)
during the summer. Gunnar was to tend the cattle of the
widow of Rimul.

It was at Rimul, where his father took him to put him
in charge of his new mistress, that Gunnar looked upon a girl
for the first time in his life. This one had a scarlet bodice and
golden hair, plaited in a long braid hanging down her back.

"Are you the Hulder?"* he asked.

"Mother, mother," cried she, running up to the tall woman
with a white cloth bound about her head, who was talking to
his father, "what do you think he is saying? He wants to know
if I am the Hulder!"

"Be quiet, child; I am busy," said Ingeborg, sternly.

The little girl twisted the corner of her apron, and, after
some hesitation, returned to Gunnar.

"Have you got a name?" she asked.

"Yes."

"My name is Ragnhild, and this is my cousin, Gudrun."

---

* A fairy of the forest, the protecting genius of cattle.

Here she pointed to another little girl who came running toward them out of the house.

"My name is Gunnar; and my grandmother knows ever so many stories about the Hulder, the beautiful maiden that has a cow's tail, longer than your braid, that she always tries to hide behind her, and the Necken that plays on his harp behind the waterfall, and the boy who killed the Trold and married the princess."

The girls opened their eyes in wonder at such erudition, and put the corners of their aprons in their mouths. Ragnhild in particular thought there never was such a boy—an opinion, indeed, in which she never after wavered.

At this moment the cup of Gunnar's bliss was filled to overflowing by his father approaching, and, as a parting gift, handing him a fine knife, with carved haft and silver sheath. Surely he had never known his father before now! If the girls had not been by Gunnar might have been so unmanly as to burst into tears.

While Gunnar was watching the cattle upon the *saeter*, he began to draw with a charred stick upon birch-bark many a picture of the Hulder, the unhappy sprite with the disfiguring cow's tail, but every attempt, somehow, grew into a portrait of a little girl with a long braid of hair.

Hereafter he spent every summer herding the Rimul cattle, and every winter lumbering with his father, until he was old enough to prepare for confirmation. In his class at the parsonage was Lars Henjum, who was wont to boast that he would stand at its head in church on the eventful day when they were catechized.

The pastor, however, was more interested in Gunnar than in Lars, for the answers of the houseman's son revealed a keen intelligence, while those of the gardman's son, while correct, had evidently been learned by rote. Then the pastor's daughter had told him that the "Henjumhei boy" was a wonder for making pictures; and, on Gunnar's bringing him by request some of his sketches, the good man praised them highly, and invited the lad to make free with his library, which contained many engravings, beautiful beyond all the boy had imagined.

On the day of confirmation Gunnar's name was called first,

Lars Henjum's second. It was with unholy feelings that the gardman's son approached the altar.

After the ceremony was ended the pastor called Gunnar into his study, and talked with him about his future. He advised the boy to go to the capital and study art, promising if he did so, to give him an introduction to his old friend in that city, the pastor Vogt, who had a son about the age of Gunnar.

Soon after the confirmation Lars set upon Gunnar in public, expecting to crush the houseman's son with his rude sarcasm. Instead of this result, however, Gunnar fell upon Lars and beat him till he cried for mercy.

In the skee race* that winter, the first heat was a dead one between Lars and Gunnar. In racing it off Gunnar slid first. At the first of the jumps, which was out of the sight of the crowd of spectators at the finish, Lars concealed himself unnoticed by Gunnar, but not by Ragnhild, who had also hidden near by to watch every movement of her mother's handsome and graceful young herdsman. As Gunnar approached the jump at lightning speed in a cloud of snow, Lars thrust a large pine-branch on the track. Ragnhild leaped forward and threw the branch back against him. An instant after the snow-cloud swept by. Lars sneaked away through the fir-trees, down toward the crowd. A chorus of hurrahs rose from the valley; he hesitated; then turned and walked up the mountain among the trees.

The judges grew tired of waiting for Lars to slide, and gave the prize to Gunnar. He sought Ragnhild to show it to her, and finally found her as she came down the hillside.

"Where were you?" he asked. "I've been looking all over for you."

"At the first jump. Didn't you see me?"

"I couldn't see anybody. Going too fast."

"I wonder you didn't fall."

"Fall! O Ragnhild, I could slide down the steepest mountain-side if you stood by and looked at me." Two men on skees overtook them. "Hurrah, boys! here we have the prize-racer," cried one.

"Ah, the fair Ragnhild of Rimul! You are racing for a high

---

* Sliding down hill on skees, Norwegian snow-shoes, over "jumps" or artificial bunkers.

prize there, a houseman's son!" exclaimed the second. "I doubt if you win it;—the track is steep from Henjumhei to Rimul, and the river flows between." The men passed on. Ragnhild turned with burning face to her companion.

"Don't you care, Gunnar. I don't."

"O Ragnhild, and do you love me?"

"Gunnar, you have been dear to me ever since that day you asked me if I was the Hulder. I only hope my love will not work you evil, as they say hers does to the young men she regards with favor."

That night Gunnar and Ragnhild led the dance in honor of the race, and sang the *stev** after it.

Proud of the courageous love and loyalty of his sweetheart, as he shoved out on his homeward way from Rimul, whither he had escorted her, Gunnar trod, or rather skeed, on air. But, as he came near his father's humble cottage in the dark and narrow glen, his heart fell within him. Truly the track was steep from Henjumhei to Rimul!

Ingeborg heard of the gossip that connected her daughter's name with Gunnar, the houseman's son. As she and her brother Atle had planned to unite the gards of Henjum and Rimul by the marriage of their children, Lars and Ragnhild, she ordered her daughter to refuse to receive the attentions of Gunnar; and, when Gunnar called at Rimul a few days after the skee-race to see Ragnhild, he was driven from the door with scorn for his pretensions.

Lars Henjum was standing by at the time, and burst into mocking laughter as Gunnar turned away in dejection. The houseman's son turned upon the gardman's, and thrust his clenched fist in his face. Lars shrank behind Ingeborg.

"Lars, you are a coward," she said; and she thought with a sigh, "Even Sigurd was not that."

Ragnhild had a will of her own and disobeyed her mother. She went with Lars to the next wedding, but deserted him for Gunnar as partner in the dance. A half-drunken man jeered at Lars: "It's clear the houseman's son has cut you out there."

Mad with jealous hatred, Lars lay in wait for Gunnar out-

---

* An antiphonal dialogue in song by a man and woman.

side the door, and, as the houseman's son emerged, struck him unawares.

"It is Lars Henjum," cried Gunnar; "the blow was from behind!"

The wedding-guests crowded out with firebrands to see the fight that all had known was brewing. Wild was the combat. Blows came quick and strong on either side. At last Gunnar struck Lars on the head; blood streamed from his mouth and nostrils; he reeled and fell to the ground. Gunnar was turning to go, when his opponent drew a knife and sprang to his feet. In the twinkling of an eye Gunnar tripped Lars, who fell upon the point of the knife. A red stream gushed from his side.

Ragnhild, feeling that the tragedy was the result of her disobedience, flung herself down by the wounded man. "O Gunnar!" she cried, looking up at her lover, "go, go, and may God be merciful to thee!"

Gunnar walked away into the night.

The next morning he set out for Christiania. There he entered the Academy of Art. In three years he won the highest prize with a picture of the Hulder. He sent home to his proud father a newspaper criticism of the work, which closed with the words:

"A little bird has sung to us that Mr. Henjumhei caught the inspiration of his picture from a fair damsel in his native valley, whither he will shortly go with his friend, the son of Pastor Vogt. We are confident he will win for his own the wayward sprite, for he is a youth of whom any damsel, yes, old Norway herself, may justly be proud."

Lars in time entirely recovered from his wound. Atle and Ingeborg went on with their preparations for his marriage to Ragnhild, who, in mingled repentance and despair, had withdrawn all opposition.

When the wedding was imminent, however, and she heard that Gunnar was coming home with his honors thick upon him, she went to the pastor to find a way of escape from the odious fate prepared for her.

"Father," she said, "they say Gunnar Henjumhei is coming home."

"Yes, and a proud day it is for the valley. A nobler youth the parish never bore."

"Then it is no sin for a maiden to love him?" asked Ragnhild.

"H'm," said the pastor, seeing how he was being committed, "if the maiden's parents are willing."

"Then please speak to my mother, and get her consent to let me marry Gunnar instead of Lars, whom I hate as much as I love Gunnar. Oh, it is wicked to force me to marry a man I hate!"

"Hush!" said the pastor, "He that honoreth not father and mother—"

Ragnhild smiled, for she knew where his sympathies lay. She interrupted:

"Thou shalt obey God, rather than men."

The old man paused awhile in thought. Then he remarked: "The paper says that a young man named Vogt is coming with Gunnar. I think that he can intercede with Ingeborg better than I."

Ragnhild and her cousin Gudrun were together upon the mountain pasture when Gunnar and Vogt came walking toward them. Gudrum and Vogt considerately strolled off by themselves to leave the lovers alone. The suggestion of this pairing off was inevitable—and very agreeable to the parties concerned. Young Vogt, like his father, had lost his heart to a beautiful mountain maid, and, unlike him, had a free heart to love. And Gudrun, like her aunt Ingeborg before her, responded at once to the fascination of the handsome, well-bred city man. Before the walk was ended they knew in feeling if not in words that they were affianced lovers.

Ragnhild, left alone with Gunnar, laid her head on his breast and burst into happy tears. "O Gunnar, I knew you would come. Every year before now, when the cuckoo came, I heard his call first in the north, which means grief. But this year he sang in the east, which means a wedding, and nearer to me than to the other girls, which means my wedding. And three times I whispered your name, and made a wish, and each time he sang; so I knew I was to marry you."

Thor Henjumhei went with his son to Rimul to make a

formal request on the young artist's behalf for the hand of Ragnhild. The houseman presented his petition to the haughty woman with a dignity that filled Gunnar's heart with filial love and pride; and, as on the day when his father gave him his first knife, tears sprang into the son's eyes.

Ingeborg was more moved than she cared to show, for she respected the houseman deeply; and the emotion of the young man revealed a loving sympathy between parent and child that was in poignant contrast to her estrangement from her daughter.

She did not trust herself to say much, and so rejected the suit as curtly as possible, on the ground that the hand of Ragnhild was pledged to Lars Henjum.

"But not her heart, mother," said this young lady, who had slipped into the room during the interview, and now seated herself on Gunnar's knee and threw her arms about his neck.

"Thor Henjumhei," cried Ingeborg helplessly, "take your son away!"

"Yes, father, and me with him," added Ragnhild.

At that moment, a tall, slender young man entered the door, carrying a long-tasseled college-cap in his hand.

"The pastor told me I would find you here," he said to Gunnar, "and that I was to add my request to your father's," —here he turned to the mistress of Rimul—"that she who was once Ingeborg Henjum"——

"O God, my God!" cried Ingeborg, staring at the young stranger as if he were an apparition, "what would I do! Condemn my daughter to the loveless life that has been my lot? No. Let Lars take Rimul if he will, but not Ragnhild!"

Vogt stood transfixed with astonishment at the result of his words. Observing this, Ingeborg rose and took him by the hand. "Mr. Vogt," she said, "you have your father's features, and I imagined he stood before me. He was once a welcome guest in my father's house. I beg that you will consider yourself as such at Rimul so long as I remain its mistress."

MARY ELIZABETH BRADDON

(MRS. JOHN MAXWELL)

(England, 1837)

LADY AUDLEY'S SECRET (1862)

This was the first successful novel written by Miss Braddon, and it is probably her best known work. On its publication it gained immediate notoriety and widespread popularity, and later was dramatized successfully.

UDLEY COURT was a noble place that visitors fell into raptures over. It had fine old timber, luxuriant pastures, beautiful approaches of avenues of ancient trees, a clock-tower, lawns, sundials, orchards, a fish-pond, a moat, high hedges of box and holly, kitchen-gardens, terraces, ruined walls picturesquely overgrown with ivy, moss and stonecrop, graveled walks, ruins of an old nunnery, a beautiful deer-park, shaded with oaks, elms and beeches, a lime-walk terminating at a stagnant well, cool and sheltered, hidden away in the shrubbery behind the gardens, with rolling rope and rusted handle, where in the cool of the evening the owner loved to stroll. The interior of the many-gabled and chimneyed mansion was redolent of luxurious medieval and Tudor times.

The owner, Sir Michael Audley, was fifty-six years of age, and he had married a second wife three months after his fifty-fifth birthday. He was tall and stout, with a deep sonorous voice, handsome black eyes, and a white beard—a white beard which made him look venerable against his will, for he was as active as a boy, and one of the hardest riders in the country. For seventeen years he had been a widower with an only child, Alicia Audley, a young lady of eighteen, devoted to fox-hunting and all out door sports, and by no means pleased at having a step-mother brought home to the Court, where she had reigned supreme since her earliest childhood.

Lady Audley, becoming the wife of Sir Michael, had made one of those apparently advantageous matches which are apt to draw upon a woman the envy and hatred of her sex. She had come into the neighborhood as a governess in the family of a surgeon in the village near Audley Court. No one knew anything of her, except that she came in answer to an advertisement. She came from London; and her only reference was to a lady at a school at Brompton, where she had once been a teacher. But the reference was so satisfactory that none other was needed; and Miss Lucy Graham was received by the surgeon as the instructress of his daughters. Her accomplishments were so brilliant and numerous that it seemed strange she should have answered an advertisement offering very moderate remuneration.

Lucy Graham took joy and brightness with her wherever she went. Her amiable and gentle nature, her charming manners and striking girlish beauty made her adored by rich and poor alike. She had the most wonderful blue eyes and a wealth of golden curls, soft and feathery, which framed her beautiful pink and white face in a pale halo of golden sunlight. She was blessed with that magic power by which a woman can charm with a word, or intoxicate with a smile. Everybody loved, admired, and praised her. When the Baronet deprecatingly offered her his hand, he was chilled by her frank avowal that from her babyhood she had never seen anything but poverty, that her father was a gentleman, clever, accomplished and handsome, but poverty had made a pitiful wretch of him. She could not be disinterested, therefore, nor blind to the advantages of such an alliance. She had been selfish from her babyhood, and did not love anybody in the world. Such was his infatuation, however, that he was willing to be married for his fortune and position. When they returned from their honeymoon on the Continent, Lady Audley was as successful socially among the county families as she had been as a nursery governess. She was accompanied by a domestic in the surgeon's household, named Phœbe Marks, who was devoted to her and whom she had promoted to be her confidential maid. Phœbe was engaged to a cousin, a rough farm-hand, whose ambition was to be the landlord of an inn. At their first meeting on her return, Phœbe, in the absence of her mistress, showed her lover her mistress's new and splendidly furnished apartments, and while there discovered a baby's shoe and lock of hair in a secret drawer, whereupon she promised her brutish lover that he should have his public house.

Sir Michael had an orphaned nephew, Robert Audley, a barrister, whose father had left him four hundred pounds a year, who spent his time principally in smoking his pipe, reading French novels, strolling in the Temple gardens, and complaining to his brother benchers of his over-work. He always spent the hunting-season at Audley Court, though he never went further than the covert at the meets. Robert was a great favorite with his uncle, and still more so with his pretty cousin, over whom he, however, was only mildly enthusiastic. Her indignant letter announcing her father's marriage one morning only made him hope that Alicia and her stepmother wouldn't quarrel in the hunting-season, because rows always upset a man's digestion.

Shortly afterward, in the city, Robert ran across an old Eton chum, who had just arrived from Australia, where he had made £20,000 in gold-mining. His name was George Talboys, who, before accepting Robert's hospitality, insisted on going to a coffee-house, where he expected a letter from his wife. On the way, he told Robert the story of his life since they had last met. George was the son of a rich country squire, as stern as Junius Brutus. When an ensign in a cavalry regiment, quartered at a seaport town, he had fallen in love with the beautiful daughter of a half-pay naval officer, a drunken old hypocrite ready to sell his daughter to the highest bidder. It was a case of love at first sight; and, George being the highest bidder at the moment, they made a match of it. When Mr. Talboys, senior, heard of it, he wrote saying that he would never hold any communication with his son again, and cut off his allowance. Thereupon George sold out for £2,000; and the youthful pair lived in splendor till the money was nearly gone, when they returned to her father, who fleeced them of the remainder.

When George could not find employment to support his wife

and babe, his bride bitterly reproached him for giving her nothing but poverty and misery, whereupon he wrote a letter telling her that he was going to seek his fortune in Australia; and, believing her asleep, he departed in the night. After innumerable hardships and disappointments, he had succeeded; and, notifying his wife, he had taken the first ship for England. Now he was on his way to receive her expected letter.

On their arrival at the coffee-house, to George's bitter disappointment, there was no letter. Moodily staring at the *Times*, his eye caught the following paragraph in the death column:

"On the 24th inst. at Ventnor, Isle of Wight, Helen Talboys, aged 22."

Robert carried George to his rooms, and did his best to care for and comfort him. The next morning they took the first train; and, after some trouble, discovered the lodgings of Captain Maldon, who sorrowfully confirmed the sad tidings. George visited his wife's grave, arranged for a monument and for the keep and education of his son, who was living with the Captain, his wife's father, and appointed his friend Robert guardian of the boy, intending himself to return immediately to the antipodes. But Robert persuaded him to defer his departure from time to time, till a year had passed, during which time the two friends were inseparable.

At the opening of the shooting-season, Robert insisted on taking George with him to Audley Court, and wrote for permission. In return, a letter came from Alicia, saying that Lady Audley persisted that she was too ill to entertain visitors, though nothing ailed her. Robert, pig-headedly, nevertheless dragged his friend down there, and put up at the village inn. He quickly made the acquaintance of his fascinating aunt, and was charmed with her; but met with constant impediments in his attempts to introduce his friend. When Sir Michael invited the two friends to dinner, she sent Phœbe Marks to London on dress-making business, and next morning received a telegram saying that her old school principal, Mrs. Vincent, was dangerously ill. Accompanied by Sir Michael, she immediately set out to comfort the old lady's last hours. In her absence, the two friends visited Audley Court, wandered through the rooms, and, by a secret passage, found their way into my Lady's boudoir, where was a life like painting of herself. As they set out for the inn, Lady Audley and her husband unexpectedly arrived.

The next day was spent by the two men in fishing till two in the afternoon, when George suddenly left his friend and called at Audley Court. The servant said Sir Michael was out, and my Lady was walking in the lime-tree avenue. An hour and a half afterward, she returned, singing, from the opposite direction, with her skirt full of meadow flowers; and, retiring to her boudoir, rang for Phœbe Marks, and asked her what she had been doing in her absence. Phœbe said she had been altering the blue dress, in her own room, sitting at the window. They gazed at each other for a moment, and then her Ladyship said: "You are a good, industrious girl, and while I live and am prosperous, you shall never want a firm friend or a twenty-pound note."

Robert Audley waited for his friend in vain for some time, and then returned to the inn. Not finding him there, he went to Audley Court and heard that Mr. Talboys had called, and gone away. He then went to the railway station, and became satisfied that George Talboys had returned to London in one of his moody fits. Next day he followed, and was astonished not to find George in his chambers. He therefore proceeded to Southampton, and learned from Captain Maldon that George had been there the night before and had left again for Liverpool. Robert followed, but could find no trace of him there. Now thoroughly suspicious, he determined to prosecute his search within a short radius of Audley Court.

By the generosity of Lady Audley, Phœbe Marks was soon married to her cousin, Luke, who was very ungrateful, even after sulkiness had induced her to double her original offer of the money required to set them up in business in a ramshackle inn three miles from the Court.

Robert spent Christmas at the Court, and the long duel between him and its mistress began. Robert suspected his step-aunt of having a hand in the disappearance of his friend, and did not attempt to conceal his suspicions from her. Finally, she got rid of him by hinting to her husband that Robert was paying her too much attention, whereupon his uncle dismissed him in a very delicate manner.

Robert, though determined to unravel the mystery, was anxious to save his uncle's feelings and the honor of the family from any public scandal, and doubted whether he ought to go any further in the matter. Instead of returning to London, he took up his quarters at the Castle Inn, at Mount Stanning, where he made the acquaintance of the drunken landlord and listened to his grumblings over the stinginess of some folks. Phœbe almost collapsed when Robert sympathetically said: "What indeed is a hundred pounds to a man possessed of the power which you hold, or rather, which your wife holds over the person in question?"

The next morning he was astonished to receive a visit from Lady Audley, who came to apologize for the treatment he had received. In the course of conversation, the question of his interest in George's disappearance came up, and he outlined his plans for continuing the search. On his return to his chambers, among other things he was going to search his friend's effects for anything that might throw light upon the mystery. When he refused to accept her apology for what had occurred, he escorted her to her carriage. Presently it drove into the inn-yard empty; and he learned that my Lady had just taken the train to London. He followed by the next train, and met Lady Audley on the platform there on her return journey. Proceeding to his chambers, he learned that they had been entered, and on searching George's trunks he found nothing but a book, in which, by chance, he found an inscription in a well-known hand, presenting it to George Talboys by Helen Maldon.

Robert's worst fears were now confirmed. He went to Southampton, interviewed the maudlin Captain Maldon, who was greatly agitated when told that Robert knew that George had never been to Southampton, removed little Georgie from the Captain's care and put him in a good school.

Robert's next step was to seek an interview with Mr. Harcourt Talboys, whose estate was in Dorsetshire. He tried to induce the old gentleman to take an interest in the fate of his missing son; but found him inflexible. The father said that George was staying away for effect, but he never would obtain forgiveness that way. However, in George's beautiful sister, Clara, Robert found one who offered to spend her whole fortune in discovering her brother's murderer. She forwarded to Robert letters written to her by George during his honeymoon, in which he minutely and ecstatically described his wife's features, fondly dwelling upon every grace of form, beauty of expression and charm of manner. This forged another link in the chain connecting Helen Maldon and Lucy Graham.

Sir Michael fell ill, and Alicia summoned her cousin to the Baronet's bedside. While at the Court, he interviewed Dr. Dawson and learned that the latter knew nothing of his late governess's antecedents, except that Lucy Graham had answered an advertisement and referred him to a Mrs. Vincent, the proprietress of a school in which she was then teaching. The replies to his inquiries proving satisfactory, he engaged the governess, who had always given perfect satisfaction. Dr. Dawson, however, was able to supply Mrs. Vincent's address. On his return to town, therefore, Robert looked up Mrs. Vincent; and the result of his visit was the discovery of an old bandbox, on which, among many labels, one was pasted over another: the upper one bore the name of Miss Graham; the under one, that of Mrs. George Talboys. Robert next wrote to Clara Talboys for the name of the town where George had first met his bride, and learned that it was Wildernsea, Yorkshire, for which place he took the first train. He learned that Captain Maldon had been well known there, and that his daughter was a great favorite. After her husband's desertion, she supported herself by giving music-lessons, and her father spent most of the money in drink. She finally disappeared, leaving her child out at nurse. The landlady was able to produce the Captain's letter to her on the day of his daughter's disappearance. He enclosed Helen's farewell note to him. It closed with the words: "Forgive me if I have been fretful, capricious, changeable. You should forgive me, for you know why I have been so. You know the secret which is the key to my life." The Captain's letter, with Helen's note enclosed, was dated two days before Lucy's entrance into Mrs. Vincent's school.

Robert determined next to establish the identity of the woman lying in Ventnor churchyard. On his arrival in London, he found a letter from Alicia, saying that Sir Michael was much

better, and, for some unexplainable reason, Lady Audley was
very anxious for him to pay them a visit. He still shrank from
the anguish that his uncle would suffer by his instrumentality,
and determined to give Lady Audley one more warning. If
only she would run away! On his arrival in the village, to his
amazement, he had a chance encounter with Clara Talboys, who
was visiting in the neighborhood, and she again solemnly
adjured him not to allow her brother's fate to remain a mystery.

At the Court he met Lady Audley returning from a drive,
and insisted on having a private interview, to which she
assented, and accompanied him to the shadows of the lime-
walk. There he forced her to listen to the story of George
Talboys, laying before her all the circumstantial evidence he
had collected. She resolutely defied him to do his worst, and
refused to take to flight before the exposure he threatened.
She declared that he must be insane to make such accusations.
He left her, saying that he had wished to have pity upon the
living, but henceforth he would remember only his duty to the
dead. He was so upset with the outcome of the interview that
Alicia, whom he met in the garden, could not induce him to
visit her father; but he promised to return the next day.

Lady Audley immediately sought her husband and told him
part of what Robert had said, insinuating that he was undoubtedly insane and should be put under restraint. To this Sir
Michael regretfully agreed. She succeeded in persuading her
husband that constant brooding over the death of his friend
had made Robert Audley a monomaniac.

Having convinced her husband of Robert's lunacy, my
Lady retired for the night, and dismissed her maid. Her tortured musings were interrupted by a knock at her door; and at
her invitation Phœbe Marks entered with apologies for intrusion.
She had come to beg for assistance: the bailiff was in possession
for unpaid rent, and her drunken husband was insistent. Lady
Audley also learned, with rage and terror, that Robert was at
the Castle Inn. She bitterly complained that nearly all her
jewels had been pawned and her pin-money overdrawn to
satisfy similar demands. However, she quickly formed a
sinister plan. She herself would accompany Phœbe home, and
pay the money in person. Waiting till the household was

asleep, she slunk out through a French window, joined Phœbe in the avenue, and walked the three miles to the Castle Inn, arriving at three o'clock. There she paid the bailiff, and asked Phœbe to stay downstairs while she refreshed herself in her bedroom. Passing the room to which Robert had been assigned, she double-locked his door, and, escorted by Phœbe, returned toward home. As they reached the top of a hill, a mile away, Phœbe looked back and saw a red light in the sky, and instantly realized that the inn was on fire. Comprehending at once the means my Lady had taken to get rid of Robert and the black-mailing Luke, Phœbe was horror-stricken; but Lady Audley mocked at her terrors and stalked away in the darkness, leaving her kneeling in the road.

At evening she walked alone down the avenue to the entrance arch. There she met Robert Audley. She made no resistance to his command to accompany him to the house. Leading her into the library, he denounced her for the horrible deed she had committed, in addition to her former crimes. No lives had been lost in the fire, as he had slept in another room, and had been able to alarm the household in time. He promised her public exposure and the utmost penalty of the law, unless she would confess her misdeeds to her husband and accept from Sir Michael and himself such mercy as they might be inclined to extend. Then she finally gave up the struggle. Robert went for his uncle; and, in utter abandonment, Lady Audley told the story of her life.

As a child she had never known her mother; but after a few years she learned that she was in a madhouse. When she was ten years old, her father took her to visit her mother, young and beautiful, but a harmless maniac. The child went away to brood over the knowledge that madness was her inheritance, for her grandmother also had been insane. When admiration and flattery told her she was more beautiful, bewitching and gifted than others, it encouraged her to hope that she might make a better marriage than they and thus escape the poverty she hated and obscurity she shrank from. When, therefore, the fairy prince arrived in the person of George Talboys, she thought her dreams were realized. When his money was gone, she complained loudly and bitterly that this fine marriage had only given her a year's gaiety and extravagance after all. When he deserted her she was desperate, and the hereditary taint began to show itself in fits of violence and despair. She deserted the child she disliked and began life again under a new name.

A month after her second marriage, she read in one of the papers of the return of the lucky gold-seeker. The ship would soon arrive. She went to Southampton and confided her peril to her father, who was not greatly shocked at her conduct. They determined to advertise her death on the arrival of the ship. It happened that the landlady's daughter was at the point of death from consumption, and money induced the landlady to enter into their plans. A house was taken at Ventnor, and thither the woman was removed under the name of Mrs. Talboys, with the boy. In a few days she died, and was buried under that name.

At this point Sir Michael Audley rose, unwilling to hear more. He asked Robert to assume the duty of caring for the lady whom he had believed to be his wife, leaving everything in his hands as the author of the discovery. He went straight to his room, and ordered his valet to pack a portmanteau and accompany him to London by the next train. Robert sought Alicia, and induced her to accompany her father, who was suddenly called away by very important matters. Sir Michael left everything to Robert's discretion, begging him not to be cruel.

Robert immediately telegraphed for a specialist in mental diseases, who arrived the next morning. After leaving the details of the case, he interviewed Lady Audley, and declared that she had the hereditary taint in her blood: "She has the cunning of madness, with the prudence of intelligence. She is dangerous." He gave Robert a letter to the director of a palatial sanitarium in an obscure town in Belgium, where she could be safely immured and well treated. Thither Robert forced her to accompany him. Before leaving her in her living grave, he had a talk with her, in which she revealed the mystery of her husband's disappearance. He had found her in the lime-walk, and there had been a terrible scene beside the well. She concluded, "It was then that I was mad; it was then that I drew the loose iron spindle from the shrunken wood, and saw him sink with a horrible cry into the black mouth of the well."

After much troubled reflection, Robert determined to leave his friend's body in its unhallowed resting-place and to keep from his uncle the knowledge that his wife was a murderess. On his return to town he received a letter from Clara Talboys, saying that Marks was at the point of death from the injuries received during the fire, and was very anxious to see him. He hurried down to Mount Stanning, and the dying man confessed that on the night of George's disappearance he had been passing through the shrubbery when he found a man with torn clothes and a broken arm, covered with slime. For a rich reward, he took him to his own home in the dead of night and cared for him, and early next morning put him on the train. Two letters had been left in his care; one for Lady Audley, and one for Robert. The letter to his wife was one of forgiveness; that to Robert merely said that the writer was suddenly leaving England, and thanked him for all his kindness.

Soon after these events, Robert visited Dorsetshire and managed to ingratiate himself with old Mr. Talboys and gain his consent to his daughter's marriage. Robert said the honeymoon was to be spent in a voyage to Australia to seek the missing man. This, however, proved to be unnecessary, for one evening on returning to his chambers he found George installed there. The latter explained how his mining experiences had served him in good stead. Being able to climb like a cat, he had ascended by the rope and stone-work of the narrow well, even with a broken arm. Instead of going to Australia, he had taken another vessel for New York, where he stayed till homesickness compelled his return. Lady Audley did not long survive her incarceration.

JOHN MARCHMONT'S LEGACY (1863)

This story was the third of Miss Braddon's successful novels, and has been called "a tale of Destiny." The scene is laid mainly in two English counties, Lincolnshire and Hampshire, and the time of the narrative is 1838-1854.

OHN MARCHMONT, once a teacher, later a lawyer's hack by day and at night a supernumerary at Drury Lane Theater, met one evening a former favorite pupil, Edward Dangerfield Arundel, a lad of seventeen, the second son of a wealthy Devonshire squire. Young Arundel had always been kind to the poor teacher, and the latter, who was slowly dying of pulmonary consumption, and who knew that Edward possessed a noble nature, confided to him his hopes and fears regarding his only child, Mary, a little girl of eight years. John Marchmont, who was the heir-presumptive to a fortune in Lincolnshire, explained to Edward that three lives stood between him and his inheritance, and that his one desire was that when he should no longer be alive to protect his idolized child, there might be someone who would be a friend to her and guard her interests should the Marchmont property ever come to her. John said also that his cousin, Paul Marchmont, and his two sisters, were the next heirs after Mary, and that, unreasoningly perhaps, he feared and hated Paul. But, as he had perfect confidence in Edward Arundel, he begged him to be the protector of little Mary, saying: "The legacy of a child's helplessness is the only bequest which I can leave to the only friend I have." Arundel, with boyish enthusiasm, accepted this legacy, saying that he would fight her battles for her if she ever needed help. But two years later Edward Arundel was sent with a cavalry regiment to India, to the sorrow of little Mary Marchmont, who regarded the handsome boy with almost idolatrous affection.

Three years after Edward's departure, the lives that stood between John Marchmont and his inheritance having been removed by accidental death, he became the proprietor of the vast Lincolnshire estate and master of Marchmont Towers, removing thence with Mary, where the gentle girl soon endeared herself to all the tenantry.

When Edward Arundel returned to England for his first visit he was enthusiastically welcomed to the Towers by John Marchmont and his daughter. Young Arundel spent several months at Marchmont Towers, and during his visit Mr. Marchmont and Mary made the acquaintance of Edward's cousin, Olivia Arundel, a young lady of twenty-three years, who lived with her father, a poor rector, several miles from the Towers. Olivia Arundel, both in looks and character, was a striking contrast to Mary Marchmont. She was beautiful, but as cold and impassive as Mary was impulsive and affectionate. Olivia regulated all her actions by the stern, uncompromising rule of duty, in which neither affection nor compassion had the slightest part; yet everyone praised Olivia for her goodness, while at the same time no one really loved her except her father.

John Marchmont's mind was never free from the thought that his life could not last long, and that his innocent Mary would be without a legal protector when he was gone. He heard praises of Olivia Arundel on all sides, and decided to ask her to become his wife for the sake of Mary, who needed a mother's care. When John offered himself to Olivia, he frankly explained his motive, telling her also that he could leave her a good income of several thousand pounds. But Olivia had a jealously guarded secret. The one person in the world who had the power to move her cold nature was her young cousin, Edward Arundel. She loved him with an intensity that surprised herself, but she realized that he was indifferent to her and that he never would love her. Therefore, when she learned that her father wished her to marry John Marchmont, she argued herself into the belief that it was her duty as well as to her interest to marry John and to crush out her unrequited love for her cousin. So she told Marchmont that she would faithfully perform her duty to his motherless child; and soon after their marriage she began the education of the sadly neglected girl; but no spark of affection for her stepdaughter accompanied this work. Mary had resolved to be submissive and obedient to her stepmother although she knew instinctively that she never could love her.

Olivia proved a dutiful wife, tending her husband with great care through his frequent illnesses, and when he died, two years after their marriage, he left Mary to the guardianship of his wife, who was also the executrix of his will. On the day of her husband's funeral Olivia received a call from Paul Marchmont, the artist cousin whom John had so disliked and feared. Paul accepted Olivia's invitation to remain at the Towers for a few days, and although he saw Mary but once during his visit, he left the mansion saying to himself "The little girl is as feeble as a pale February butterfly; a puff of frosty wind might wither her away. But that woman, that woman!—how handsome she is, with her accurate profile and iron mouth; and what a raging fire there is hidden somewhere in her breast, devouring her beauty by day and night! What is her mystery? What is her secret, I wonder—for she must surely have one." Olivia's secret was her love for Edward Arundel, which she had allowed to fill her heart again as soon as she was free to think of him without sin.

About three years later, Captain Arundel came again to England and to Marchmont Towers, where Mary, overjoyed to see her faithful friend once more, was happy for the first time since her father's death. Olivia watched in terror and jealous rage Edward's evident interest in Mary, and when at last, by eavesdropping, she overheard the two acknowledging their love for each other, she was nearly mad with despair. She hated Mary as intensely as she loved Edward, and, meeting the young girl alone one night just after she had parted from her lover, she upbraided her in cruel words for her actions, accusing her of having offered herself to Edward; assuring her that he cared nothing for her and that all he sought was her fortune. The wicked woman so wrought upon the feelings of the unsuspicious girl that she believed her stepmother was right in saying that Captain Arundel could not love her, though she would believe nothing against him. The next morning a letter was given to Edward in which Mary told him that she knew that he could not love her for herself, but that she did not blame him; that she wished him to have her fortune and that she intended to leave Marchmont Towers forever. Captain Arundel, half stunned by this news, and learning that Mary had fled from her home, noticed a strange look on Olivia's face, which instantly told him the source of poor Mary's sorrow. He turned upon her, saying in passionate indignation:

"This mischief is some of *your* work, Olivia Marchmont! It is you who have slandered and traduced me to my dead friend's daughter! It is you who have whispered shameful insinuations into this poor child's innocent ear! I scarcely need the confirmation of your ghastly face to tell me this. It is you who have driven Mary Marchmont from the home in which you should have sheltered and protected her! You envied her, I suppose—envied her the thousands which might have ministered to your wicked pride and ambition; the pride which has always held you aloof from those who might have loved you; the ambition that has made you a soured and discontented woman, whose gloomy face repels all natural affection. What other motive could you possibly have had for doing this deadly wrong?"

"No other motive!" Olivia thought, as she crouched at her cousin's feet.

"Listen to me, Olivia Marchmont," the young man continued. "Wherever this girl may have gone, driven hence by your wickedness, I will follow her. My answer to the lie you have insinuated against me shall be my immediate marriage with my old friend's orphan child. *He* knew me well enough to know how far I was above the baseness of a fortune-hunter, and he wished that I should be his daughter's husband." So saying, Arundel left the Towers and hastened to London, where he found Mary; and, after convincing her that he really loved her and that her stepmother's words were wickedly false, he told her that she needed immediate protection from Olivia's evident hatred, and that they must be married as soon as he could arrange matters.

After their marriage Edward took his bride for a honeymoon to a little Hampshire village, telling her that while there he would write to her lawyers, her stepmother, and others, announcing their marriage; but day after day slipped by without the letters having been written, until one afternoon he received a summons to his father's deathbed. Mary lived in absolute terror of her stepmother, and dreaded to have Edward leave her; but he told her he would return for her in a few days. On his journey home that night, however, an accident occurred to his train and he was the most seriously injured of any of the passengers.

Meanwhile Paul Marchmont, who was visiting his sister, Mrs. Lavinia Weston, at Kemberling, had persuaded Olivia that it was her duty to find Mary, who, he insinuated, was under the influence of Captain Arundel, and force her to return to her home; he said also that he would discover her present hiding-place. Consequently, a few days after Edward Arundel had met with the accident that rendered him helpless, Mary Arundel was found and carried back to the Towers.

For three months Edward Arundel lay in a state of coma, his skull having been fractured in the railway accident; and when, after a critical operation, he finally recovered consciousness, he told his mother of his hasty marriage to Mary Marchmont, and how he had carelessly postponed writing the news to their friends, and asked the reason why his young wife had not come to him. Learning from his mother that no news of Mary had ever come to Dangerfield, he was nearly frantic with anxiety for her welfare. Weak as he was, Edward hastened to Marchmont Towers, and, confronting his cousin Olivia, passionately demanded to be told what had happened to his wife and where she was. Olivia, with a cold, evil smile, replied that no one had believed Mary's assertion that she was married to Captain Arundel, especially as she had no evidence other than her word to substantiate her claim; that the girl, being unhappy after her return to the Towers, had left the house about a month previously, and that although every effort had been made to find her, she never had reappeared since that day. Late that afternoon she had been seen walking by the riverside, on the bank of which one of her slippers was afterward found. The river had been dragged, but her body was not recovered; nevertheless, Olivia declared that the general opinion was that Mary had been drowned. This Edward would not believe; but furiously denounced his cousin for her treatment of his innocent wife, by which she had been driven to despair. When he learned also that Paul Marchmont was a frequent visitor at the Towers, and had disbelieved Mary's story about her marriage, he excitedly exclaimed that he remembered poor John Marchmont's warnings to him against this very man, and declared that he believed Paul Marchmont to be a villain, playing an infamous game to win the fortune that would be his if Mary were out of the way. He added that if he or anyone else had foully dealt with her, he himself never would rest until he had avenged her; and that he would hunt the world over to find his wife, for he would not believe her dead.

Olivia explained further that Paul Marchmont had found Mary where Edward had left her in Hampshire, and that when she herself had gone with him to conduct Mary back to the Towers, the unhappy girl refused to go until after she had been informed by Paul of the accident that had befallen Edward; then she was seized with brain-fever as a result of the news, having been attended through her illness by Dr. Weston, a brother-in-law of Paul Marchmont. Although the latter refused to take possession of the estate at present, he had built a painting-room adjoining the boat-house and went there every day to paint, and there Edward Arundel sought him. The boat-house and the pavilion above it had been repaired, and the painting-room had been so built that it enclosed the only entrance to the pavilion. Paul Marchmont, having heard from Olivia of Edward Arundel's proposed visit, received him with an air of frankness, and replied to all his questions with coolness and imperturbability. He asserted his entire ignorance of anything that could explain the mystery of Mary's disappearance, but said that he had always considered her rather deficient in mental power and that nothing she might do would astonish him. Realizing that no present satisfaction was to be obtained from this man, Edward, more and more wretched, and blaming himself for not having guarded his wife better, searched everywhere for her in vain; and in another interview with Olivia he accidentally saw a printed notice of his own death, with a letter from Paul Marchmont to Olivia directing her to show the notice to Mary immediately.

"I understand everything now," said Edward Arundel; "it was with this printed lie that you and Paul Marchmont drove my wife to despair, perhaps to death. My darling, my darling! I refused to believe that you were lost to me. I can believe it now!"

At last Edward believed that his wife, while nearly mad with grief, had committed suicide; and his one purpose henceforth was to make Paul Marchmont answer to him for her life. He resolved to wait and watch for evidences of the villain's guilt. Accordingly, Captain Arundel sold his captaincy in the army and went to live in a cottage between Kemberling and Marchmont Towers. When Paul heard that Edward had established himself so near the Marchmont estate, he went to his sister, Mrs. Weston, and talked long and seriously with her, finally saying:

"He must be terribly in earnest, or he would not have sacrificed his position. He has planted himself here, close upon us, with a determination of watching us. We shall have to be very careful."

Months rolled by and still Edward Arundel was no nearer the solution of the mystery of his lost wife's disappearance. The next summer Edward made the acquaintance of Belinda Lawford, a schoolmate of his sister Letitia, and a sweet girl, as good as she was beautiful. Belinda had heard from Letitia the sad story of her brother's marriage, and she pitied him from the depths of her tender heart. Edward's loneliness was relieved by frequent visits to Lawford Grange, where his sister was staying; and yet he bitterly reproached himself for enjoying an hour's happiness while his darling wife was still unavenged; and when Letitia left the Grange he determined to go there no more.

Paul Marchmont had announced his intention of taking possession of the estate a year and a day from the date of Mary's disappearance; and to celebrate the event he intended to give a grand hunt-breakfast. For many months it had been reported that Olivia was to marry Paul, and later scandalous things were said of her. On the night before the hunt-breakfast, Edward Arundel met his cousin Olivia on her way to the boat-house and remonstrated with her for her persistence in remaining at the Towers; but she refused to listen to his advice, and suddenly Edward heard the cry of a child coming from the pavilion. Startled, he turned to Olivia, whose face had grown livid, and asked whose child it was. Upon her reply that she could not tell him, and that he should trample her to death before he entered the room to see the child, he flung her from him in disgust, saying that he knew the secret between Paul Marchmont and herself and cared little what became of her. Nevertheless, he determined that before he left Lincolnshire forever, as he had decided to do, he would let the whole county know what he thought of Paul Marchmont. Accordingly, the next morning, after that vain person had finished feasting with his guests and, inflated with a sense of his grandeur and importance, was descending the steps of the terrace, he was suddenly confronted by Edward Arundel, who seized the artist by the collar, and before the eyes of all the county magnates proceeded to give him a sound horsewhipping. Then, turning to the astonished crowd, Edward told them that Paul was a scoundrel, and, mounting his horse, he rode away to find distraction in foreign lands. Paul, like a whipped cur, crawled back to his room, and, frightened by the words Edward had whispered in his ear: "I know the secrets you hide in the pavilion by the river," he remained in seclusion until Edward's departure from Lincolnshire a week later.

After this event Paul Marchmont tried by a display of hospitality to win back the attention he feared he had forfeited from his neighbors; but, although many accepted his invitations, Major Lawford and his family declined all his advances. Belinda was a firm friend of Edward, as well as of Letitia Arundel; in truth, her interest in and pity for the brave young soldier had ripened into love; and when, a year and a half after Mary Arundel's disappearance, Edward returned from his wanderings and asked Belinda to be his wife, she gladly consented; knowing, however, that while he loved her dearly he still thought with a remorseful sorrow of his lost bride.

Paul Marchmont was jubilant when his sister Lavinia Weston took the news of Edward's engagement to him, but told her it would be well to keep it from Olivia, who was fast losing her mind, and remained shut up in her rooms at the Towers. But on the last day of June, the night before Edward and Belinda's wedding-day, Dr. Weston (the surgeon who had attended Mary in her illness), the stupid, "hen-pecked" husband of Lavinia and the tool of his wicked brother-in-law, went to Olivia late at night and told her that Edward Arundel was to be married the next morning. Then he angrily exclaimed that he would be trodden under foot no longer and that if she didn't speak he would. At the mention of Edward's name and the news that he was about to be married, all Olivia's wits were aroused—all her mad jealousy was revived; and, rushing into the room where Paul Marchmont was, she demanded to know the truth of what she had just heard. On his confirming the report, she wildly ordered him to prevent the marriage. He coolly replied that he would do nothing of the kind, and that neither should she, and ran to the door to lock it. Then there was a sudden crash of broken glass, and Olivia Marchmont had fled out into the night through one of the long French windows. Knowing that it was useless to attempt to find her in the darkness, Paul rode in great haste to Lawford Grange, reaching there about two o'clock in the morning, and told Belinda's father that Olivia was mad, warning him not to permit her to enter the house or to approach his daughter. This the Major promised, thanking Paul warmly for the warning.

At Hillingsworth church the following morning the service that was to unite Edward Arundel and Belinda Lawford had begun; but suddenly the ceremony was interrupted by Olivia Marchmont, who, with disheveled hair and gasping for breath, hurried up the aisle and in wild accents told Edward that his wife—his beloved Mary—was alive, and only an hour's ride from the church.

"My wife!" said Edward Arundel; "Mary, my poor, sorrowful darling—alive?"

Olivia repeated her statement and urged him to follow her, which Edward and Major Lawford did, leaving Belinda to be taken home by her mother. Edward, in his impatience, urged the driver of their carriage to hasten, and soon they reached the home of a humble friend of Mary's, and in that dwelling Edward saw his lost wife, and by her side was a beautiful boy a year old. Mary fell fainting into her husband's arms, while Edward sobbed out thanksgivings for the return of his darling. At last Olivia told Edward her reason for her hatred of Mary, and why she had consented to become the tool of Paul Marchmont; so, for the first time, Edward knew that Olivia had loved him always; and that this jealous love and her own violent passions had finally driven her mad.

When Mary was able to talk she told Edward her sad story: how she had been very ill for a long time, and how Paul Marchmont and his sister always refused to believe in her marriage to Edward; how cruelly her stepmother had talked to her when she received the false news of Edward's death. In her misery she had rushed madly out into the park and sat down by the river, and after a long time Paul and his sister had come and carried her into a room in the boat-house pavilion, where Dr. Weston again attended her. She had been very ill for many months and was kept in the boat-house after her baby was born, and until the following autumn, when her jailers removed her and the boy to a lonely farm-house and placed them in the care of an old woman. She had made no effort to escape, because she believed that Edward was dead, consequently, life held nothing for her. Then she told how Olivia had taken her and the boy away that morning and brought them to the house where Edward had found them.

When Edward had heard all this piteous story he clasped his wife in his arms and promised never to speak of her cruel wrongs again; but in his heart he vowed to punish Paul Marchmont.

That heartless scoundrel, knowing that all his vile schemes had come to naught and that punishment swift and sure would overtake him, remained in hiding until the night of the day that had reunited Edward and Mary, and then in the darkness he returned to the Towers, from which all the house servants but one had fled. Having sent this man to Mrs. Weston with all his jewelry and valuables, he set fire to the house and coolly locked himself into a room to perish with it, first throwing the key out of the window to prevent escape should his courage fail him. Although search was made for his body among the ruins of Marchmont Towers, no remains ever were found, but Mrs. Weston knew his fate.

Edward Arundel took his wife and child to Nice, and in that sunny clime they were very happy—but for a brief time only, for in less than a year Mary succumbed to the same disease that had ended her father's life, and Edward Arundel again went to fight in India, leaving his baby boy with his grandmother at Dangerfield.

Four years later Edward, now Major Arundel, returned to England, and, seeking Belinda Lawford, again asked her to be his wife, to make sunshine in his empty home and be a mother to his boy.   And the gentle Belinda, still faithful to the love of five years before, willingly gave her hand where her heart had been for many years.

FREDRIKA BREMER

(Sweden, 1802-1865)

THE NEIGHBORS (1835)

This is perhaps the most popular of all its author's charming pictures of domestic life in Sweden. It met with an enthusiastic reception in England in 1843, when it was translated by Mrs. Howitt, who pronounced Fredrika Bremer "the Jane Austen of Sweden." Mrs. Howitt felt that little was known in England of the rich treasures of intellect and literature in Sweden, and she devoted much time to translating all this writer's best works into English. She chose *The Neighbors* first of all to present to her countrymen, regarding it as a particularly characteristic production. This story is written in the form of a series of letters, and extracts from letters, penned by Franceska Werner to her friend Maria ——.

ERE I am now, dear Maria, in my own house and home, at my own writing-table, and sitting by my own Bear. And who is Bear? you probably ask: who should it be but my own husband, whom I call Bear because the name suits him so well.

First of all you shall have his portrait. Of middle size, but proportionably, not disagreeably, stout and broad; a handsome, well-curled peruke, made by the Creator's own hand; light eyelashes; small, clear grey eyes, with a certain penetrating glance, under large bushy yellow-grey eyebrows; the nose good, though somewhat thick; mouth large, with good teeth—large hands, but well made and well kept; large feet, the gait like a bear; but this gives no idea of his exterior, if you do not take into account an expression of open-hearted goodness and cheerfulness, which inspires a joyful confidence in the beholder. His inward self, best Maria, I have not yet myself studied. Betrothed to him only within two months, wife since fourteen days, I have not had great opportunity to become acquainted with a man who is generally silent, and whom I have not known more than half a year. But I trust and hope all for good!

In the first place, he is much older than I am; he is nearly fifty, and I want yet three years of thirty; further, he has been so long an old bachelor, has his good and bad habits, and these last I do not find at all agreeable; but they shall not destroy our domestic happiness; of that I am determined. Some of them I shall accustom myself to, some of them I shall wean him from.

You asked me if I really loved him and in reply I say I certainly liked him and found him an excellent man, otherwise I should not have married him. You know I was poor and obliged to get my own bread by the sweat of my brow, for teaching music is no light labor. I was not young any longer, had no beauty, nor talent beyond that little bit of music, and he, from a family of consequence, of a respectable station in life, and universally esteemed on account of his character, knowledge and ability, selected me from many richer, handsomer, and better than I. He attended me during my severe fever with utmost kindness; and when my mother would have recompensed his trouble with the remains of our hoarded-up money, he put it aside and requested my hand. Then he was kind to all who belonged to me; gave presents to my brothers, and through him prosperity entered into our formerly needy house. Should I not be grateful? Should I not like him? Should I not endeavor with all my power, with my utmost ability, to make him happy? Ah, yes! that will I, that shall I; with his virtues and his defects, in jest and in earnest, in good and in evil, will I make him happy, and a voice within me says that I shall succeed.

On the day of my coming to my new house, before we reached the pleasant cottage where Bear had lived and which he had in readiness for his bride, we drove into a courtyard and drew up at the door of a large, handsome house while my husband explained, "Here lives *ma chère mère*."

"What, must we alight here?" I asked.

"Yes, my love," was his reply.

This was to me by no means an agreeable surprise; I would much rather have gone on to my own house; much rather have made preparation for this first meeting with my husband's stepmother, of whom I stood in great awe from the anecdotes I had heard of her, but I saw that it was no time for opposition.

It was Sunday, and as the carriage drew up I heard the sound of a violin.

Bear took me by the hand and in spite of my reluctance led me to the hall-room whence proceeded the sounds of music and dancing.

Here my terror was considerably abated by finding that the great room contained merely a number of cleanly dressed servants, men and women, who leaped about lustily with one another, and who were so occupied with their dancing as scarcely to perceive us. Bear led me to the upper end of the room, and there I saw sitting upon a high seat a very tall and strongly built gentlewoman, apparently fifty years of age, who was playing with remarkable fervor upon a large violin, and beating time to her music with great power. Upon her head was a tall and extraordinary cap of black velvet, which I may as well call helmet, because this idea came into my head at the first glance, and after all I can find no better name for it. She looked handsome but singular. This was the Generalska (wife of the General) Mansfelt, this was the stepmother of my husband, this was *ma chère mère!*

She instantly turned her large dark-brown eyes upon us, ceased playing, laid down her violin, and arose with a proud bearing, but with, at the same time, a happy and open countenance. Bear led me forward; I trembled a little, made a deep curtsy, and kissed her hand; in return she kissed my forehead, and embraced me as warmly as her stepson. And now came his turn; he kissed her hand most reverentially, but she presented her cheek; they regarded each other with the most friendly expression of countenance, she saying in a loud, manly voice the moment afterwards: "You are welcome, my dear friend; it is very handsome of you to come here to me before you have been to your own house; I thank you for it. I might, it is true, have received you better if I could have made preparations; but at all events, this I know, that a welcome is the best dish. I hope, my friends, that you will remain till evening with me."

Bear excused us, saying that he wished to reach home soon, as I was fatigued with the journey, but that we could not have passed Carlsfors without paying our respects to *ma chère mère*.

"Nay, good, good!" said she, apparently satisfied, "we will soon have more talk within, but first I must speak a few words with these people here. Listen, good friends!" and *ma chère mère* struck the back of the violin with the bow till general silence prevailed through the hall. "My children," continued she, in a solemn tone, "I have something to say to you—zounds! wilt thou be quiet there below?—I have to tell you that my beloved son Lars Anders Werner takes home his wife, this Fransiska Buren, whom you see standing by his side. Marriages are determined in heaven, my children, and we will now pray Heaven to bless its work in the persons of this couple. This evening we will drink together a *skal* to their well-being. So now you can dance, my children! Olof, come here, take the violin and play thy very best."

When our visit was concluded and we were about to take our departure *ma chère mère* told us to fill up our glasses with the very good punch with which she had provided us, and drink to the people; for she said "trouble man may keep to himself, but pleasure he must enjoy in company." Then leading the way to the dancing-room she addressed the assembly in this manner: "One must never triumph before one is over the brook; but if people sail in the ship of matrimony with prudence and in the fear of God, there is a proverb which says, 'Well begun is half won,' and therefore, my friends, we will drink a *skal* to the new-married couple whom you see before you, and wish, not only for them, but for those who come after them, that they may forever have place in the garden of the Lord!"

"*Skal! skal!*" resounded on all sides. Bear and I emptied our glasses, and then went round and shook hands with so many people that my head was quite dizzy.

From this time I saw much of *ma chère mère* and became greatly attached to her, as she had many noble qualities which made one overlook her eccentricities. I learned from my husband that a blighting sorrow overhung her life and that her stern exterior hid a broken heart.

Ma chère mère, who had been a just and faithful mother to her four stepsons, had had only one son of her own, who was called Bruno after his father, General Mansfelt, and whom his mother completely idolized.

His birth had nearly cost her her life, and that which she bought so dearly seemed more precious to her than life itself. The relation between mother and son was extraordinary, and the passionate affection which existed between them was most unusual. Both were of the same powerful, determined character, and this in spite of the intense love they felt for each other, brought about much strife. It would have been impossible to find anywhere a handsomer boy than her Bruno: and yet, although his mother worshiped him in her heart, her sense of justice was so great that she never even in the slightest instance favored him to his stepbrothers' disadvantage. Bruno was naturally extravagant and prone to dissipation, and in order to secure the money to gratify his thirst for pleasure he would purloin small sums from his brothers or from the domestics. At last came the day when a large sum of money was missed from the desk of the bookkeeper of the estate and it was understood that there was a thief in the household.

The servants were all searched at once and finally one in anger suggested that her ladyship might seek nearer home for the culprit. *Ma chère mère* was filled with rage, but at once acceded to the suggestion and had the belongings of her stepsons thoroughly examined without leading to any discovery.

"Now then, there are only the things of the young Baron left," said one of the old servants respectfully, "but the chest is locked: and besides this, it is not necessary."

"That may be," exclaimed *ma chère mère*, "but he must fare like the rest. The box shall be broken open."

"But the young Baron is not at home," said the servant anxiously; "we cannot—"

"His mother commands it," said she, warmly.

"It is done."

With her own hand the mother took out books and clothes, which had been thrown in in great disorder. Presently the hand was withdrawn, as if it had been burned by a red-hot iron; she had stumbled upon a bundle of notes. It was the missing money. She took it out; turned it about in her hand; examined it, as if she could not believe her own eyes; grew paler and paler; and then a cry of inexpressible anguish rose from her breast: "My blood!" exclaimed she, "my own flesh and blood!" and she sank without a sigh as if lifeless to the floor. Terrible was her awakening. But she shed no tear, uttered no word of anger or complaint. She appeared strong and determined.

That evening Bruno returned from his temporary absence and upon being sternly accused by his mother of the crime he haughtily acknowledged his guilt.

"Fall upon your knees and receive your punishment," commanded his stern judge, but Bruno stood unmovable.

Ma chère mère raised herself. "Fall upon your knees, sinner!" exclaimed she in an awful voice, but still Bruno refused to obey; and finally in a voice which made the blood freeze in one's veins she asked him whether he would submit to her will or receive her curse?

Mother and son looked at each other with eyes of flame and defiance. For a long time they stood thus. Again she repeated the question; and then followed terrible words on both sides. Again all was still. The curse-speaking lips became stiff, the haughty glances dimmed. Mother and son both sank in a deep swoon.

That night Bruno disappeared, taking nothing with him but the clothes he wore and leaving a note addressed to his brother in which he said: "I have met severity with scorn, might with might; and this has made me appear more criminal than I truly am. This last theft (and I had sworn that it should be last) was not entirely theft. The day after to-morrow the money would have been returned. My mother refused me a loan—and now I took only of that which at one time would be mine—it was discovered and she—she must bear the consequences of that which has happened and may yet happen.

"Farewell for ever.

"BRUNO."

Ma chère mère tore the paper out of my hand, and read the contents. "He has stolen more than once, then," said she passionately. "I have then brought a thief into the world!" She tore the letter into a thousand pieces.

From this moment she spoke not one word for three years. She shut herself in her own room, which was darkened; would endure neither light nor the sight of man; ate and drank but little; slept scarcely at all; spoke with none.

At the expiration of that time she arose from her bed and came once more among her people. Her hair had turned white and her countenance bore traces of most painful suffering, but she again took up the reins of government and assumed the control of her estate which she had for so long left to the care of others.

The name of Bruno was never mentioned, and *ma chère mère* shortly moved from her large estate, named Ramm, and took up her abode at Carlsfors, where she has since resided.

Our little place, named Rosenvik, was on the latter estate and my husband rented it of his stepmother, as he was fond of his garden and of country life.

Sixteen years had elapsed since Bruno had disappeared, when a rich stranger known as M. de Romilly bought the estate of Ramm, which had remained vacant for so many years, and came there to live. For some time the black-bearded stranger was regarded as a mysterious personage by his neighbors but eventually was recognized by my husband as his long-lost brother Bruno.

When the recognition took place a most affecting scene ensued and Bruno, pressing his brother warmly to his breast, kissed him and embraced him, stammering out, "Brother!— brother, can you yet remember me, will you acknowledge me and love me as before?"

Bruno then explained how he had returned to his home, after years spent in the West Indies, where he had acquired great wealth, in the hope of becoming reconciled with his mother. He told how her curse hung over him and caused him untold misery and declared that until he could persuade her to revoke it he could never know peace.

Bruno begged my Bear and me to do what we could to bring his mother to leniency, but when we endeavored to approach the subject in the most cautious way, we found her as bitter as ever.

Visiting at our house at this time was Serena Löfwoen, a

lovely young girl, who was the orphaned grandchild of some dear old neighbors of ours, and who as a child had been a great pet and favorite of Bruno's. The love which he had felt for her as a child developed into a deep and ardent passion, and she in her turn seemed to reciprocate his affection. He finally disclosed his identity to her and she acknowledged that she loved him but could not marry him while he was under his mother's curse, as she knew her grandparents would never consent to the union.

At last came the day when a startling and unexpected event was to bring matters to a crisis.

I had been invited to drive with *ma chère mère* to a neighboring town for some visits and shopping, and it was dark before we were ready to start on our homeward way.

Ma chère mère took the reins and drove the spirited pair of horses, as was always her custom. I was in an anxious mood and noted uneasily that my companion was *distraite* and appeared not to drive with her usual vigilance. As the darkness increased it seemed to me that we had forsaken the accustomed road and were traversing an unfamiliar locality; the horses flew on, more and more rapidly, until we were close upon the large estate which we thought to be Carlsfors—but a sudden flash of lightning showed us our mistake; we were at Ramm with its dark façade and huge wings.

In the sudden shock of surprise which ensued *ma chère mère* lost control of the horses, and they, terrified by the lightning, dashed recklessly down through the shrubbery towards the lake.

Then a dark and sturdy form suddenly sprang toward us and seized the reins; then ensued a struggle, the horses reared, and the form seemed to be trampled to the ground. I lost consciousness, but before I did so I recognized Bruno.

Thus it was that the son endeavored to atone for the past. I was unhurt, but *ma chère mère* was in a serious condition and Bruno was wounded and bleeding. Unmindful of his injuries, however, he watched by his mother for a sign of returning consciousness, declaring that he would receive no ministrations until he had won her forgiveness.

"Mother, I have suffered so much," he cried; "I have

wandered about without peace: I am destitute of peace yet: peace can never be mine while I am thrust from thy bosom. I have suffered; I have suffered much; I have repented— I can and will atone. But then you must pardon, you must bless me, mother. Mother, take away the curse!"

It was not long before the words he had longed to hear came faintly from her lips:

"I take away the curse which I once laid on the head of my son—I bestow on him full forgiveness." She opened her arms and they held one another in a long and close embrace. Thus the reconciliation took place. For a time the life of the mother was despaired of, and that of the son hung in the balance, but both were happily spared to us, much thanks being due to the medical assistance rendered by dear Bear.

Untiring also were the ministrations of the beautiful Oriental serving-maid, Hagar, who showered passionate devotion upon Bruno, and exhibited unrestrained grief at the thought of his having been fatally injured.

It was during the golden wedding festivities of the aged Dahls, Serena's grandparents, that her betrothal to Bruno unexpectedly took place.

The course of true love had not run smoothly with these two young people, but of late circumstances had been drawing them ever closer together, and this evening proved a climax in their affairs.

As the aged Dahl advanced into the dance salon on the arm of his granddaughter a sudden movement was visible in the great chandelier overhead, which with its sixty lights immediately fell to the floor with a deafening crash. Bruno, realizing on the instant Serena's danger, dashed forward in time to snatch her from under the falling mass, himself receiving a heavy blow on the head which partially stunned him. At this Serena crying "Bruno, Bruno!" caught him in her arms as he fell to the ground.

I confess that there was a great sensation in the little company, and I soon found myself in a dimly lighted chamber. Bruno lay upon a sofa with a family group about him, and my good Bear soon succeeded in arousing him from his temporary stupor. As he regained consciousness Bruno exclaimed.

"Ah, where is she? I had her in my arms—she was mine —it was so beautiful—thus let me die! Serena," exclaimed he, still more passionately, "where art thou? My bride, will thou let the world separate us? The world—men—what are they to us?"

Then he continued to beg that Serena's grandparents would give her to him that day for his bride, and after his own mother had warmly interceded for him the others reluctantly gave their consent, and the evening of the golden wedding closed with the glad betrothal of the lovers.

A horrible event has occurred at the Dahls', and my hand in consequence still trembles so that I can hardly guide my pen. This event was preceded by forebodings experienced by Bruno, who had been troubled by an evil dream; at the end of its recital to Serena, he had exclaimed:—

"How little do I deserve a love like this—how unworthy— Serena! thou sweet angel! thou who shalt be my wife—"

"Never shall she be it!" cried a wild, piercing voice, and Hagar, more like a fury than a woman, darted into the room. A dagger flashed in her hand—in the next instant it seemed sheathed in Serena's heart. But with the speed of lightning Bruno had seized Hagar's arm; the blow was turned aside, and the dagger only wounded Serena's shoulder. With the gesture of a madman Bruno wrenched the murderous weapon from Hagar's hand, pushed her fiercely back, seized with one hand her hair, and the steel glittered above her breast.

"Wretch!" he exclaimed, with a hollow voice and white lips—"Curse of my life—die!"

"Bruno! O my God!" cried Serena, as she sprang forward and hung on his arm. Bruno moderated his fury, his wild look became more composed, his lips murmured—"A woman!" and the dagger fell from his hand. He looked at Serena, saw her blood flow, caught her in distraction in his arms, and bore her to a sofa.

"Thy will shall be done!" cried Hagar wildly. "See here, Bruno, thy victim; it would only die at your feet!" She ran to him, plunged the dagger into her own breast, and fell before him, drenched in her blood. "Bruno, for thee! for thee!"

muttered her lips, then were silent; and her eyes closed.

This tragic occurrence cast a gloom over all, and Bruno, who had begun to feel assured that at last happiness was in store for him, was plunged into the depths of despair.

He cried out that his lot must remain ever one of sorrow and bitterness, and that he could bring only misery to any woman who loved him; then he rushed away from his beloved.

The days which followed were hard ones for Serena, but she bore them nobly; she cared with tender pity for the wounded girl, who hung between life and death, now accusing Bruno of crime and then declaring that he was blameless, and begging that he would come to her. Finally in response to a plea from Serena, he came to give comfort to the distracted creature, who breathed her last blessing Bruno and hoping for his and Serena's happiness.

When she had gone Bruno turned passionately to Serena and poured forth the recital of all that was dark and evil in his past career, assuring her that he was unworthy to be linked with the one woman he had ever loved, and bidding her tell him to depart.

But she stooped toward him with silent tears of affection in her eyes, and said—"I go with thee, Bruno. O my friend, my husband! It cannot be otherwise. Together let us wander on the earth, together one day kneel before the throne of the All-Merciful!"

ANNE BRONTË

(ACTON BELL)

(England, 1821-1849)

AGNES GREY (1847)

This was the first of the two novels written by the youngest of the three Brontë sisters. She had had some experience as a governess, which, according to her sister's biographer, is "pretty literally" described in *Agnes Grey;* she seems to have used also some incidents of Charlotte's brief service as a governess. By the seaside boarding-school established by her mother we are reminded that the three sisters had at one time an ambition to found a school of their own for girls, and that they chose Burlington, a seaside place, for its site. It was an ambition, happily, perhaps, for their fame, never to be realized. For after the wreck of this hope they turned to writing as their only resource against poverty and their only solace in the dreary winter of 1845-'46, while their father was becoming almost helpless with growing blindness, and their brother was sinking ever deeper into dissipation. The reception of their volume of poems (1846) was not encouraging; and more than a year passed before a publisher was found to accept any of the three novels—*The Professor, Wuthering Heights,* and *Agnes Grey*—which at first they sent out together; but when one publisher after another had returned them, they sent them separately, and late in 1847 *Agnes Grey* and *Wuthering Heights* were accepted, on terms somewhat impoverishing to the two authors, and published in December of that year, Charlotte's second novel, *Jane Eyre,* having appeared in October. In 1850 Charlotte edited a new edition of these two novels by her sisters.

I our pleasant parsonage in the north of England we lived comfortably on my father's income from his incumbency and his snug little private fortune. My mother, a squire's daughter, had married against the wishes of her father, who had therefore cast off and disinherited her. But when I was eighteen my father's property was swept away in a speculation by which he had hoped to double it. His depression and remorse on his family's account were intense; but my mother took the blow with the cheerful serenity and courage she had kept through life.

I was not needed to help my mother and elder sister in the household; and that I might not be a burden, I evolved a plan by which I hoped even to add a little to the family resources and I finally gained permission to carry it out. This was to become a governess.

Of my first experience—with the Bloomfield children—I need say but little. It was sharp but short. My second engagement was with the family of Mr. Murray, of Horton Lodge. My pupils were Rosalie, about sixteen, Matilda, fourteen, and two boys younger. To my relief, Master John was sent to school the next year, and Charles a year later, both, I must confess, in scandalous ignorance of Latin as well as of the more useful though more neglected subjects.

Miss Murray was a very pretty girl at sixteen, and in two years she had become beautiful in face and figure. She was lively and light-hearted, but vain and supercilious; her intellect was somewhat shallow, and she would apply herself only to the more showy accomplishments. At seventeen her whole mind was absorbed in the ambition to attract and dazzle the other sex.

Miss Matilda was a big, awkward hoyden, full of animal life and vigor, but ignorant, indocile, headstrong, violent and unreasonable. From her association with her father and the grooms—for she was fond of hanging about the stables—she had learned to swear like a trooper—a habit her mother believed I could have little difficulty in correcting.

While I was at home on a vacation Miss Murray made her social début at a grand ball given by her mother, and on my return she gave me a glowing description of it, dwelling mainly on her own great success—her dress, the compliments to her beauty, her conquests, the envy of her rivals. Among her most ardent admirers were the rector, Mr. Hatfield, and Sir Thomas Ashby, "rich and wicked," but she said complacently that she supposed she was to be Lady Ashby, and she did not mind the wickedness.

Incidentally she told me there was a new curate, Weston by name, whom she described as "a beast, an insensate, ugly, stupid blockhead." I discovered later that these epithets, being interpreted, meant that, unlike the enamored rector, he had shown no interest in the occupants of the squire's pew.

On Sunday afternoon the despised curate gave us a sermon which was to me truly refreshing after the prosy discourses of his predecessor and the still less edifying harangues of the rector, which usually were on church discipline, rites and ceremonies, apostolic succession, the duty of reverence and obedience to the clergy, the atrocious criminality of Dissent, the presumption of attempting to think and interpret Scripture for one's self, and, occasionally, the duty of deference from the lowly to their superiors in rank and station.

One bright day in February, after I had been reading to poor, lonely, half-blind Nancy Brown, she spoke of the new curate, and compared his way of administering comfort to the afflicted or troubled in mind with that of the rector. When she told Mr. Hatfield her fear that she loved neither God nor man as she should, he said, giving "a sort of whistle and with a bit smile on his face:

"'Oh, it's all stuff! You've been among the Methodists!'"

Assured that she had not, he prescribed for her regular attendance at church and close attention to his sermons.

"But if you get no comfort that way, it's all up."

"Then, sir, should you think I'm a reprobate?"

"Why, if you do your best to get to heaven and can't manage it, you must be one of those that seek to enter in at the strait gate and shall not be able.' And then he asked me if I had seen any of the ladies of the Hall about that mornin'; so I told him where I'd seen the young missis go; and he kicked my poor cat across the floor and went off after 'em as gay as a lark. But I was sad."

Then she told me how afterward she overheard him tell the curate she was "a canting old fool." But Mr. Weston visited her the next day, listened to her doubts with sympathy, and gave her wise and tender counsel, which she repeated to me. By his advice she had begun to do little kindnesses to her uncongenial neighbors, "for," he said, "if you cannot love them, you can try to do to them as you would they should do to you; and the very effort will make you love them in some degree."

In other cottages I heard similar tales of his sympathy with the troubled and of his generosity to the needy; and in a few chance interviews I learned to know for myself his independence of mind and his kindness of heart.

I had so long been restricted to the society of perverse children and ignorant, wrong-headed girls, that I had seemed to feel my intellect deteriorating, my heart petrifying, my soul contracting; and I trembled lest my moral perceptions should be deadened and my distinctions of right and wrong confounded. The gross vapors of earth were gathering around me and closing in upon my inward heaven. But now Mr. Weston rose like the morning star on my horizon, saving me from the fear of utter darkness. I was glad to see that not all the world was made up of Bloomfields, Murrays, Hatfields, Ashbys; that human excellence was not a mere dream of the imagination.

One Sunday, on the way from the afternoon service, I had fallen behind, as I usually did when the young ladies were joined by others. As I was trying to reach three primroses that grew high on the bank beside the road, I was startled by the words, "Allow me to gather them for you, Miss Grey." It was Mr. Weston, of course. Who else would trouble himself to do as much for me?

As we walked on we naturally talked of flowers and I spoke of my love for primroses because of associations with my home; this led him to say what a great consolation it must be to me to have a home, even if I could spend but a small part of my time there.

I said I could not live without it—and immediately repented of my over-enthusiastic and rather silly assertion.

He told me that he once thought existence could hardly be endured if he were deprived of home and its affections; that a year before he had lost the last and dearest of his early friends, his mother; yet he was not wholly destitute of hope and comfort even for this life; still, he almost envied even the humblest cottagers when he saw them gathered about the hearth at the close of the day.

After he had left me, and the Murrays' friends had entered their home, I joined my pupils, only to be irritated by their foolish jests about my "flirtation" with the curate, until they resumed the discussion of the attentions of the Captain and the Lieutenant, leaving me to turn my thoughts into a pleasanter channel. Having entered my room, I fell upon my knees and offered a fervent, impetuous prayer. That prayer men and

women would have scorned me for—"But, Father, Thou wilt
not despise!" I said. I believed that another's welfare was as
ardently desired as my own—nay, even that it was the principal
object of my heart's desire.

About this time Mrs. Murray was alarmed at the discovery
that Rosalie was meeting Mr. Hatfield in walks upon which
she contrived to set out alone. I soon found that she was
encouraging him only for the gratification of her vanity; and
later she described to me with great glee the high-bred scorn,
as she thought it, with which she had received his presumptuous
proposal of marriage, and the distress and despair with which he
was overwhelmed. But she missed his attentions, and sighed
for other victims.

One morning in returning from the village we came upon
Jane and Susan Green, whom Rosalie welcomed in default of
more inspiring company. I walked by myself as usual till
I was joined by Mr. Weston. Our conversation turned upon
books, and I thought he was less intent upon expressing his
own thoughts and preferences than in discovering mine. "And
why should he interest himself at all in what I think or like?"
I asked myself.

When Jane and Susan had left her, Miss Murray turned
to us and Mr. Weston would have passed on; but Rosalie gave
him one of her sweetest smiles and immediately engaged him
in conversation with a gentle, playful vivacity which I thought
must be peculiarly pleasing to a man of his temperament. I was
quite left out, and I felt wronged.

When he was gone she laughed and said, "I thought I
could do it."

"Do what?"

"Fix that man."

"What in the world do you mean?"

"I mean that he will go home and dream of me. I have
shot him through the heart. I know by the look of reverential,
tender adoration he gave me when he went away."

"Oh, God avert it!" I cried internally, "for his sake, not for
mine!"

This was but the prelude to many meetings planned by
Rosalie to complete the subjugation of the curate. In this

she was aided by Matilda, who now went with Rosalie on her walks, leaving me behind on one pretext or another, and even preventing me from going with them to the afternoon service. Meantime Rosalie had become engaged to Sir Thomas Ashby, but insisted upon keeping it secret, that she might lose no possible attention from others.

They took great pleasure in describing to me their interviews with Mr. Weston, asserting things flattering to them, which I knew must be exaggerations or perversions of the truth, if not utterly false, and other things that I feared might be true; but my anxiety and my indignation had to be concealed under an assumption of indifference. On one occasion Matilda told me he had asked if I were ill, and Rosalie had said I was well but didn't wish to go to church, "So he'll think you're turned wicked!"—another time, that she had said I was so buried in my books that I cared for nothing else!

One source of grief I had at this time which may seem trivial, but it cost me many tears. Matilda had given her little wire-haired terrier Snap into my care when he was ill, and he had naturally attached himself to me. Disgusted that he should prefer anyone to her, she gave him, in spite of my entreaties, to the village ratcatcher, a brute notorious for his cruelty to his canine slaves. But a more serious trouble came upon me; my father's health was failing fast.

Rosalie's wedding was over, and Matilda was ordered to avoid the stables and walk with me. One morning when we had seen and talked with Mr. Weston he met us again, bringing me a bunch of bluebells and saying that, though he had seen so little of me the past two months, he had not forgotten that they were among my favorite flowers. It was something to find my unimportant saying so well remembered, and something to know that he had noticed the time I had been secluded—not much, but enough to give me a cheerful evening, a night of pleasing dreams and a morning of felicitous hopes—foolish dreams, unfounded hopes—yes!

Alas! that very morning a letter summoned me home on account of a serious turn in my father's illness; and I hastened away, only to find him gone.

Our home was now broken up, and my mother, refusing

the invitation of my sister and brother-in-law to live with them, determined to find a suitable house where she and I might take a few boarding and day pupils—a plan to which I willingly assented.

During my further stay of six weeks at Horton Lodge I saw little of Mr. Weston until he overtook me to say good-bye on my last Sunday afternoon.

"It is possible we may meet again," he said, retaining my hand in his a few seconds. "Will it be of any consequence to you whether we do or not?"

"Yes, I should be very glad to see you again," I answered dully.

We began our school with nine pupils. I set myself to work with energy and for six weeks was by no means unhappy. "Will it be of any consequence to you whether we meet again?" These words were my secret solace and support. But as the weeks passed by I began to see upon how frail a twig I had hung my hopes.

In the Easter holidays I visited Rosalie at Ashby Park, by her earnest entreaty. I found her discontented, detesting her husband, as she said; she had not found him as indulgent as she had expected; angered at her flirtations in London, he was keeping her in the country with only himself and his mother.

The third morning after my return I was strolling on the sands near which we lived, when I heard a snuffling sound behind me and a dog came frisking and wriggling to my feet. It was my own Snap! When I spoke to him he leaped up in my face and yelled for joy. But how came he there? I looked round and beheld—Mr. Weston!

He told me that he was now Vicar of F——, about two miles distant from our town.

I hoped he liked his new parish and that I might congratulate him.

"You may congratulate me," he said. "I have a pleasant parish, and no one to interfere with me. I have nothing but solitude to complain of, and nothing but a companion to wish for."

I felt myself flushing, and in a confused attempt to disclaim a personal application of the remark, I answered to the effect that if he waited till he was well known in the neighborhood he might have numerous opportunities for supplying the want among the residents and visitors at F—— and in the vicinity, not considering the compliment I implied till his answer made me aware of n.

"I am not so presumptuous as to believe that, though you tell me so; but if it were so, I am rather particular in my notions and might not find one to suit me among the ladies you mention."

"If you require perfection, you never will."

"I do not; I have no right to require it, being so far from perfect myself."

Promising to call upon my mother the next day, he departed with Snap, who hesitated as to which of us to follow till called by his new master.

My mother and Mr. Weston got on extremely well together, and he became a frequent visitor. Ceremony was soon dropped between us; he even called me Agnes, and seemed to prefer it. So did I.

One evening in the last week of our vacation he came in unexpectedly.

"A beautiful evening, Mrs. Grey! Agnes, I want you to take a walk with me."

We fell into silence as we went through the village, and again when we were ascending a hill to get a view of the sunset and the sea—a silence he was, as usual, the first to break.

"My house is desolate yet, Miss Grey; and I am acquainted now with all the ladies in my parish and several in this town too; and many others I know by sight and by report; but not one of them will suit me for a companion; in fact, there is only one person in the world that will, and that is yourself; and I want to know your decision."

"Are you in earnest, Mr Weston?"

"In earnest! How could you think I should jest on such a subject?"

I said something about my mother's consent, and not wanting to leave her.

"I settled everything with Mrs. Grey while you were putting on your bonnet. She said I might have her consent if I could obtain yours. And so now I have overruled your objections on her account. Have you any other?"

"No, none."

"You love me, then?"

"Yes."

THE TENANT OF WILDFELL HALL (1848)

With more immediate success than the better work by her sisters, this novel of Anne Brontë's went into a second edition the year of its publication. Like her first story, it has some foundation in the experience of her life. The witty, attractive, reckless, drunken profligate of the book, Arthur Huntingdon, is easily identified with her brother Bramwell, whose worst escapade, carried on in the house where she lived as governess and he as tutor, had caused her intense suffering. The publisher sold advance sheets to an American firm as the latest and best work of the author of *Jane Eyre* and *Wuthering Heights*, no doubt honestly believing that the three Bells were one and the same person; so that Charlotte and Anne were obliged to go to Cornhill to convince him of their separate existence. The story purports to be told in letters from Gilbert Markham to his brother-in-law, Mr. Halford, who had asked him for an account of the most remarkable event of his life.

 OU must go back with me to the year 1827. I need hardly remind you that I was then carrying on my father's farm, in accordance with his last wishes, but contrary to my own preferences, which pointed to a more ambitious career. Then our family consisted of my mother, my sister Rose, my brother Fergus, and myself.

My mother's great anxiety at that time arose from my preference for Eliza Millward— the pretty, kittenish, coquettish daughter of our stern, ponderous, vain old vicar, whom she thought not good enough for me.

One evening in October my sister Rose announced as an important piece of news that the long-deserted Wildfell Hall had been let and for more than a week inhabited by a lady of five or six and twenty, Mrs. Graham; that she wore a sort of mourning, but not widow's weeds, and lived alone except for one servant, an old woman. Moreover, Jane Wilson and her mother had called and had imparted to their neighbors such details as they could learn by observation, having failed to elicit any information from the lady herself, who was civil but reticent, and evidently relieved when the visit was over. Eliza Millward, too, had been heard from; her father intended to inquire into the cause of the stranger's non-appearance at church on her first Sunday.

The Mrs. Wilson I mention was a narrow-minded, tattling old widow. Her son Robert was a farmer, and Richard was studying with the vicar for the Church. Jane, who was twenty-six, had a boarding-school education, which, as she thought, raised her above the farmer caste, was considered a beauty, and was ambitious to rise, so gossip said, by marriage with Frederic Lawrence, the young squire, whose family had deserted their old home, Wildfell Hall, for a more modern house in a neighboring parish.

My sister Rose, who called at the Hall with my mother, roused my curiosity by her enthusiastic description of Mrs. Graham's beauty; and on the following Sunday I saw for myself that the occupant of the pew appertaining to the Hall was a very beautiful woman. While I was gazing at her, her eyes met mine, but in an instant were dropped to her book with a look of quiet scorn that was peculiarly galling to me.

The following Tuesday I was out hunting on Wildfell Hill; and when near the garden wall I saw a beautiful little boy looking over with great interest at my setter Sancho. Then he tried to climb over, but was caught and suspended from a branch of a ragged cherry tree outside. I ran and caught him, and called Sancho, to divert him from his fright; but just as he put out his hand to stroke the dog, Mrs. Graham darted from the gate and snatched him away in excitement and agitation absurdly disproportioned to the occasion.

When I explained, she apologized and said, "I did not know you. I thought"——but did not tell what she thought.

When she returned my mother's call she brought her little boy, saying that she never left him away from her. In the course of conversation we got into an argument about the policy of shielding children from temptation rather than training them to overcome it. She, of course, said she would do both, that enough would come in any case to test their strength. I thought that in her remarks to me she seemed bent on letting me know that her opinion of me fell far below that I entertained of myself.

This naturally nettled me and made me anxious to show her

that I was not the conceited fop she took me for; and from that time I seized every opportunity to meet her—often when she was out sketching; for she was an artist of considerable ability, and sold her paintings, she told me for a needed addition to her income. Little Arthur was a great help to me. We had formed a close friendship, through Sancho at first; then his mother had allowed him to receive a little setter puppy I brought to him. If he caught sight of me when he was out with his mother—and I took great pains to be where he could—he would run to meet me; then I could take him back and talk with her.

I had not met Mrs. Graham many times before I began to realize the insipidity of Eliza Millward's conversation; but I did not altogether discontinue my visits at the parsonage until she began to annoy me with ill-natured raillery and innuendos about Mrs. Graham.

Meantime our friendship was progressing, and though Mrs. Graham was chilly and repellent at times, I had hopes that I was becoming, as the phrase is, not wholly "indifferent to her"; as for me, I was growing ever more and more deeply in love.

Thus I was no less enraged than horrified to learn, at first through hints from the vicar's daughter, then from sources that could be traced to the Wilsons, that the mystery in regard to Mrs. Graham's antecedents had been wrought into a scandal and spread through the community; and Frederic Lawrence's name was slyly coupled with hers. Lawrence was my friend; but he was naturally reticent; and long as I had known him I never felt that I knew him well. I was far from believing for an instant the calumnies of the Wilsons and Millwards; but I began to look upon Lawrence as a possible rival, and some little things served to confirm my suspicions.

On one occasion when I had snubbed him in my wrath he guessed something of the cause and said:

"Let me tell you, Markham, that if you have any designs in that quarter they will certainly fail; and it grieves me to see you cherishing false hopes and wasting your strength in useless efforts, for—"

"Hypocrite!" I exclaimed. He turned white, and left me without another word.

When, not long after this, I ventured on some expression

of my affection, Mrs. Graham told me that there must be no more of it; that if I could not be content to regard her only as a friend we must be strangers for the future. When I promised to be a friend or a brother or anything she wished, but urged her to tell me why I could be nothing more, she said she might tell me some day but not then.

Three weeks later the vicar called at our house and told my mother that he had been to see Mrs. Graham and had talked to her about the reports of her misconduct as he thought it incumbent upon him to do; and that he had been repulsed and as good as turned out of the house. I was nearly boiling over with rage, and when he turned his pastoral impertinence upon me—"As for you, young man—"

"As for me, sir," I began, but my fury choked my utterance, and I bolted from the house and off to Wildfell Hall.

I could not enter upon the subject at once; and I stayed on until she reminded me that it was getting late, and that her kind neighbors were on the watch. The subject was broached; and in my excitement I declared my love and implored her to be my wife. It could not be; she had wronged me from not understanding that my regard was more than fraternal or at most a passing fancy. She would tell me all—not then, for she had had misery enough for one day, but the next day, if I would meet her about noon on the moor.

I had gone part of the way home when I turned to look at the Hall, and something drew me nearer—an irresistible desire to take one more look at her. Scaling the wall, I looked in at the window. As I turned away, seeing that the room was vacant, the door opened and she came out with—Frederic Lawrence! As they passed me I heard a few words—"I must leave this place, Frederic."

"But where can you find a better one? So secluded, so near me; and I will be more cautious in future." They went on, and I saw him put his arm about her waist while she rested her hand on his shoulder.

In my agony I half rushed, half staggered from the spot threw myself over the wall and on the ground in despair.

Some days later I was riding over the lonely road to L—— in the rain, when Lawrence overtook me. I fell back to let him pass, but he kept beside me and attempted to converse in spite of my sullen silence.

"Markham," he said at length, "why do you quarrel with your friends, because you have been disappointed in one quarter? How am I to blame? I warned you beforehand—"

He said no more; for, impelled by some fiend, I seized my whip and brought the heavy handle down upon his head. He reeled and fell, and the blood rushed from the bruise. Scornfully rejecting my offers to help him on his pony, he sat on the wet grass, wiping his forehead with his handkerchief, and I rode on.

Hearing rumors that he was dying, I sent inquiries the next day by Fergus, who brought intelligence that he was laid up with a broken head from a fall, and a cold from lying on the wet ground, but nothing worse. So he did not intend to accuse me.

On one of the wretched days that followed I was out with the reapers, when Mrs. Graham sent Arthur to ask me to come and speak to her. She asked why I did not come to the moor that day; she evidently thought I had been listening to slanders against her. At length I told her what I had seen and heard, and upbraided her with the injury she had done me.

"I don't say," she answered, "that I can clear myself altogether. But would you be glad to discover that I was better than you think me?"

Upon my eager answer she took from her desk a thick written volume, and tore a few leaves from the end, then gave it to me, asking me to read and return it, and to tell no one of what I should learn from it.

It was a journal beginning in 1821 and brought down to the time she came to Wildfell Hall.

Briefly, it told of her life with an Uncle and Aunt Maxwell at their home, Staningley. They had taken her at her mother's death when she was a child. Then there was much of the courtship of Arthur Huntingdon, whom she married against her aunt's judgment. Then her gradual disillusionment as she discovered that her handsome, genial husband was wholly without principle, selfish and sensual, proud of the dissipation and license of his past life, and not inclined to give them up. The journal recorded his lying excuses when he wanted to get away from home to his disreputable friends, and described some of their disgusting orgies under his own roof. So her life went on, growing always less endurable, until about three years after their marriage, when she discovered a low intrigue of her husband with Lady Lowborough, a visitor in the house, with whom he had flirted before the marriage of either. Then she desired a separation to take her child and go away, which her husband refused; and so she dragged out two years more at Grassdale Manor; but as the child grew older the father was doing his best to make him like himself, teaching him to drink and swear, baby as he was, to despise his mother, and to enjoy the orgies of his father's boon companions.

She resolved to steal away with little Arthur and hide, perhaps in America; but she must have means of support, and she did not want to apply to her brother; so she began to practise painting, for which she had a talent, hoping to gain skill enough to take care, by it, of herself and her child. This design was discovered and thwarted by Huntingdon. She had then no resource but her brother, whom I had guessed to be Frederic Lawrence before I had read this far in the journal. At her request, he promised to prepare some rooms for her in the old Hall, but advised her not to go until she found it impossible to stay at Grassdale. That time came soon after, when Huntingdon brought into the house an adventuress, on the pretext of providing a governess for the boy. She timed her escape well, and so far had succeeded in keeping her whereabouts from the knowledge of her husband.

The last entry before the torn leaves was written soon after her arrival at Wildfell: "I have made some further acquaintance with my neighbors. The fine gentleman and beau of the parish (in his own estimation at least) is a young——" myself, evidently. Well, I could forgive the contemptuous remarks that had doubtless followed, now that I knew the kind of men her experience had shown her.

Of course I went to her at once. She forgave me my distrust, begged my forgiveness for the injury she had unintentionally done me, and said that we must meet no more, a decision from which all my entreaties failed to move her.

The next tale that Eliza Millward brought to our house

about Mrs. Graham, some months later, had more foundation in fact. "Perhaps you know," she said, "that her husband is not really dead and that she has run away from him; but perhaps you did not know that she is now gone back to him, and that a perfect reconciliation has taken place! Only think what a fool the man must be!"

As soon as I was free I rushed off to Lawrence, who had readily forgiven me my brutality when he learned its cause. He said that she had indeed gone to her husband, who had had a fall from his horse and was in a serious but not hopeless condition.

"Why did she take this infatuated step?" I exclaimed angrily. "What fiend persuaded her to it?"

"Nothing persuaded her but her own sense of duty."

"Humbug!"

"I was inclined to say so myself at first, Markham, for I detest that man as fervently as you can do, except, indeed, that his reformation would give me greater pleasure than his death. It was not by my advice she went."

"He will make her all manner of lying promises and she will believe him and be ten times worse off than before."

"There doesn't seem much ground for believing so at present," he said, and showed me a letter from her, telling how she found her husband and his ungracious reception of her.

As time went on Lawrence showed me other letters. Huntingdon was gaining under her careful nursing, was treating her more decently, and at length was nearly out of danger, but as he felt returning strength he grew unmanageable; declared he would not be treated like a baby any longer, that she wanted to keep him weak so as to have him under her thumb; but by the Lord Harry he would have no more humbug! In defiance of her efforts he one day ordered the butler to bring a bottle of the strongest wine from the cellar, and never rested till he had drunk it dry. This brought on a relapse, ending in his death.

She was free! but I could not venture to believe she would think of me when the shock was over. It seemed to me that the awful scenes through which she had passed must have effaced from her heart the transient affection she had felt for me, which, if she thought of it at all, must seem like a fleeting dream. Moreover, there was a wide difference, from a worldly point of view, between the Lady of Grassdale Manor and poor Mrs. Graham of Wildfell Hall, a difference that it seemed to me influenced her brother to give the barest possible answers to my inquiries about her.

Months passed, and I thought I might write to her, perhaps see her at Grassdale, when Lawrence told me that her uncle was dead and that she would stay for some time at Staningley with her aunt. I asked where it was, and he told me the shire, nothing more; and I would not ask.

It was more than a year after Huntingdon's death when I went to Grassdale and there was directed to Staningley, where she was still living. Two of my fellow-travelers on the coach made me aware when we reached the grounds.

"Fine land, this," said one.

"Ay; it's old Maxwell's, I suppose."

"It was; but he's dead now and has left it all to his niece."

"She'll be a fine catch for somebody."

"She will so. I should think she'll marry none but a nobleman, myself. Look ye, sir, that's the hall—grand park, you see, and all them woods; plenty of timber there, and game!"

I alighted at the park gates, but I could not go in. If I could only get a glimpse of her! But she must not see me; for what could have brought me here but the hope of reviving that fleeting attachment and of obtaining her hand? How could I bear that she should think me capable of such presumption? I would go; I would not even pain her with the thought of my fidelity and my suffering.

But yet I could not go. I leaned against an old tree beside the road. Presently a carriage came around the corner. I did not look at it till I hea.d a child's voice from within.

"Mamma, here's Mr. Markham!"

And another voice, "Oh, aunt, here's Mr. Markham, Arthur's friend! Stop, Richard!"

I cannot tell you all that passed after we had gone into the house, Arthur joyously leading me after the carriage. She did not at first divine my scruples and the cause of my strangeness; but we came to an understanding at last. We were married the following summer; and I need not tell you, Halford, how happily we have lived and loved through these passing years.

CHARLOTTE BRONTË

(CURRER BELL)

(England, 1816–1855)

JANE EYRE (1847)

In the summer of 1846 Charlotte Brontë was in London with her father, who was under treatment for cataract. While there she began *Jane Eyre*. August 24, 1847, it was sent to the publishing house of Smith and Elder, was accepted, and published October 16th. This firm had declined *The Professor* in a letter "containing," as she said, "a refusal so delicate, reasonable, and courteous as to be more cheering than some acceptances." A few copies were sent to literary friends, among them Thackeray, and all praised it highly in their letters of acknowledgment. The literary journals in general gave qualified praise, but the *Examiner's* commendation was most hearty and yet discriminating. Meantime the novel had begun to make its way with the public and was called for by the libraries; early in December the rush began. A second edition, with a dedication to Thackeray, appeared in January. Its success in the United States was great and immediate. Not until the summer of 1848 did even the publishers learn of the identity of "the Bell brothers." The original of "Lowood," as is well known, was a school at Cowan's Bridge, a hamlet between Leeds and Kendal, to which the elder sisters, Maria and Elizabeth Brontë, were sent in July, 1824, and Charlotte and Emily in September. "Helen Burns" is an exact portrait of Maria; and the incidents of her sufferings at the hands of Miss Scatcherd are literal descriptions of what actually happened. In the spring of 1825, the year of the fever, Maria became so ill with consumption that she was taken home, and died a few days later. Elizabeth was sent home soon afterward and died in the summer. Charlotte is reported as saying she would not have written as she did of Lowood if she had known it would be so readily identified, although she had given a true picture of the institution as she knew it.

MY recollections of my first ten years are those of a helpless dependent under the grudging care of my uncle's widow, Mrs. Reed of Gateshead, where I was constantly reminded of my inferior position not only by the family but by the servants, rebuked and punished for faults not my own, subject to cruel and violent abuse by my cousin, John Reed, and to the disdain and contempt of his spoiled sisters, Eliza and Georgiana, all of whom were older than I.

The next eight years I passed at Lowood, a school for

Portrait of Charlotte Brontë (p. 230)
Photogravure from a contemporaneous engraving

Portrait of Charlotte Brontë (p. 230)

Photogravure from a contemporaneous engraving

orphan girls, supported in part by charity, where my aunt sent me to rid herself of my hated presence. During the first few months of my stay the school was controlled exclusively by the Rev. Mr. Brocklehurst, whose mother had been one of its founders. He was a pompous, narrow-minded man, who considered it a Christian duty to repress any tendency to vanity by keeping the girls in a hideous and absurd uniform, and to discourage carnal appetites by half starving them on coarse and insufficient food; he was liberal only in promises of future torments in hell to real or supposed offenders.

But in the spring an epidemic of typhus broke out in the school; forty-five of the eighty girls were ill at one time and many died. This drew public attention; and an inquiry disclosed the low, miasmatic nature of the site, the quality and quantity of the food, the fetid water, the insufficient clothing and wretched accommodations, to the indignation of the public and the mortification of Mr. Brocklehurst. He was retained as treasurer, but the management was entrusted to men of more liberal ideas, and a new building on a better site was provided for.

That spring was saddened for me by the death of Helen Burns, a girl of noble intellect and beautiful spirit, bearing with meekness and yet dignity the persecutions visited upon her for minor faults by one of the teachers, Miss Scatcherd. Her friendship and that of the superintendent, Miss Temple, were my solace and delight during that first miserable winter.

My last two years at Lowood were passed as teacher. At the end of that time Miss Temple married and removed to a distant county. Then it was no longer a home to me; in one afternoon I tired of its routine and its narrow life.

I had but one resource. I advertised and was engaged by a Mrs. Fairfax, of Thornfield, near Millcote, as governess for a little French girl, Adèle Varens, a ward of Mr. Rochester, the owner of Thornfield, who was a connection of Mrs. Fairfax by marriage and for whom she was housekeeper. As I afterward learned from her, he had come into the property nine years before on the death of his father and brother, with whom he had quarreled. The cause of this quarrel she did not know, except that these relatives had brought him into a painful position in order to make his fortune, so that the family property might go undivided to the elder brother. Since then Mr. Edward Rochester had led an unsettled life, appearing at Thornfield occasionally without warning and for very brief visits.

Before I had been many days at Thornfield I heard an odd laugh, coming from the third story, above my room—a mirthless laugh, ending in a clamorous peal. When I mentioned it to Mrs. Fairfax she said it must have been Grace Poole, a woman who sewed and assisted the housemaid. Grace proved to be a set, square, middle-aged woman with a hard, plain face, not at all the sort of being I had associated with that tragic laugh—a sound I heard not infrequently afterwards.

Not long after this Mr. Rochester came, accompanied only by his big dog, Pilot. He was perhaps thirty-five, with a dark face, stern features, a heavy brow, and fine dark eyes; on the whole what would be called by most people an ugly man. His manner was changeful, abrupt, sometimes even to roughness, and unconventional. But it put me at ease; I felt no shyness with him. Once when he caught me looking at him he said:

"You examine me, Miss Eyre; do you think me handsome?"

"No, sir." The answer slipped out before I was aware.

"Ah! By my word! there is something singular about you; you have the air of a little *nonnette:* and when one asks you a question you rap out a round rejoinder, which, if not blunt, is at least brusque. What do you mean by it?"

"Sir, I was too plain. I beg your pardon. I ought to have said that tastes differ, that beauty is of no consequence, or something of that sort."

"You ought to have said no such thing! Beauty of no consequence, indeed! And so, under pretense of softening the previous outrage, of stroking and soothing me, you stick a sly penknife under my ear!"

He talked on, asked me if I would let him dispense with conventional forms and phrases, even let him hector me a little, without thinking it arose from insolence.

"I am sure, sir, I should never mistake informality for insolence; one I rather like; the other nothing free-born would submit to, even for a salary."

"Humbug! Most things free-born will submit to anything

for a salary. But I like your answer, despite its inaccuracy. Not three in three thousand raw school-girl governesses would have answered so. Yet, for what I know, you may have intolerable defects to counterbalance your few good points."

"And so may you," I thought; and he read my thought.

"Yes, yes," he said, "I need not be severe on others. Nature meant me to be a good man, Miss Eyre; but circumstances have made me a trite, commonplace sinner, hackneyed in all the poor, petty dissipations with which the rich and worthless try to put on life. I wish I had stood firm, God knows I do! I could reform—I have strength enough yet for that, if—but what is the use of thinking of it, hampered, burdened, cursed as I am?"

"It seems to me that if you tried hard you would in time find it possible to become what you yourself would approve."

"Justly thought, rightly said, Miss Eyre; and at this moment I am paving hell with energy."

"Sir?"

"I am laying down good intentions. I pass a law this moment that they are good and right."

"They cannot be if they require a new statute to legalize them."

"They are. Unheard-of combinations of circumstances demand unheard-of rules."

"That maxim sounds dangerous; it is liable to abuse."

"Sententious age! So it is; but I swear by my household gods to abuse it."

On another occasion he had been telling me how he had taken Adèle when her mother, a French opera-dancer, toward whom he once cherished what he called a *grande passion*, had abandoned her to run away to Italy with a singer.

We were walking in the avenue. He looked up at the Hall. "I like Thornfield," he said, "and yet how long I have abhorred the very thought of it! How I do still abhor——" He stopped and looked up to the battlements with a glare in which pain, shame, ire, impatience, disgust, detestation, seemed holding a quivering conflict. But another feeling triumphed—something hard and cynical, self-willed and resolute.

"At that moment, Miss Eyre, I was arranging a point with my destiny. She dared me to like it. 'I will,' I said, 'I dare like it! I will break obstacles to happiness, to goodness—yes, goodness; I wish to be a better man. As Job's Leviathan broke the spear, hindrances that others count as iron and brass I will esteem but straw and rotten wood.'"

So happy had I now become with the new interest given me by his cordial frankness that I ceased to pine after kindred. His face, so far from being ugly to me, was the object I best liked to see. I believed that his moodiness, his harshness, and his former faults of morality, which he had frankly confessed, had their source in some cruel cross of fate.

That night I heard something groping along the gallery past my door and afterwards that demoniac laugh; a door opened and shut above; then all was still. I dressed hastily and started to go to Mrs. Fairfax, when I saw smoke issuing from Mr. Rochester's door, which was ajar. I opened it; his bed was on fire. I roused him by dashing water over him, after vainly trying to waken him by calling. When he found what had occurred he bade me wait while he went to the third story; and on his return he asked me to say nothing of the incident. I spoke of Grace Poole.

"Just so. Grace Poole. You have guessed it."

As I turned to go, "You have saved my life," he said. "I knew you would do me good in some way at some time. I read it in your eyes the first time I saw you; their expression and smile did not strike delight to my inmost heart for nothing."

Another event added to my wonder that such a person as Grace Poole should be kept in the house. This was a midnight attack with a knife on a Mr. Mason, from the West Indies, who came to visit Mr. Rochester at one time when there was a house-party at Thornfield. This time, too, Mr. Rochester kept everyone in the dark about it excepting me; for I had heard Mr. Mason's cry for help; and he sent Mr. Mason away with a surgeon before anyone was stirring.

The following day Mrs. Reed's coachman came for me. My aunt had had a "stroke" at the news of John's death by suicide. He had ruined his health and wasted his estate in the lowest dissipation. My aunt had called for me, and I went.

I soon discovered that she wanted me, not from any relenting or belated affection, but to give me a letter, dated three years before, from my uncle, John Eyre, of Madeira, asking for my address, as he wished to adopt me and leave me his possessions. She confessed that she had disliked me too much to help me to prosperity, and wrote to him that I had died at Lowood.

"You were born to be my torment," she said. "My last hour is racked by the recollection of a deed which but for you I should never have been tempted to commit."

Living she had hated me; dying she must hate me still. She died that night.

At the time of the house-party before mentioned, it had been regarded as settled that Mr. Rochester was to marry Miss Blanche Ingram, one of the guests; I had told him that I thought Adèle, whom Miss Ingram evidently disliked, should be sent to school before his marriage; that I also wished to be out of the house before that event. He had acquiesced, but told me not to seek another situation, that he would find one for me.

When I returned from Gateshead, the subject came up again. I was anxious to get away. He talked of a place in Ireland he had heard of for me, hectored, excited me, till I almost declared my love for him, with my firm resolve to leave Thornfield before his bride should enter there.

"My bride is here, because my equal is here. Jane, will you marry me?"

I did not answer.

"Do you doubt me, Jane?"

"Entirely."

"Am I a liar in your eyes? What love have I for Miss Ingram? None; and she has none for me. You—I entreat you to accept me."

Now indeed I was convinced of his sincerity and I promised.

"God pardon me!" he said ere long, "and man meddle not with me. I have her and will hold her."

"There is no one to meddle; I have no kindred to interfere."

"No; that is the best of it." Afterward he murmured, "I know my Maker sanctions what I do. For the world's judgment—I wash my hands thereof. For man's opinion—I defy it."

We were to be married in four weeks and go to the Continent.

Meantime, he persisted in buying fine clothes for me, to my unspeakable annoyance. Then my uncle's letter came to my mind. I thought, "If I had a prospect of one day bringing him an accession of fortune, I could better endure to receive everything from him now." I wrote immediately to my uncle, telling him why he had not heard from me before, and that I was to be married and to whom.

We went alone to the church. When the clergyman had uttered the words regarding impediments to the marriage, and was going on to the next sentence, a distinct voice behind us said, "I declare the existence of an impediment."

With a slight start, but turning neither head nor eyes, Mr. Rochester said to the perplexed clergyman, "Proceed."

"I cannot proceed without investigation into what has been asserted and evidence of its truth or falsehood. What is the nature of the impediment?" he then inquired.

"It simply consists in the existence of a previous marriage," said the voice, which belonged to a man standing behind us. "Mr. Rochester has a wife now living."

Challenged to prove it, he read an affirmation signed Richard Mason, setting forth the marriage of Edward Fairfax Rochester to Bertha Mason at Spanish Town, Jamaica, fifteen years before, and to prove that she was yet living he called forward Richard Mason himself.

"She is now living at Thornfield Hall. I saw her there last April."

"Impossible!" said Mr. Wood, the clergyman. "I have never heard of a Mrs. Rochester at Thornfield Hall!"

"No, by God!" muttered Mr. Rochester. "I took good care that no one should hear of it. Enough," he said aloud. "Wood, take off your surplice; John Green, leave the church; there will be no wedding to-day."

He continued hardily and recklessly: "Bigamy is an ugly word! I meant, however, to be a bigamist; but fate or Providence has checked me. I have been married and the woman lives. She is mad; her mother, the Creole, was a mad woman and a drunkard, as I found after my marriage; for they were silent on family secrets before. Bertha copied her parent in both points. Oh, my experience has been heavenly! I had a charming partner, pure, wise, modest! Briggs, Wood, Mason, I invite you all to come to the house and see *my wife!* You shall see what I was cheated into espousing, and judge whether I had a right to break the compact and seek sympathy with something at least human. This girl knew no more than you, Wood, of the disgusting secret; she never dreamt she was going to be entrapped into a feigned union with a defrauded wretch, already bound to a bad, mad, embruted partner. Come, all of you!"

Still holding me fast, he left the church, the three gentlemen following, went to the Hall, led the way to the third story and let us look at the repulsive lunatic in Grace Poole's charge, who was running back and forth like a hyena. She sprang at him and grappled his throat viciously; he would not strike but wrestled with her until he mastered her arms and tied her down with a cord Grace handed him. With a smile both acrid and desolate he turned and sent us away.

I learned from the solicitor that my uncle had received my letter when Mr. Mason, with whom he had a business connection was with him; and, having heard Mason speak of a Mr. Rochester, had mentioned to him the intended marriage. On learning the facts he had implored Mr. Mason to go to England and prevent it. He himself was too ill, and, Mr. Briggs thought, very near death.

They departed; and I went to my room to wrestle with my misery. When I saw Mr. Rochester again he showed such deep remorse, such unchanged love, that I could but grant, not outwardly, but in my heart, the forgiveness he asked.

"You know I am a scoundrel, Jane?"

"Yes, sir."

"I was wrong to attempt to deceive you. I should have appealed to your magnanimity. I should have asked you to accept my pledge of fidelity and to give me yours. Jane, give it me now."

I was silent. I was experiencing an ordeal. Terrible moment—full of struggle, blackness, burning! No human being that ever lived could wish to be loved better than I was loved, and him who thus loved me I absolutely worshiped; and I must renounce love and idol. One drear word comprised my intolerable duty—"Depart!"

"Jane, you understand what I want of you? Just this promise: 'I will be yours, Mr. Rochester.'"

"Mr. Rochester, I will *not* be yours."

He besought me to think what his life would be without me. "Is it better to drive a fellow-creature to despair than to transgress a mere human law, no man being injured by it?—for you have no relatives or friends to offend by living with me."

This was true; and while he spoke my very conscience and reason turned traitors against me and charged me with crime in resisting him. They spoke almost as loud as feeling, and that clamored wildly, "Oh, comply! Think of his misery, his danger when left alone; remember his headlong nature; consider the recklessness following on despair; soothe him; save him; love him; tell him you love him and will be his. Who cares for you? Who will be injured by what you do?"

Still indomitable was the reply: "I care for myself. The more solitary, the more friendless, the more unsustained I am, the more I will respect myself. I will keep the law given by God, sanctioned by man. I will hold to the principles received by me when I was sane and not mad, as I am now. Laws and principles are not for the times when there is no temptation; they are for such moments as this, when body and soul rise in mutiny against their rigor; stringent are they; inviolate they shall be. If at my individual convenience I might break them, what would be their worth? They have a worth—so I have always believed; and if I cannot believe it now, it is because I am insane, quite insane, with my veins running fire and my heart beating faster than I can count its throbs. Preconceived opinions, foregone determinations, are all I have at this hour to stand by; there I plant my foot."

I did. He read it in my countenance. His fury was wrought to the highest; he stormed and pleaded. I bade him farewell.

"God bless you, my dear master!" I said. "God keep you from harm and wrong, direct you, solace you, reward you well for your past kindness to me!" And I left him.

The next morning early I stole away, not knowing whither, only to be gone from Thornfield. I had but twenty shillings; I took a coach as far as that would carry me. When I left it I forgot my little packet containing my linen and some articles of jewelry. Then I wandered about for two days, tasting food but twice. I slept in the open air two nights. I applied for work without success.

When I was spent with fatigue and starvation I was taken in by a family at whose door I had fallen, after having been repulsed by their servant. When I recovered they urged me to stay till I could find some employment. In a short time Mary and Diana Rivers and I had become warm friends. They were governesses on a vacation at their home, all their father had left them of the property he had lost in an investment which had been recommended to him by his brother-in-law. He had thought that, though they had quarreled, the uncle would make up the loss to the children by his will. But while I was there they heard that he had died and left everything to a cousin they had never seen.

Their brother, St. John Rivers, a clergyman, gave me employment in a school in his parish not far away. I had given my name as Jane Elliott, telling them it was not my real name, and that I could tell them little of my story. But when Mr. Briggs wrote to St. John, asking his help to find the heiress of their uncle, Jane Eyre, who had disappeared under such and such circumstances, my identity was easily guessed.

I was, then, the possessor of £20,000, which I insisted upon dividing into four equal parts and sharing with my cousins. As it was, in a way, an act of justice, they gracefully consented to accept it.

I had settled down contentedly to live with Mary and Diana, when their brother, a man of ability and many fine qualities, but hard, stern and ascetic, who was preparing to go to India as a missionary, asked me to go with him as his fellow-laborer and his wife—not that he loved me, or professed to, but because he thought I could be useful. I offered to go as a fellow-laborer, not as his wife. That, he said, was impossible. Under the pressure of his importunities, I began to think it might be God's will and my duty.

Alone with him one Monday night when all the house was still, I was about to yield, when something like an electric shock passed through me, and I heard a voice, Edward Rochester's voice, "Jane! Jane! Jane!" in pain and woe.

"I am coming! Wait for me! I will come!" I cried, and rushed into the garden. "Where are you?" But all was still.

After this I could not rest. I set out for Thornfield. Arrived there, I saw—a blackened ruin! At the inn I heard that the Hall had been set on fire the previous autumn by the lunatic. Mr. Rochester went to the roof to rescue his mad wife, who stood there shouting. He was heard to call, "Bertha!" was seen to approach her, when she screamed, sprang, and in an instant lay dead on the pavement. As Mr. Rochester came down, a burning beam fell upon him, crushing one hand and destroying his sight. He was now living at Ferndean Manor, a desolate spot, attended by two of his old servants.

When I arrived at Ferndean Pilot knew me; but it was long before his blind master could believe that I was a reality, not a dream. A few days passed and I had satisfied him that I still loved him, and had put aside his scruples about attaching my life to one so scarred and crippled, so wrecked as he.

"Jane," he said, "you think me an irreligious dog, but my heart swells now with gratitude to God. I did wrong. I would have sullied my innocent flower; He snatched it from me. I almost cursed the dispensation. Divine justice pursued its course; disasters came thick upon me; I was forced to pass through the valley of the shadow of death. Of late, I began to see the hand of God in my doom, to experience remorse.

"Last Monday night a singular mood came over me. I had long had the impression that since I could nowhere find you, you must be dead. I asked God to take me from this life, asked if I had not been long enough desolate, afflicted, tormented. I longed for you, and I called 'Jane Jane! Jane!' and a voice—your voice—replied, 'I am coming! Wait for me! I will come!' and a moment after, 'Where are you?' You no doubt were at that hour in unconscious sleep; perhaps your soul had wandered from its cell to comfort mine; for those were your accents—they were yours!"

SHIRLEY (1849)

Charlotte Brontë began to write *Shirley* shortly after the publication of *Jane Eyre*, but work on it was interrupted by the illness and death of her brother and her sisters, so that it was not published until October, 1849. The inspiration of many a character in *Shirley* is from some one or other of the author's acquaintances. She herself said that many traits of the heroine were drawn from her sister Emily; that Shirley Keeldar was what Emily Brontë would have been had she had a prosperous and happy life. The incident of the mad dog was taken from an adventure of Emily's, who behaved as Shirley is described as doing; and Emily had a companion in her dog, Keeper, even as the heiress had in Tartar. Caroline Helstone is a picture of an intimate friend, Ellen Nussey. Rose and Jessie Yorke are portraits of Mary and Martha Taylor, school friends; Martha died in Brussels in 1842, while Charlotte was a teacher in Madame Héger's school, and Mary some years later went to live in New Zealand. The boys of the Yorke family, Mrs. Pryor, and the three curates had their prototypes near Haworth. During the author's schooldays at Roe Head she was in the district of the Luddite riots, of which she heard accounts from her acquaintances; and from Miss Wooler, her schoolmistress, she heard the story of the burning of a mill that may have suggested the account of the assault on Hollow's Mill given in the story.

N 1811 conditions in Yorkshire mill towns were in a state of unrest. The "Orders in Council" had closed the American market to English clothiers, and the Continental markets were so glutted that nothing remained but to fill warehouses in the hope of better times to come. The manufacturers discharged many hands because of the business depression and the introduction of machinery. Consequently, the clothiers were unpopular and perhaps the most so was Robert Gérard Moore. His father had been a partner in a prosperous firm of Yorkshire clothiers and had married a daughter of the house of Gérard of Antwerp. In the shock of the French Revolution, the house of Gérard, with its allied English firm, was ruined. When Robert rented Hollow's Mill he was regarded as a semi-foreigner; when he proved himself a progressionist he was abominated. It galled him that his desire for progress was thwarted by his limited capital, and he did not deliberate

much as to whether his own advance was or was not prejudicial
to others. Then the time came when the new machinery for
which he had risked the last of his capital was destroyed: and
the steps he took toward punishing those guilty rendered the
people of Briarfield more bitter against him than before.

With the rector of Briarfield lived his niece Caroline, the
child of parents separated soon after her birth. Her mother
was the half-sister of Robert's father, her father was Mr.
Helstone's brother—a man of a character best not recalled.
Caroline was at this time eighteen and had the dower of beauty;
her shape was girlish and pliant; her face was expressive and
gentle; her eyes were handsome and spoke a winning language.
She had a pretty mouth, a delicate skin and a picturesque
profusion of brown curls. The rector was little suited to have
the care of a young girl, and Caroline's reticence allowed her to
make few acquaintances, so that her life had been dull and
sad till two years before, when her cousins, Robert and Hortense,
came to Briarfield. The daily sharing of French lessons with
Hortense brightened her life; and as time passed she realized
that in the existence of another inmate of Hollow's cottage
she had pent all her universe. Occasionally she remained to
spend a delightful evening, when Robert was wont to relax
and become almost animated, gentle and friendly. Yes, he
felt Caroline's charm, but he was ambitious and she was poor;
so, after one of these social evenings, he became colder than
ever. Yet the day after the destruction of the machinery he
asked his cousin to remain for tea; and so kind was he that
Caroline returned home joyously excited. She felt sure the
morrow would not show Robert cold and chill: her expectations seemed warranted, and the foundations on which they
rested appeared solid.

"When people love, the next step is they marry," was her
argument. "I love Robert and I am sure Robert loves me;
I have thought so many a time; to-day I *felt* it."

In undiminished gladness she met Robert next day. He made
his greeting brief; it was cousin-like, brother-like, friend-like,
anything but lover-like: the nameless charm of last night had
left his manner. That evening he came to the rectory; her
diffident, downcast air must have shown him how the check of

the morning had operated; and now was the opportunity to carry out his determination with effect. He asked her to give a message to her uncle in regard to the apprehension of one of the destroyers of his machinery. Caroline begged him not to prosecute and thereby make himself a target for revenge.

"Don't fear for me, Lina."

"How can I help it? If anything happened—"

"Nothing will happen. To speak in your own language, there is a Providence above all—is there not?"

"Yes, dear Robert. May He guard you!"

"You pray for me sometimes?"

"Not *sometimes*, Robert."

"So I have imagined. When a man lives only to make money it seems odd to utter his name in a prayer—that a good, pure heart should harbor him. If I could guide that benignant heart, I should counsel it to exclude one who professes no higher aim in life than the patching up of his fortune, the wiping from his escutcheon of the stain of bankruptcy."

Shortly after this Robert and Mr. Helstone came to a decisive rupture on political questions, and the latter intimated to his niece that her intercourse with Hollow's cottage must end. She acquiesced in his mandate because it coincided with her own previous judgment. Caroline mused over the mystery of "business" and tried to comprehend its perplexities, liabilities, duties, exactions; and she contrived to get a glimpse of the light of truth. "Different, indeed," she concluded, "is Robert's mental condition from mine; I think only of him; he has no leisure to think of me. The feeling called love is and has been for two years the predominant emotion of my heart; quite other feelings absorb his reflections and govern his faculties."

In spite of her efforts, the heaviness of a broken spirit and of pining moods and palsying faculties overshadowed her buoyant youth. Yet she refused tamely to succumb; she had native strength in her girl's heart and she used it; but daily she grew more wan and joyless. A deep, anxious yearning to know her mother strengthened daily; but with the desire was coupled a dread—if she knew her could she love her? Never had she heard that mother praised; and this suggested the conclusion that it was, perhaps, better never to know than to know and not like her.

Shortly after Caroline's intercourse with Hollow's cottage ceased, Fieldhead, a large house near Briarfield, was opened to receive the heiress who owned it, as well the property of Hollow's mill. Shirley Keeldar possessed a graceful form and a face naturally pale, but intelligent and of varied expression; her eyes were of the darkest gray—transparent, pure, neutral gray; and her hair was of the darkest brown. Her features were distinguished, mobile and speaking; but their changes were not to be understood, nor interpreted, all at once. Although she made the acquaintance of the families round, it appeared she found none of them very congenial; but after their first meeting she frequently sought Caroline, who soon acknowledged that her new acquaintances were of value to her; for Mrs. Pryor, Shirley's former governess, who lived with her, seemed as well disposed to cultivate her friendship as did the young heiress. Shirley's predilection increased greatly when she discovered that her own way of thinking and talking was understood and responded to by Caroline, whose tastes too were like her own. Shirley had just come of age and was glad to be independent in property; but her exaltation was singularly inoffensive and her serious thoughts tended elsewhere. To admire the great, reverence the good, and be joyous with the happy, was the bent of her soul; she mused on the means of following this bent far oftener than she pondered on her social superiority. She was fearless, warm-hearted and sympathetic; quite self-possessed, and always spirited and easy; conscious of her social importance, yet never presuming upon it; it was enough to give one courage just to look at her. In her frequent conferences with Robert on business connected with the mill she took a tone at once animated and dignified, confidential and self-respecting: she was all interest, life and earnestness, but there was nothing coquettish in her demeanor: but she seemed happy in conversing with him, and her joy appeared twofold—a joy of the past and present, of memory and of hope. It was painful to Caroline to witness these interviews, but she felt that Shirley was the wife for Robert—rich, youthful and lively; Shirley was wealth and power while she herself was but poverty and incapacity: she believed that they loved each other and tried to resign herself to the thought of being forgotten by both.

In the summer an uncle, aunt and two cousins of Shirley's arrived at Fieldhead, and Caroline, disinclined to seek her friend in the midst of her fine relatives, was once more limited to the gray rectory. During a walk one evening she caught a fever in whose symptoms there seemed at first no violence. But when she had been ill a fortnight Mrs. Pryor, who had visited her daily, installed herself in the sick-room. Thereafter loneliness and gloom were banished from Caroline's bedside; protection and solace sat there instead: yet she fell into a condition of prostration. One evening she said to Mrs. Pryor:

"I believe grief is and always has been my worst ailment. I sometimes think if an abundant gush of happiness came on me, I could revive yet."

"Do you wish to live?"

"I have no object in life."

"Do you love me, Caroline?"

"Very much—very truly."

"Then if you love me it will be neither shock nor pain for you to know that you are mine—my daughter—my own child."

"Is what I hear true—no dream? My own mother! Is she one I can be so fond of as I can of you? If you are my mother, the world is all changed to me. Surely I can live—"

"You must recover. We have been long parted; I return now to cherish you."

Mrs. Pryor explained that when she saw in her infant daughter the features of its father she feared they hid a nature like his, which she dared not encounter after the sufferings of her married life.

It was not until a hot, dry August gave way to cool, pleasant weather that there was hope, that a genuine convalescence began. When Caroline was able to walk to Fieldhead, she saw there Robert's younger brother Louis, who had recently arrived with his pupil, Henry Sympson. He was not so handsome a man as Robert, but one felt that he had a nature slower and more benignant than his brother's: he had the air of a man whose faculties were walled up in him, and were unmurmuring in their captivity. To Caroline's surprise she found that to Shirley her cousin seemed as much a mere teacher, as little a man, as to the correct Misses Sympson: she was not, perhaps, haughty to him, but she barely recognized him. At first Caroline believed him to be a stranger to Shirley and excused her prejudice on that ground; but soon she learned that the heiress had been, during a two years' residence at Sympson Grove, Louis' pupil in French. Habitually she bore herself toward the tutor with strange alternations of cold reserve and docile respect; now sweeping past him in all the dignity of the moneyed heiress, and anon accosting him as abashed school-girls are wont to accost their stern professors.

One morning a sudden change came over Shirley. She had been in one of her sunniest moods, then within a brief ten minutes a new and peculiar shadow came over her countenance that did not pass like a light summer cloud. During the following fortnight a strange quietude settled over her looks, her movements, her very voice. Soon it became evident that to notice this change was to annoy her. She declared herself perfectly well and made an effort to appear gay, but her face grew thin, her large eyes looked hollow. At last Henry told his tutor how troubled he had been by a recent conversation with Shirley, in which she told him that she had made her will and explained to him its provisions and her reasons for making them. From this and from her manner, though she never referred to her health, the boy feared his cousin thought she was going to die. When Louis had heard what Henry had to tell, he sent his pupil to ask Shirley to come to the schoolroom. When alone he said to himself:

"I can speak to Henry as if, in my eyes, she and he were both children. Let me see if I can keep up the same rôle with her. I am poor and it behooves me to look to my self-respect—not to compromise an inch of it. A strange, sweet ecstacy steals through my veins at moments; I'll not encourage—I'll not remember it."

When Shirley came in, a soft youthful shyness depressed her eyelids and mantled her cheek.

Louis explained the reason of his desire to see her and she declared that her health was perfect.

"Do you not think it wrong to affirm and reaffirm what is substantially untrue?"

"I say I am well."

"But why, then, are you altered? Your spirits are always at ebb: besides there is a nervous alarm in your eye."

"Mr. Moore, you have exactly hit it. I am nervous."

"You nervous! Yes: and if Miss Keeldar is nervous it is not without cause. The ailment is not physical. Your pain is mental. I wish I had the gift of persuasion and could incline you to speak willingly. I believe confession in your case would be half equivalent to cure."

"No," said Shirley abruptly, "I wish that were at all probable."

For some moments she sat in reflection, then she lifted her eye, to his: he looked calm, strong, trustworthy.

"I had better tell you than my relatives. You can bear a little shock?"

"A great one, if necessary."

Moore, though tortured with suspense, did not demand quick explanation; his tranquillity tranquillized Shirley.

"Look here, Mr. Moore." She showed a small healed indentation in her arm. "Small as that is, it has taken my sleep away, and made me nervous, thin and foolish. One day about three weeks ago I lingered in the lane after a walk with my cousins. Phoebe, one of Mr. Wynne's pointers, came running up with her head down, her tongue hanging out; she looked as if bruised and beaten all over. I called her and when I attempted to pat her head, she turned and bit my arm so as to draw blood, and ran on. Directly the keeper came up and told me he was after Phoebe to shoot her, for she was raging mad."

"And you sought no help? You did nothing?"

"Yes, I walked into the laundry. I took an Italian iron from the fire and applied the glowing tip to my arm: it cauterized the little wound."

"You apprehend the effects of the virus? You anticipate an indefinitely threatening, dreadful doom?"

She bowed.

"Make yourself easy; I am easy, though I value your life as much as I do my own chance of happiness in eternity."

"I want your promise."

"Dictate."

"You know, in case the worst I have feared should happen, nobody in the house will be self-possessed but you: now promise to befriend me—to keep them all away: lock the chamber door against the surgeons; and lastly, if I give trouble, with your own hand administer to me such a sure dose of laudanum as shall leave no mistake. *Promise to do this.*"

"I promise all you ask without comment, without reservation."

"That is good in you," she said, looking up at him as he bent above her and smiling.

Moore leaned on the back of her chair and after a prolonged pause he said:

"Is the shadow gone?"

"Wholly. As I was two hours since, and as I am now, are two different states of existence."

After this Shirley's spirits resumed their serenity. Louis found means to relieve her from every nervous apprehension; and, indeed, from the moment of giving him her confidence, every fear seemed to have taken wing. On inquiry he found that probably only ill-usage had driven the dog from home, and, right or wrong, it is certain that the bite proved innocuous.

One evening when Shirley and her guests were out at dinner Louis wandered through the parlors till he came to a little work-table with a desk upon it and a chair near it.

"Her mark; here she has been, called away in haste, doubtless, and forgetting to return and put all to rights. Why does she leave fascination in her footprints? Whence did she acquire the gift to be heedless and never offend? There is always something to chide in her and the reprimand never settles in displeasure on the heart. Am I muttering? Stop that!"

He drew a chair opposite that near the work-stand, sat down, and took out a small book of blank paper in which he began to write in a cramped, compact hand.

"I used rather to like solitude, to court her serenely. Since that day I called S. to me in the schoolroom and she opened the trouble of her mind to me—asked my protection—appealed to my strength, I abhor solitude. What a child she is sometimes! I see her now, looking up into my face, and confessing that she was not so self-sufficing, so independent of sympathy as people thought. She imagined I despised her. Despised her! I worship her perfections: but it is her faults, or at least her foibles, that bring her near me. All her little failings would, I know, be a source of irritation to my brother Robert; if they vex me, it is a most pleasurable vexation; I delight to find her at fault, and were I always resident with her, I am aware she would be no niggard in thus ministering to my enjoyments. She would just give me something to do: a theme for my tutor lectures.

"What a difference there is between S. and that pearl C. H.! Caroline, I fancy, is the soul of conscientious punctuality and nice exactitude; she would precisely suit the domestic habits of a certain fastidious kinsman of mine; so delicate, dextrous, quaint, quick and quiet; she would suit Robert; but what could I do with anything so faultless? *She* is my equal; poor as myself; she is certainly pretty; but where is there anything to alter, anything to endure, anything to reprimand, to be anxious about? My wife, if I ever marry, must stir my great frame with a sting now and then; she must furnish a use for her husband's vast mass of patience."

"Oh, my pupil! Never shall I do more than see, and worship, and wish for thee!"

In the early days of Caroline's illness Robert Moore had gone to Birmingham and then to London and all Briarfield wondered at his absence, prolonged till late October. Shortly after his return he was one evening shot and wounded severely by an avenger of the leaders in a mob attack on his mill, whom he had pursued with relentless severity. Through all November and into December he lay in grave danger at the house of his friend Mr. Yorke; but at last he was convalescent and able to return to Hollow's cottage. The first evening there he persuaded Hortense to send for Caroline. After tea he said: "Cary, I must tell you that I wanted to marry Miss Keeldar for the sake of her money, though I had not an emotion of tenderness for her. I suppose I was truly tempted by the mere gilding of the bait. Caroline, what a noble fellow your Robert is—so disinterested!"

"But not perfect; he made a great blunder once, and we will say no more about it."

"And shall we not despise him in our heart?"

"Never! We will give no scorn—only affection."

"Which won't satisfy, I warn you of that. Something far stronger, sweeter, warmer, will be demanded one day. Be calm, Lina, I have no intention, because I have no right, to perturb your mind now; don't look as if you would leave me; we will make no more agitating allusions."

It was near Christmas and the Sympsons were departing, when Louis again discoursed with his little blank book.

"She is lovelier than ever. Since that little cloud was dispelled, all the temporary waste and wanness have vanished. This morning I found her with Henry in the schoolroom and I dared not only *wish* but *will* an interview with her, and dismissed Henry. It was not my intention to utter one word of love. Presumptuous I never have been; presumptuous I never will be; rather than seem selfish and interested, I would resolutely rise and seek, on the other side of the globe, a new life. My design was to take of her a near scrutiny—to know *what* I was leaving; therefore I spoke to move her, and she was moved. At length her eyes emitted an eager flash; her lips opened; she made a movement all haughtiness and fire and impulse. She turned to leave me. Could I now let her part as she had always parted from me? All the encumbrance of doubt, all the rubbish of indecision must be removed at once, and the plain truth must be ascertained. She must take her part and tell me which it was. I must take mine and adhere to it. What change I underwent, I cannot explain; but out of her emotion passed into me a new spirit. I neither was crushed nor elated by her lands and gold. I saw only herself.

"My pupil, I have to tell you that for four years you have been growing into your tutor's heart, and that you are rooted there now. I have to declare that you have bewitched me, in spite of sense and experience and difference of station and estate; you have so shown me your faults and your virtues that I love you—love you with my life and strength."

"Well, Mr. Moore, what then?" was the answer in a tone that faltered.

"Am I to die without you, or am I to live for you?"

"Do as you please; far be it from me to dictate your choice."

"Reply, Shirley, my pupil, my sovereign—reply."

"Die without me, if you will. Live for me if you dare."

"I dare live for you and with you, from this hour till my death. I will never let you go; I have chosen my wife."

"Dear Louis, be faithful to me; never leave me. I don't care for life, unless I pass it at your side."

Then she gave me a change.

"But sir, at your peril, never again name such sordid things as money, or poverty, or inequality."

My face grew hot. I did once more wish I were not so poor, or she were not so rich. She saw the transient misery; and then, indeed, she caressed me. Blent with torment, I experienced rapture.

"Mr. Moore," said she looking up with sweet, open, earnest countenance, "teach me and help me to be good. I do not ask you to take off my shoulders all the cares and duties of property; but I ask you to share the burden. Be my companion through life; be my guide where I am ignorant; be my master where I am faulty; be my friend always."

"So help me God, I will."

Caroline was asked to act as bridesmaid that summer, but fortune decreed otherwise. One June evening she said to Robert:

"Will the repeal of the orders do you good—immediate good?"

"The repeal of the 'Orders in Council' saves me. Now—now, I can seek a wife. Will Caroline, who meekly hopes to be forgiven as she forgives, will she pardon all I have made her suffer? Will she forget what she knows of my poor ambition—my sordid schemes? Will she let me expiate these things? Will she suffer me to prove that, as I once deserted cruelly, I can now love faithfully, treasure tenderly? Is Caroline mine?"

"Caroline is yours."

VILLETTE (1853)

The writing of *Villette*, the last of Charlotte Brontë's novels, was much delayed by the author's failing health during the winter of 1851-2; but it was completed in November, 1852, and published in the following January. The scene of this novel is taken from the school of Monsieur and Madame Héger, near Brussels, where Charlotte and Emily Brontë passed the year 1842 as pupils, and where Charlotte was the teacher of English in 1843. In this story are transcribed many of her experiences as teacher; and on the character of M. Héger is founded that of Monsieur Paul Emanuel. Her father's wish was that *Villette* should end happily, but the idea of M. Paul's death at sea was so strongly fixed in the author's plan of the story that she could but veil the close and leave interpretation to the reader. In a letter to her publisher she speaks of Lucy Snowe, whose lines she never meant to appoint in pleasant places, as both morbid and weak at times, partly because her character was not of unmixed strength, partly because of her life, and declares that she must not marry Dr. John, whose wife must be young, rich, and pretty, for he must be made very happy. In reply to a criticism that the interest is latterly transferred to a new set of characters, she said: "It is not pleasant, and it will probably be found as unwelcome to the reader as it was, in a sense, compulsory upon the writer. The spirit of romance would have indicated another course, far more flowery and inviting; it would have fashioned a paramount hero, kept faithfully with him, and made him supremely worshipful; he should have been an idol, and not a mute, unresponding idol either; but this would have been unlike real life—inconsistent with truth—at variance with probability."

 HEN I was about thirteen my godmother, Mrs. Bretton, came in person to claim me from the kinsfolk with whom at that time was fixed my permanent residence, for my semi-annual visit to Bretton. I believe she then plainly saw events coming whose very shadow I hardly guessed; yet of which the faint suspicion sufficed to impart a settled sadness, and made me glad to change scene and society; for at my godmother's side time flowed smoothly. The charm of variety there was not, nor the excitement of incident; but I liked peace so well and stimulus so little that when the latter came I almost felt it a disturbance and wished it had held aloof. This stay was in part enlivened by the presence of the daughter of a connection of the late Dr. Bretton, Paulina Home, a strange,

quaint, self-controlled, fairy-like child of six, who at first betrayed in her silent fretting for her father that one-idea'd nature, that monomaniac tendency, which I have ever thought the most unfortunate with which man or woman can be cursed. After the return home of Mrs. Bretton's son, Graham—at this time a handsome, spoiled, whimsical boy of sixteen—Paulina ceased to fret and became absorbed in him. He regarded her as an amusing companion and playmate when nothing else offered, whereas she regarded him with a devotion that made me wonder how she would bear the shocks and repulses, the humiliations and desolations prepared for all flesh.

Little did I think that I was never again to visit Bretton. Eight years filled with troubles passed, and impediments raised by others had cut off my intercourse with my godmother, though I heard that her property had been lost and that her son, having adopted a profession, had taken his mother away.

I was left at this time dependent on my own exertions, and I became the companion of Miss Marchmont, a woman of fortune, a crippled invalid. At first the idea of living in that close room, a watcher of suffering, sometimes the butt of a temper sorely tried by physical and mental anguish, appeared almost intolerable, in spite of the life I had lately led; but soon I found that I could respect my mistress's character, wait on her with calm and sympathy, even regard her with attachment. I became content in my world of two hot, close rooms, with a crippled old woman my all, and I could have crawled on thus for twenty years; but Fate, with whom I had tried to compromise, would not be pacified so, would not let me escape occasional great agonies by submission to a whole life of privation and small pains.

One February night came a voice near the house, heard by all, but translated, perhaps, by only one. After a calm winter, storms were ushering in the spring, and the wind that had wailed all day took on a new tone—an accent keen, piercing, almost articulate. Three times in my life events had taught me that these strange accents in a storm—this restless, hopeless cry—denote a state of the atmosphere unpropitious to life. That night Miss Marchmont's doom came; quietly and painlessly she died, and I was once more alone, the possessor of fifteen pounds, of health worn but not broken, and of spirit in similar condition.

Impelled to seek something beyond the wilderness where I had dwelt, I set out for London. I made no plans; but Fate took me in her strong hand, and within a few days I found myself in the city of Villette, capital of Labassecour, as English *gouvernante* to the children of Madame Beck, proprietress of a *Pensionnat des Demoiselles*, a boarding and day-school for young ladies.

Madame Beck was a very great and capable woman. She possessed high administrative powers and ruled to perfection a large establishment, without effort or bustle. Always occupied, rarely busy, she controlled by a system of surveillance, of espionage. On her *souliers de silence* she glided ghostlike through the house, watching and spying everywhere, peering through every key-hole, listening behind every door. Yet not all her system was bad, for nothing could be better than her arrangements for her pupils; in these her method was easy, liberal, salutary, and rational. She was charitable but merciless; of sympathy she had none, and, as interest was the master-key of her existence, it was useless to rely on her beyond the point where it was to her interest to be trustworthy. No one could browbeat her, nothing could irritate her nerves, exhaust her patience or overreach her astuteness. She was wise, firm, faithless, secret, crafty, passionless; watchful and inscrutable; acute and insensate, and withal perfectly decorous.

I was not left long as the instructress of the children. Madame had watched me, tested me, examined all I had, until I believe she esteemed herself cognizant of all I was; then she made me the English teacher in the school. I got on in my new sphere very well after some sharp contests, and by degrees I acquired fluency and freedom in the French language; but I had little intercourse with any of my pupils save one—Ginevra Fanshawe, an English girl, who had a habit of making me convenient and whom I tolerated, although I do not know why, unless it was because of a certain directness of speech which was the sole preservative ingredient of a character otherwise not formed to keep. I tried the other teachers, three, and chose solitude.

The Professor of Literature in the Rue Fossette, who filled the chair of *belles-lettres* in the College, was Monsieur Paul Emanuel, a dark little man, pungent and austere; to me he seemed a harsh apparition with his close-shorn black head, his broad, sallow brow, his thin cheek, his wide and quivering nostril, his thorough glance and hurried bearing. On examination-day M. Paul did his best to make my part easy, and we parted friends when the school broke up. The pupils scattered for the long vacation; Madame joined her children at the seaside; the house was left quite vacant but for me, one servant, and an imbecile pupil.

Never shall I forget that vacation! How long were the days! How vast and void seemed the desolate premises! My spirits had long been gradually sinking; now that the prop of employment was withdrawn, they went down fast. To look forward was not to hope; the dumb future gave no inducement to bear present evil in reliance on future good. A despairing resignation to reach the end of all things earthly often oppressed me. The first three weeks were hot, fair and dry, but the fourth and fifth were tempestuous and wet, and that change made a cruel impression on me, crushed me with a deadlier paralysis; my nervous system could hardly support what it had for many days and nights to undergo in that huge empty house. I often walked all day, through the burning noon and the arid afternoon and the dusk evening, and came back with moonrise. At last I took perforce to my bed, and for nine dark and wet days, bewildered with sounding hurricane, I lay in a strange fever of nerves and blood. Sleep came but once, then in anger bringing an avenging dream that wrung my whole frame with an unknown anguish, and conferred a nameless experience that had the hue, the mien, the terror, the very tone of a visitation from eternity. One evening—and I was not delirious—I dressed myself and forth I set. The bells of a church arrested me in passing; I went in and knelt with others. When the *salut* was over a few of the worshipers remained to confess. I watched. A pale lady near me whispered:

"Go you now; I am not quite prepared."

Mechanically I rose and went. I knew what I was about. To take this step could not make me more wretched; it might soothe me. The priest received me kindly when I told him that I was not a Catholic. The relief of communication in an ear human and sentient, yet consecrated, did me good and I was already solaced when he bade me go, saying that he was not prepared with counsel fitting the circumstances, but that, believing me made for his faith, he would not lose sight of me; and as I withdrew he told me to come to his house next day. As I glided away I did not contemplate venturing again within his reach. I knew myself not wholly impervious to his sentimental French kindness, and I knew how it would have ended; but of that benign old priest I must ever retain a grateful recollection, for he was kind when I needed kindness. As I left the church I turned as I thought to the Rue Fossette, but soon discovered that I had lost my way; then suddenly I seemed to pitch headlong into an abyss. I remember no more.

I had met frequently, during his attendance on Madame Beck's children, a young English physician, always addressed as Dr. John, whom I had long ago recognized as John Graham Bretton. He saw in me only Mademoiselle Lucie, as I was called, not the Lucy Snowe he had known in his boyhood. When I became conscious I learned that Père Silas, the old priest, had followed me, and when I fainted had summoned Dr. Bretton, who was passing, and who, recognizing me, had brought me to La Terrasse, where he and his mother dwelt. When I made myself known I was joyously welcomed by my godmother; and the remainder of my vacation was spent in happiest surroundings, with pleasantest companionship. In these weeks I gained ample knowledge of John Bretton and came to realize the fineness of his nature, the outlines of which were shaped with breadth and vigor, though the details embraced workmanship of almost feminine delicacy. But because the sympathetic faculty was not prominent in him—for to feel and to seize quickly another's feelings are separate properties—his acute sensibility was seldom betrayed save when some over-sharp contact with his nerves betrayed by its effects the exquisite perfection of this gift of sensibility. He was a kind, generous man, but one must make his needs known.

When I returned to the *pensionnat*, having admitted to Dr.

Bretton that I should feel the solitariness of my life there after the pleasure of my visit, he offered to write to me. Reason told me not to expect this, not to build on such a promise, told me not to reply, or but briefly, if he should write; to indulge no delight of heart, no expansion of feeling, no genial intercommunication. I groaned under Reason's bitter sternness; always has she been toward me vindictive, envenomed, and long ago should I have died of her savage, ceaseless blows, but for that kinder Power who holds my secret and sworn allegiance. Yet in spite of Reason, as the weeks passed and letters came regularly, a new creed became mine—a belief in happiness. Vital comfort they brought, and though after years showed them to be but kind, pleasing letters because composed by one well-pleased, when I first tasted their elixir, it seemed juice of a divine vintage. Yet I disclaim with utmost scorn every sneaking suspicion of what are called "warmer feelings"; for women do not entertain these where throughout an acquaintance they never have been cheated of the conviction that to do so would be to commit a mortal absurdity. Nobody ever launches into Love unless he has seen or dreamed the rising of Hope's star over Love's troubled waters. I felt a closely-clinging and deeply-honoring attachment that wished to attract to itself all that was painful in the destiny of its object; but Reason rightly prevented all expression of such feeling.

I had received five of these treasured letters when there came a blank, and for seven weeks I had no letter, no word, no token from La Terrasse; then I was taken by my godmother for a half-holiday with her. I found as fellow-guests the Mr. Home of Bretton days, who had succeeded to the title and estates of a French relative and was now the Count de Bassompierre, and his daughter, in whom the promise of interest and grace had become beauty, a refined and tender charm that lay in a subdued glow from the soul outward. I observed the intercourse of Paulina and Dr. Bretton; it was now seven weeks since they had last met, and I saw that the past decade had in no wise lessened the sympathy between them, and that both were natures of which the mutual influence is that the more they say the more they have to say.

From this time I went out a good deal to La Terrasse and

to see Paulina, in whom intimate intercourse, close inspection, disclosed only what was delicate, intelligent and sincere; therefore my regard for her lay deep. No more letters came to me, and I realized that no more would come. Paulina and Dr. Bretton loved, and I, from that infatuation of egotism that there is in lovers, was forced to be a witness of their happiness.

In all this time I saw much of M. Paul, and was treated now with capricious irritability and suspicion, now with kindness and helpfulness, so that our intercourse was a series of quarrelings. He was a spirit of caprice and ubiquity; one never knew either his whim or his whereabouts. I found him severe and suspicious toward me; he never lost an opportunity of intimating that mine was a fiery and rash nature—adventurous, indocile and audacious. He was wont to charge me with being too airy and cheery—too volatile and versatile—too flowery and ardent. The harsh little man, fierce and frank, dark and candid, testy and fearless, a pitiless censor, called me to account for every poor scattered sin of vanity; and after I was habituated to being passed by as a shadow in Life's sunshine, "a being inoffensive as a shadow, with over-gravity in tastes and manner —want of color in mind and costume,"—this being the opinion of my friends and myself—it was a new thing to see one testily lifting his hand to screen his eyes because of an obtrusive ray. In spite of all this, in spite of his habit of casting to the winds all dignity and self-control, I did not dislike M. Paul. Constantly I used to find in my desk exercises left full of faults corrected, books welcome and refreshing, fresh, interesting new works, or classics, mellow and sweet in ripe age, and many a paper of chocolate comfits. At times his silence was full of friendliness and no words could inspire a pleasanter content than did M. Paul's wordless presence; but when overwrought he became acutely irritable, unreasonable; and in his love of power, his eager grasp after supremacy, his was an absolutism that verged on tyranny. Having heard me acknowledge ignorance in some branch of education, M. Paul took me in hand and became my teacher. At first he taught me with pleasure; he was very kind, very forbearing with the incapacity, the preternatural imbecility which has marked the beginning of all my efforts; but when my faculties began to struggle themselves free and I voluntarily increased the tasks he set me, his kindness became sternness, sarcasms of which the severity amazed and puzzled me harassed my ears. Before I penetrated motives these sneers made my heart ache; I feared I had lost M. Paul's affection. I soon found, however, that it was his impulse to compel a peculiar talent appearing within his range to prove itself, and how difficult he made that proof!

One day in early May M. Paul took the boarders and teachers to breakfast in the country. When we reached the farmhouse we all sat on a knoll and he told us a story. Well could he narrate: in such diction as children love, and learned men emulate—a diction simple in its strength and strong in its simplicity. He told a beautiful little tale with sweet glimpses of feeling and hues of description that never have faded from my memory. M. Emanuel was not a man to write books; but I have heard him lavish, with careless, unconscious prodigality, such mental wealth as books seldom boast; his mind was indeed my library, and whenever it was opened to me I entered bliss.

When we sat at breakfast, with what a pleasant countenance he watched us! He was a man whom it made happy to see others happy; he liked to have movement, animation, abundance and enjoyment round him. At the worst, it was only his nerves that were irritable, not his temper that was radically bad; soothe, comprehend, comfort him, and he was a lamb. After the meal he called me to sit beside him under a tree and read to him. While I read he listened with a sweetness of calm the more impressive from the impetuosity of his general nature; the deepest happiness filled his blue eye and smoothed his broad forehead. I, too, was happy, happy with the bright day, happier with his presence, happiest with his kindness.

He asked me whether, if I were his sister, I should always be content to stay with such a brother as he. I said I believed I should; and I felt it. He inquired whether, if he were to leave Villette, and go far away, I should be sorry; and I made no reply. The gentleness with which he treated me went to my heart. It was too tender, it was mournful. The day would have been perfect but for the breathing of melancholy that had dimmed its sunshine.

About this time I found myself an object of solicitude to Madame Beck and Père Silas. I was told of M. Paul's early love, Justine Marie, who became a nun when her parents opposed her suitor, and died soon afterward. I was told how he had been faithful to this love for twenty years, and how he was bound to constancy for the future because he had undertaken the support of Justine Marie's grandmother, Madame Walravens, and her old servant, and his old teacher, Père Silas. Thus they opened up the adytum of his heart—showed me one grand love, so strong and perfect that it had laughed at Death himself, and had watched beside a tomb for twenty years; and Madame Beck laughed to me, "*Oubliez les professeurs!*" Thus they took a sage plan to make me forget him! They showed me how good he was; they made of my little man a stainless hero.

Next I found that Rome was tempting me—M. Paul gave me books to read, Père Silas talked to me, I was taken to see the great ceremonials of the Church, until at last when I spoke my mind to M. Paul, showed him that I had a mind to keep my reformed creed—that in times of doubt and sorrow, my heart only longed to cry, "God be merciful to me a sinner"—there came a tone accordant, one sweet chord of harmony in two conflicting spirits, and M. Paul murmured:

"Whatever say priests or controversialists, God is good, and loves all the sincere. Believe, then, what you can; believe it as you can; one prayer, at least, we have in common; I also cry, *O Dieu, sois appaisé envers moi qui suis pecheur!*"*

For a month after this, M. Paul hourly grew better and kinder to me; mutual understanding was settling and fixing; feelings of union and hope made themselves profoundly felt in the heart; affection and deep esteem and dawning trust had each fastened its bond. Through his indulgent help, fond guidance and tender forbearance, a new feeling and a strange thought found a course. Could it be that he was becoming more than a friend or brother? Did his look speak a kindness beyond fraternity or amity?

Following upon these quiet lesson-hours came the sudden announcement that in a week M. Emanuel would sail for Basse-

---

*O God, be merciful to me, a sinner!

terre in Guadaloupe, where Madame Walravens had an estate, long sequestered, which now a competent agent might make highly productive. M. Paul was to be that agent. I saw that three persons actuated by self-interest—Madame Walravens by desire for her property, Père Silas by desire to keep his pupil from the influence of a heretic, and Madame Beck by the determination that another should not win what she could not obtain, M. Paul's love—had banded together and beset the one unselfish. No living being ever humbly laid his advantage at M. Emanuel's feet, or confidingly put it into his hands, when he spurned the trust.

For that week I did not see him, a week of suspense, with blank yet burning days, I remember, but I cannot describe its passage. On the last day he came to the school, but Madame Beck followed me, took her kinsman's attention, got him away, and then there seems, to my memory, an entire darkness and distraction in a few certain minutes I passed alone, a grief inexpressible over a loss unendurable. What should I do when all my life's hope was thus torn by the roots out of my riven, outraged heart?

Days passed, and I learned that M. Paul had postponed his departure a fortnight, and still I did not see him till within two days of the sailing of the *Paul et Virginie*. Then he came, he took me to see the work that had occupied him during these past weeks. He had prepared for me what I had planned to do for myself when I should have saved a thousand francs, a modest little day-school where I should occupy myself in his absence.

"Here," he said, "you shall have a school; you shall employ yourself while I am away; you shall think of me sometimes; you shall mind your health and happiness for my sake, and when I come back—"

I promised to do all he told me, to be his faithful steward during the three years of his absence. Before we returned to the Rue Fossette, these words caressed my ear:

"Lucy, take my love. One day share my life. Be my dearest, first on earth."

We parted; he gave me his pledge, then his farewell. The next day he sailed.

The three years that succeeded were the happiest of my life. I worked hard and prospered, and all the time I believe that hardly a being lived so remembered, so sustained, dealt with in kind so constant, honorable and noble. The years passed, and M. Paul was to be with me ere the mists of November should come. But November sent his fogs in advance, the wind took its autumn moan, rose, swelled, shrieked out long, and by one midnight all sleepless watchers heard and feared a wild southwest storm. That storm roared frenzied for seven days. It did not lull till the deeps had gorged their full of sustenance.

Here pause. Trouble no quiet, kind heart; leave sunny imaginations hope. Let them picture union and a happy succeeding life.

THE PROFESSOR (1857)

As early as 1840 Charlotte Brontë had written at least a small part of a novel which was to have been in several volumes, and of which she left some fragments in manuscript. It is said that she sent the beginning of it to Wordsworth, who must have given an unfavorable opinion, judging from her reply (quoted by Mrs. Gaskell), in which she said she "could give it up without much distress." In the preface to *The Professor* Miss Brontë said she had gotten over her taste for the "ornamental and redundant in composition," probably having in mind the first form of that story. *The Professor*, her first completed novel, was refused by the many publishers to whom it was sent in 1847, and did not see the light till after her death. It reads like a study for *Villette*, especially in its protrayal of Belgian types, the teaching experience, and the character and methods of the directress of the *pensionnat des demoiselles*. The location given to this school in the story, by the way, is the actual one of the school attended by the Brontës in 1842, which was in the Rue d'Isabelle of Brussels, at the foot of the staircase just beyond the statue of General Belliard.

OR my ten years at Eton I was indebted to my maternal uncles, Lord Tynemouth and the Hon. John Seacombe. My father had become bankrupt shortly before his death, and when I was born, six months later, my mother did not long survive. Until I was nine, I and my brother Edward, ten years older, lived with my uncle Crimsworth, my father's brother.

When he learned that Mr. Seacombe was standing for a borough not far from us, he wrote him a fierce letter, threatening that if he and Lord Tynemouth did not do something for their sister's orphans the public should know how they had treated that sister, solely because she had married a manufacturer, and had left her without help in the poverty of her widowhood.

Compelled by this threat, they consented to provide for my education. When I left Eton they advised me to study for the Church, Lord Tynemouth promising to give me the living of Seacombe and my Uncle John hinting that I might have one of his six daughters (all of whom I disliked) to preside over my rectory.

I declined both the Church and matrimony. Lord Tynemouth demanded sternly whether I had thought of engaging in trade, like my father. I had not, neither did I think I had the qualities essential to a successful tradesman. But the sneering tone in which he spoke of my father roused my indignation, and I said, "I cannot do better than follow in my father's steps. I will be a tradesman." We parted with mutual disgust.

I wrote asking for employment to my brother, who had married the daughter of a rich mill-owner and was now the proprietor of the business that was my father's before he failed. I received a cold assent, which, however, did not prepare me for the antipathy he exhibited and the indignity with which he treated me during the four months that I had charge of his foreign correspondence at ninety pounds a year.

Yorke Hunsden was a mill-owner whom I often saw in Bigben Close, my brother's place. I owed him a sort of involuntary grudge because he had more than once been witness of Edward's insults to me. But on a few occasions he sought my company and talked to me with a freedom and bluntness which on the whole I did not dislike. His singular character puzzled and interested me. He asked me at one time if it was my intention to become a tradesman.

"It was my serious intention three months ago."

"The more fool you! You look like a tradesman! What a practical, business-like face you have!"

"My face is as the Lord made it, Mr. Hunsden."

"The Lord never made either your head or your face for X—. What good can your bumps of ideality, comparison, self-esteem, conscientiousness, do here? But if you like Bigben Close, stay there."

At another time I had demurred when he called me a fossil. "I say," he said, "that when a man endures patiently what ought to be unendurable, he is a fossil. I've been in your counting-house when Crimsworth treated you like a dog; and how patient you were! If you are patient because you expect to make something eventually out of Crimsworth, you are what the world calls interested and mercenary, but may be a very wise fellow; if you are patient because you think it a duty to meet insult with submission, you are an essential sap, and in no shape the man for my money; if you are patient because your nature is phlegmatic, flat, inexcitable, and you cannot get up to the pitch of resistance, why, God made you to be crushed; and lie down, by all means, and lie flat, and let Juggernaut ride well over you!"

And again, "What a nobleman you would have made, William Crimsworth! Look at the features, figure, even to the hands; distinction all over—ugly distinction! But you're wrecked and stranded on the shores of commerce, forced into collision with practical men, with whom you cannot cope; for *you'll never be a tradesman.*"

For the first part of what he said I did not care; I only wondered at the perverted judgment of my character; but the last sentence shook me; for it was true.

When I went to the counting-house the next day, my brother met me with brutal abuse and charges that I had complained to outsiders of his treatment. When I demanded an explanation, he said that at a public meeting the day before the speaker opposed to him had insulted him with "cant about natural affection, family despots, and such trash; and when I rose to answer I was met by a shout from the filthy mob, and your name was mentioned. I looked round and saw that treacherous villain Hunsden acting as fugleman. And I know you have been with him. Deny it if you can!"

"Oh, I shall not deny it! And if Hunsden hounded on the people to hiss you, he did quite right. You deserve popular execration; for a worse man, a harder master, a more brutal brother than you are has seldom existed!"

There was more; but enough to say my service as clerk at Bigben Close was ended.

Hunsden came to me that evening. I made a grievance of his having deprived me of my living, which he took in earnest; but when I spoke of having been torn from my brother's affectionate embrace by his interference, he saw my real feeling. After much talk, in which he declared that he cared nothing for me personally, but loved to track a rascal, he advised me to go to the Continent and see what would turn up for me there, ending by writing me an introduction to a friend of his in Brussels.

By means of this I obtained a place as teacher, or "professor," of English and Latin in Monsieur Pelet's school for boys. M. Pelet did not look the schoolmaster; I wondered how a man seemingly so gentle could control a great school; but I found later that the least murmur or whisper was instantly stilled by a glance of that mild eye.

After listening to my first lesson he said, "I see that Monsieur has address; that pleases me, for in teaching address counts for as much as knowledge."

I pass over my experience with the young Flemings, who were dull but singularly stubborn, heavy as lead, with short memories, dense intelligence, and feeble reflective powers. It was necessary to require only moderate application, to be gentle, considerate, and even yielding up to a certain point; but beyond that point, firm as a rock. If they exceeded the limit, submission or expulsion. The system answered, and my influence was firmly established.

As for M. Pelet, he was very friendly toward me, and I was willing to take him for what he seemed, though he was sometimes too insinuating, and I discovered that his mildness was more in appearance than in reality. I suspected laxity in his code of morals, and hated his fashion of mentioning love. But he felt the difference in our notions, and kept off debatable ground, confining himself to intellectual subjects, on which he talked well.

After some time I received an offer from Mademoiselle Zoraïde Reuter, who conducted a girls' school, the grounds of which adjoined our own, to give lessons there at hours when I was at liberty. I accepted the offer and found myself instructor of a roomful of girls from fourteen to twenty years of age, among whom good features, blooming complexions, large, brilliant eyes, and forms full even to solidity seemed to abound.

After my first lesson, Mademoiselle Reuter detained me for a long conversation, evidently with some special aim; I soon found that she was feeling after my real character. She was searching for salient points, weak points, eccentric points. She was applying now this test, now that, hoping to find some chink, some niche where she could put her little, firm foot and stand upon my neck, mistress of my nature. It was no amorous influence she wished to gain; at that time it was only the power of the politician to which she aspired.

M. Pelet was curious about my impressions of his "little neighbor."

"Did she find out your weak point?"

"What is my weak point?"

"Why, the sentimental. Any woman sinking her shaft deep enough will at last reach a fathomless spring of sensibility in thy breast, Crimsworth."

"Some women might, Monsieur."

He went on teasingly in order to draw me out, and himself described some of her characteristics—"something of the cat and something of the fox."

"Will she ever marry, do you think?"

"Of course, when she finds a suitable match. No one likes better to captivate in a quiet way. I am mistaken if she will not yet leave the print of her stealing step on thy heart, Crimsworth."

I will not dwell on the subsequent verification of his words so far as Mademoiselle Reuter's efforts were concerned, and their success to some slight extent with me; or on my accidental discovery, through an overheard conversation between M. Pelet and Mademoiselle Zoraïde, that they were affianced lovers; that he was, or pretended to be, jealous of me; that both were convinced that I was in love with her; and that M. Pelet's attitude of friendship for me was insincere and treacherous. As for Mademoiselle, my slight illusion was over.

About this time a new pupil came into my class, Mademoiselle Henri, who gave lessons in lace-mending and embroidery. I had seen her occasionally in passing her class, but noticed little except that she had no control over her pupils. Now she wished to perfect herself in English, Mademoiselle Reuter told me, and recommended her to my indulgence—quite needlessly, and so ostentatiously that I wondered why, till I concluded that it was to impress me with her own exalted goodness and considerateness.

"She has not received a regular education. Perhaps her natural talents are not of the highest order. Monsieur will then, I am sure, have the goodness to be considerate and not expose her backwardness. She already has difficulty in enforcing her authority, and, should it be increased by new discoveries of her incapacity, she might find her position too painful to be retained, which I should regret for her sake; for she can ill afford to lose it."

At the first reading lesson after this, I had been tortured as usual by the uncouth mouthing of my native language by my Belgians, when a full, low voice read out a paragraph in correct English with pure accent, needing only firmness and assurance to be the counterpart of what any educated lady in Essex or Middlesex might have enounced.

It was Mademoiselle Henri. I had already discovered that she was not a Belgian. Afterward I found that her mother was English, her father a pastor in Geneva; both were dead, and she lived with an aunt whose only income was an annuity of twelve hundred francs.

Thereafter when I attempted to get a word with Mademoiselle Henri after lessons, I was invariably interrupted by Mademoselle Reuter on one pretext or another. My curt answers of late to her effusiveness only increased her desire to propitiate me. Her manner had been almost cringing since I had begun to treat her with hardness and indifference. It was her nature to regard modesty and disinterestedness as foibles, and pride, hardness, and selfishness as proofs of strength.

In the course of time I grew more interested in Frances Evans Henri, as I found that she was no ordinary pupil. Her exercises showed taste and fancy; more than that, imagination. Her interest in her lessons and the encouragement I gave supplied a stimulus that improved her in spirits and appearance. She took a new footing in the school, with an air of animation and firmness that compelled obedience in her class.

The public reading of one of her essays completed the revelation of her talents to the school. Mademoiselle Reuter gently took me to task for it. Mademoiselle Henri, she said, was hardly a concurrent with the others, being older—she was nineteen years old, and her sphere of life was somewhat beneath theirs; hence a public distinction might suggest comparisons not conducive to her real welfare. Then her *amour propre* was such as to need repression rather than encouragement. "Besides," she added, "I think that ambition, especially literary ambition, is not to be cherished in the mind of a woman. She may never marry; her poverty and obscurity, her health—for I think she is consumptive, her mother died of that complaint—make it unlikely. But even in celibacy it would be better that she should remain a respectable and decorous woman."

A fortnight later Mademoiselle Henri disappeared from my class. After a week I made inquiries and found that she had left the school for good. No one could give me her address. The pupils, the portress, who was plainly lying, Mademoiselle Reuter herself, lying also—none of them knew it. The following week I tendered Mademoiselle Reuter my resignation, to take effect a month later.

For four weeks I sought in the boulevards, the park, the churches and chapels, all to no purpose. The fourth Sunday, as I was taking a stroll outside the city, I came to a long, high white wall enclosing what seemed to be a garden. Wondering what it might be, I went on to the gate and entered, soon discovering that it was the Protestant cemetery.

Passing up an avenue, I came to a grove of yews, where I saw among their trunks a woman pacing to and fro, who presently went to a seat screened by the trees and facing a little stone set against the wall at the head of a new-made grave. Standing back of her, I saw the name on the stone—"Julienne Henri, aged 60"—her aunt!

Frances sat in tears looking at the stone. I put my hand on her shoulder. She turned quickly, saw who it was, and exclaimed with a flush of joy:

"*Mon maître! Mon maître!*"

She told me that she had had leave of absence when her aunt was very ill; that Mademoiselle Reuter had come to the house, had been very affable and expressed much sympathy, then told Frances how she regretted parting with her, and offered the remnant of salary that was due.

"Do you, then, mean to discharge me?" Frances had asked.

Mademoiselle Reuter smiled at the inelegance of the phrase, and said that their business connection was indeed dissolved, but that she hoped they would still remain friends.

One night before this, about the middle of July, Pelet had come home in a state of wild intoxication, abusing every one, raving about "that accursed Englishman, Creemsvort," and threatening to cut his throat on the hall table. Then he anathematized Zoraïde Reuter, who had thrown herself away on an adventurer in a fit of vicious caprice.

Now, it was precisely about this time that it became evident to me that the directress, excited by my suspected preference for Mademoiselle Henri, had fallen into her own snare, was caught in the meshes of the passion wherewith she had meant to entangle me; and in some way, as it now appeared, she had betrayed herself to Pelet. One of his drunken exclamations was: "And the jade dotes on your youth, you raw blockhead, and talks of your noble deportment, as she calls your accursed English formality, and your pure morals, forsooth!"

"How well disdain becomes him!" I had once overheard her say to her mother. "He is an Apollo when he smiles with that haughty air!"

And the jolly old dame had laughed. "For me," she said, "he makes me think of a screech-owl, with his spectacles!"

Pelet had forgotten the events of the night when he came to himself. In a fortnight his quarrel with his *fiancée* was made up and the time for the marriage was announced, I, in the meantime, having made evident my determination to find Mademoiselle Henri, and resigned my post at Mademoiselle Reuter's. Now, I felt that I could no longer be an inmate of M. Pelet's house, and I therefore resigned from his service also, thus leaving myself wholly without means of living.

When I returned to my room I found a letter from Frances, telling me that through the good offices of an English lady, who had called her in to mend some costly old lace for her daughter's wedding, she had been introduced to the directress of the first English school in Brussels, and engaged to teach certain subjects in the French language at twelve hundred francs a year.

Two persons whose desires are moderate may live well enough in Brussels on an income which would barely afford a respectable maintenance for one in London, simply because the English surpass in folly all the nations on God's earth and are more abject slaves to custom, to opinion, to the desire to keep up a certain appearance. Had I retained my sixty pounds a year, I could, now that Frances was in possession of fifty pounds, have gone straight to her this very evening and spoken out the words, which, repressed, kept fretting my heart with fever. Now, for the first time, did I truly feel what it was to be poor; now did the sacrifice I had made in casting from me the means of living put on a new aspect.

I sat down and thought an hour—two hours—vainly. Then I remembered something that seemed to shed a ray of hope. Three months before this I had, without much risk to myself, rescued from drowning Jean Baptiste Vandenhuten, one of my pupils. His parents believed that I had shown a bravery and devotion that no thanks could repay; and his father had made me promise that if ever I needed help I would give him the chance of discharging the obligation. I had no right to his good offices, but I needed them and I had promised.

M. Victor Vandenhuten was glad to be appealed to. All I wanted was information and recommendation; he set me on the track of several places and made efforts to secure them for me, for some time in vain. Defeat following defeat stimulated me. I forgot fastidiousness, conquered reserve, thrust pride from me. I asked, persevered, remonstrated, dunned. At the very crisis when I had tried my last chance, fortune threw a prize into my lap. I received the appointment of English professor to all the classes of a college in Brussels, with a salary of three thousand francs and the certainty of being able to make as much more by private lessons.

Now I wasted no time.

"Frances, how much regard have you for me?"

"*Mon maître*, I have much."

"Frances, have you enough to give yourself to me as my wife? to accept me as your husband?"

"Monsieur," she said after a pause, "Monsieur wishes to know if I consent?"

"*Justement.*"

"Will Monsieur be as good a husband as he has been a *maître?*"

"I will try, Frances."

Another pause. Then, "That is to say, Monsieur will always be a little headstrong, exacting, arbitrary—"

"Have I been so, Frances?"

"*Mais oui;* you know you have."

"Have I been nothing else?"

"*Mais oui;* you have been my best friend."

"But what. Frances, are you to me?"

"Your devoted pupil, who loves you with all her heart."

"Will my pupil consent to pass her life with me?"

After some moments of reflection: "You have always made me happy. I like to hear you speak; I like to see you; I like to be near you. Master, I should be glad to live with you always. Master, I consent to pass my life with you."

"Very well, Frances."

A year and a half after our marriage Frances realized her ambition to found a school, and exacted from me an hour's service a day.

Ten years rushed on—years of bustle, action, unslacked endeavor; years in which we hardly knew repose, were strangers to amusement, never thought of indulgence; and yet, as our course ran side by side, as we marched hand in hand, we neither murmured, repented, nor faltered. Now we have realized an independency, not entirely from our unaided effort, though we have worked hard; but when we had capital to invest we had two skilled counselors to advise us where to place it—Vandenhuten in Belgium, Hunsden in England.

To England we now resolved to take wing; it had been the dream of a lifetime with Frances to live in her mother's land. So, with our boy Victor, we have made our home thirty miles from X——, in my native county, a region whose verdure the smoke of mills has not yet sullied, whose waters still run pure, whose moorlands preserve in some ferny glens the primal wildness of nature, her scents of reed and heather, her free and fresh breezes.

EMILY BRONTË

(ELLIS BELL)

(England 1818–1849)

WUTHERING HEIGHTS (1847)

This, Emily Brontë's only novel, found a publisher after many rejections and appeared with *Agnes Grey*, her sister Anne's novel, in December, 1847. It received little notice at the time; its first enthusiastic praise seems to have come from Sydney Dobell, whose review in *The Palladium*, after Emily's death, spoke emphatically of the energy and genius of the book. A gray stone house, Sowdens, on the summit of Haworth Hill, is shown as the original of *Wuthering Heights;* over its door is a piece of carving: "H. E. 1659." Though not so lonely and God-forsaken as the house of the story, it doubtless afforded a suggestion of it. The character and passion of her brother Bramwell, alluded to elsewhere, are supposed to have suggested Heathcliff's; and, indeed, a claim was made for Bramwell Brontë that he was the real author of the story, a claim which the feebleness of his known writings and the character of Emily's poetry show to be untenable. Emily's acquaintance with German literature, especially Hoffman's *Tales*, is referred to as explaining to some extent the gloomy and tragic character of her imaginings.

1801. My name is Lockwood, and I am a tenant of Thrushcross Grange, belonging to a Mr. Heathcliff, who lives at Wuthering Heights, so called from the bleak and windy character of its site—"wuthering" being a provincial word indicating the tumult of a storm. It is an old farmhouse with the inscription "Hareton Earnshaw, 1500," amid grotesque carvings, over the principal door.

I have made two visits to my landlord—the last, I think; for a more strange, surly, scowling, inhospitable, unaccountable collection of human beings I have never seen and wish never to see again.

At my first call I saw only Mr. Heathcliff and the servants, not to include a bevy of dogs that rushed out from dark corners of the sitting-room. I rather liked my landlord at this time, deeming his rudeness the expression of an unsocial nature too much indulged; this led me, at leaving, to suggest coming again and to disregard the ungracious reception of my offer.

The next time, I met the other members of the family: a young man, handsome but unkempt, rude and provincial in speech, evidently a farm-worker, yet with a bearing and manner that forbade me to class him as a servant; and an exquisitely beautiful young woman, barely seventeen in appearance, a contrast to the young man by the cultivation shown in her speech, but quite as rude and insolent in manner. Mr. Heathcliff's treatment of her, at the same time contemptuous and malignant, gave me the first intimation of my mistake in judging him crusty but good-hearted.

At first I took the lady to be his wife and said something implying it; having been sneeringly corrected and informed that she was his daughter-in-law, I jumped to the conclusion that the young boor was his son and her husband—another blunder, at which Heathcliff sneered again and the young man growled:

"My name is Hareton Earnshaw, and I'd counsel you to respect it!"

I learned afterward that the young beauty was the widow of Heathcliff's only son. The only servants were Joseph, a sour, uncivil, canting old fanatic, and Zillah, the cook.

When I was ready to leave the snow was falling so fast that I saw the paths would be obliterated before I could cover the four miles to my house. My hosts refused me a guide, and Heathcliff told me I would have to share Hareton's or Joseph's bed if I stayed all night. I said I could sleep on a chair in the sitting-room.

"No, no! I'll permit no stranger the range of this place while I'm off guard!" said the unmannerly wretch.

I rushed out and seized the lantern by the light of which Joseph was milking, calling out that I would send it back on the morrow; the old fellow set the dogs on me; and but for Zillah, who came to my rescue while the men were laughing, I do not know what would have happened. From the kitchen she ushered me to a chamber, telling me to be quiet, as the master did not like anyone to lodge there.

At first I saw no bed; but on looking into a large oak case, with window-like squares cut near the top, I saw it enclosed a bed and the ledge of a window on which were a few mildewed books. The name "Catherine Earnshaw" was scratched many times on the ledge, sometimes varied to "Catherine Heathcliff" and "Catherine Linton." The margins of the books were covered with writing in form of a diary. One had a good caricature of Joseph, who appeared often in the notes as a canting tyrant forcing his prayers and sermons on the writer and Heathcliff, whose escapades together comprised most of the entries. They seemed to be under the tyranny of one Hindley also, who, with his wife Frances, excited the writer's disgust by their lover-like foolishness.

On one occasion Joseph complained to Hindley that Cathy had "torn the back off 'Th' Helmet o' Salvation'" and that Heathcliff had put his foot into "t' first part o' 'T' Brooad Way to Destruction.'"

I was wakened from my first sleep by the rattling on the window of the dry cones of a fir branch. It disturbed me when I fell asleep again, and I thought I rose and tried to open the casement; finding the hook soldered into the staple, I broke the glass and stretched my arm out to break the branch; but my fingers closed on a little ice-cold hand, which clung when I tried to withdraw my arm; and a voice sobbed, "Let me in! Let me in!"

"Who are you?"

"Catherine Linton. Let me in!"

"Let me go, then."

The finger relaxed. I snatched mine in, piled the books against the opening, and called, "I'll not let you in if you beg twenty years!"

"It is twenty years! I've been a waif twenty years!" Then a feeble scratching began, and the books moved.

I screamed. The scream at least was real; for Heathcliff appeared, evidently in extreme agitation and fright, which seemed partly relieved when he saw me, and turned into anger against whoever showed me to that room.

"If that little fiend, Catherine Linton or Earnshaw, had got in, she would have strangled me," I said. "If she has been walking the earth twenty years, it is a just punishment, no doubt, for her mortal transgressions."

He ordered me away savagely. As I hesitated at the door, not knowing my way, I saw a strange scene of superstition. Heathcliff got on the bed, wrenched open the lattice, and sobbed:

"Come in, Cathy! Do come! Once more! Oh, my heart's darling! Hear me this time, Catherine, at last!"

But the specter gave no sign; only the snow and the wind whirled wildly through and extinguished the light.

I found that I could satisfy my curiosity by encouraging my housekeeper, Ellen Dean, to gossip. She had lived at Thrushcross Grange eighteen years, and before that at Wuthering Heights from childhood. Her story, which she told with minute detail while I was kept at home by illness, was briefly as follows:

Old Mr. Earnshaw, the grandfather of Hareton, had brought home from Liverpool a dirty, ragged little boy, dark as a gipsy, strange and unable to speak English, whom he had found wandering unclaimed in a city street. His wife protested, but finally yielded to his determination to keep the child; and it was called Heathcliff after a boy they had lost—a name that had served ever since for both Christian and surname.

He seemed about the age of Catherine, who was six, and they became fast friends and allies. But Hindley, her brother, fourteen at the time, regarded him with aversion, which grew into malignant hatred as his father became more and more foolishly partial to the waif.

When Mr. Earnshaw was in failing health, Hindley was sent to college. Then, Mrs. Dean said, they might have had peace but for Cathy and for Joseph, "who is the wearisomest Pharisee that ever ransacked a Bible to rake the promises to himself and fling the curses to his neighbors."

Her characterization of Cathy is worth quoting: "Her spirits were always at high-water mark, her tongue always going, singing, laughing, and plaguing everybody who would not do the same. A wild, wicked slip she was; but she had the bonniest eye, the sweetest smile, the lightest foot in the parish. She was much too fond of Heathcliff; the greatest punishment we could invent was to keep her separate from him.

When Mr. Earnshaw died, Hindley, who had been absent three years, came home bringing a wife, a delicate, childish young woman, of whom he was dotingly fond. He deprived Heathcliff of the instructions of the curate, which had been shared with Cathy, and compelled him to labor on the farm. Heathcliff bore the degradation very well at first, because Cathy taught him what she had learned, and worked or played with him in the fields.

But harder times began for Heathcliff when Cathy became acquainted with Edgar and Isabella Linton, of Thrushcross Grange. They were fair, delicate children and had been daintily reared. Heathcliff despised Edgar as a coward and a milksop and hated him as a rival. As Hindley ordered him never to show his face when the Lintons came, and Cathy was somewhat taken up with them, Heathcliff became more sullen, lost his ambition to study, and neglected himself so that he grew slouching in his gait and dirty and savage in appearance.

Once after Hindley had flogged him and shut up in the garret for resenting ferociously a sneering remark of Edgar, "I asked him," said Ellen, "what he was thinking of as he sat moody by the fire.

" 'I'm trying to settle how I shall pay Hindley back. I hope he will not die before I do!'

" 'For shame, Heathcliff!' said I. " 'It is for God to punish wicked people.' "

" 'No; God won't have the satisfaction that I shall,' he returned."

The following summer Hindley's son, Hareton, was born, and his wife died. Hindley grew desperate; he cursed and defied, execrated God and man, and gave himself up to reckless dissipation. His treatment of Heathcliff was enough to make a fiend of a saint; and the boy took a truly fiendish delight in Hindley's increasing degradation.

The house became such an infernal den that no decent neighbor came near it except Edgar Linton. One evening after he had gone, Catherine confided to Ellen that he had asked her to marry him and that she had accepted; yet she was unsatisfied and anxious to be told she had done right.

"What are you unhappy about?" said Ellen. "You say you love him because he is handsome, young, cheerful, and rich; and he loves you. There will be no objection from either family; you will escape from a disorderly, comfortless home into a wealthy, respectable one. Where is the obstacle?"

"*Here* and *here*," said Catherine striking her forehead and her breast, "in whichever place my soul lives. In my soul and in my breast I'm convinced I'm wrong."

She could only explain by saying that once she dreamed she was in heaven weeping to come back to earth; and when the angels got angry and threw her down into the heath on Wuthering Heights, she woke sobbing for joy. "I've no more business to marry Edgar Linton than I have to be in heaven; and if the wicked man in there hadn't brought Heathcliff so low I shouldn't have thought of it. It would degrade me to marry Heathcliff now—"

At this Ellen became sensible of Heathcliff's presence in the room; he stayed to hear no more, but slipped out noiselessly. Catherine went on, "so he shall never know how I love him; and that's because he's more myself than I am. Whatever our souls are made of, his and mine are the same; and Linton's is as different as a moonbeam from lightning, or frost from fire."

When Ellen suggested that Heathcliff would be quite deserted when she married, she exclaimed indignantly,

"Deserted? Not while I live, Ellen. Every Linton might melt into nothing before I would forsake Heathcliff. When I am married I can help him to rise. Nelly, I *am* Heathcliff. He's always in my mind—not as a pleasure, any more than I am always a pleasure to myself, but as my own being."

When Heathcliff was sought that night he was nowhere to be found. It was a stormy night and Catherine would be out looking for him; but he could not be found and the wetting gave the girl a cold which was the beginning of a long illness.

Three years later Edgar, whose parents were now dead, and Catherine were married, and Ellen went to the Grange to live. Catherine was capricious but Edgar was devoted and patient; and their happiness seemed to be growing, until, within a year, Heathcliff appeared, to the almost insane joy of Catherine and Edgar's vexation, which, however, he tried to suppress for her sake.

"Heathcliff was wonderfully changed," said Ellen, "he had grown tall and strong, carried himself well, and had lost all marks of former degradation. I never knew where he had spent the years since he went away. It surprised me to hear that he was to stay with Hindley at Wuthering Heights. Why should Hindley invite him and why should he accept, old enemies as they were? I learned why later when Hindley died, leaving his whole property mortgaged to Heathcliff, who had encouraged his mania for gambling and profited by it, while Hareton was left little more than a beggar."

Before that event, however, matters had gone strangely at the Grange. Heathcliff at first used the liberty of visiting there cautiously, gradually establishing a right to be expected. Catherine was more careful about displaying her pleasure in his society; Edgar's anxiety was lulled, to be awakened later by another cause.

His sister, a charming girl of eighteen, became infatuated with the constant visitor. She grew petulant and capricious, and one day blurted out her jealousy. "You are a dog in the manger, Cathy, and desire no one to be loved but yourself!"

Catherine was surprised. "I'd as soon put that canary into the park on a winter's day, child, as recommend you to bestow your heart on Heathcliff. He's a fierce, pitiless, wolfish man. He'd crush you like a sparrow's egg, Isabella. I know he couldn't love a Linton; and yet he'd be quite capable of marrying your fortune and expectations. Avarice is growing with him into a besetting sin."

Of course this had no effect on Isabella; neither had Ellen's serious talk to her about Heathcliff's character. She thought them leagued against her happiness.

When Heathcliff came the next day Edgar was out, as he knew. Catherine told him poor Isabella's secret in the girl's presence, holding her pitilessly when she would have bolted from the room. When at length she had gone, Heathcliff asked Catherine, "You were not speaking the truth, were you?"

"I assure you I was. But don't notice it further. I like her too well, my dear Heathcliff, to let you seize and devour her."

"And I like her too ill to attempt it—except in ghoulish fashion."

"She's her brother's heir, is she not?" he asked after a brief silence.

"I should be sorry to think so. Half a dozen nephews shall erase her title, please heaven!"

Soon after, Ellen saw Heathcliff coming when Isabella was in the court. He spoke to her; then, having taken a survey of the housefront, he embraced and kissed her. Ellen called Catherine and she saw Isabella tear herself free. This led to a quarrel between Catherine and Heathcliff. When Mr. Linton came in he learned the story from Ellen and ordered Heathcliff from the house. Then Catherine turned on them both. After some violence on each side, Heathcliff went, rather than be forced by the servants from the presence of the woman he loved.

Catherine retired to her room and starved herself for two days; the third day she opened her door and called for Ellen; and a day or two later she fell into a brain fever from which she came out in two months shattered in body and mind.

Before her illness was known to the family, Isabella had run away with Heathcliff. Mr. Linton took no notice of a letter from her announcing her marriage, and asking for reconciliation and hinting that she had already repented; but Ellen went to see her after receiving a letter from Wuthering Heights, describing the horrible life she had entered upon there with the besotted Earnshaw, the child he was fast making like himself, the insolent servant, and worst of all her tyrannical and fiendish husband.

Ellen described the visit to me—the open brutality and contempt of Heathcliff's treatment, making it plain that his only object in marrying Isabella had been the Linton property, which her father had willed to her in the event of Edgar's dying without leaving a son.

Having sent his wife from the room, he told Ellen that he must and would see Catherine; that if she would not help him to enter the house quietly, he would break in at all hazards. Ellen tried to dissuade him, representing the harm it would do Catherine just as her mind was getting settled. Finding him resolved, she said she would tell her master, who would take measures to prevent his intrusion.

Then he threatened to have her kept at Wuthering Heights till after his visit. "Let us settle it at once," he said. "Will you stay here, and am I to fight my way to Catherine over Linton and his footman? or will you do what I request?"

She was at last forced to agree to ask her mistress's consent, and let him know of Linton's next absence from home. In her perplexity she thought this would be better than to risk another explosion; and perhaps, too, it might cause a favorable crisis in Catherine's mental illness.

He came on Sunday while the family were at church. It was a strange interview. Frantic caresses and wild endearments alternated with wilder accusations on both sides. In answer to Cathy's complaint that he would forget her, he said savagely:

"Are you possessed with a devil to talk so to me when you are dying? You know you lie to say I have killed you; you know I could as soon forget you as my own existence! Is it not sufficient for your infernal selfishness that while you are at peace I shall writhe in the torments of hell?"

"I shall not be at peace," she moaned. "Should a word of mine distress you hereafter, think I feel the same distress underground, and for my own sake forgive me."

More there was of the same kind. "Yes," he said, "you may kiss me and cry and wring out my kisses and tears; they'll blight you—they'll damn you! You loved me; what right had you to leave me for the poor fancy you felt for Linton?"

She was lying in his arms, when Ellen saw that people were returning from church and warned them. He would have gone, but she held him faster; and when Mr. Linton came in she was still there, but insensible. That night the Catherine I had seen at Wuthering Heights was born, and two hours later her mother was dead.

The rest is soon told. Hindley died of his excesses and Heathcliff brought up his defrauded child in ignorance, as Hindley had treated him. Isabella, who left her husband soon after Catherine's death, died twelve years later, leaving a son of that age, Linton Heathcliff, to her brother's care; but his father took him away immediately. He was a sickly, selfish, cowardly, spiritless boy, like the Lintons in color and feature. Heathcliff despised and hated him, desiring only to keep him alive till after his uncle's death, when he would inherit the Linton estates; they would then come at the boy's death to his father as his heir.

He watched, with fiendish delight, the decline of Edgar's health; and now resolved, if, indeed, he had not had it in mind for years, to marry his son to Catherine, thus making his title secure. By forcing the peevish little wretch to play upon her sympathies, he brought about secret meetings, some at Wuthering Heights where her father had forbidden her to go. At last, when Mr. Linton was near death, Catherine and Ellen were decoyed there and held, till the girl, distracted at the thought of her father's anxiety at her disappearance, consented to an immediate marriage with young Heathcliff.

When Mr. Linton was informed of what had occurred, he saw that Heathcliff's design was to secure the personal property which would come to her at his death and sent for an attorney to draw his will in order to put it in trust for her and her children. But the attorney made an excuse for delay until Mr. Linton was gone; he had sold himself to Heathcliff.

Young Heathcliff died soon after, having willed everything he possessed and what had been his wife's to his father. I had seen for myself how they had since lived at Wuthering Heights, and Mrs. Dean gave me details. She had gathered from Zillah —for Heathcliff would not allow Ellen to visit there—concerning his tyranny, Catherine's bitter and unavailing resentment, and her unconcealed contempt for poor Hareton's ignorance and boorishness, even when he was trying to learn and make himself fit to associate with her.

I had been confined to the house all winter, hearing Mrs. Dean's long-drawn out tale by instalments. In the spring I went to London, first notifying my landlord that I should keep the

Grange only till my year was up in the autumn. Mrs. Dean had slyly suggested that she would like to be permanent house-keeper at the Grange for me and young Mrs. Heathcliff as my bride; and as I rode away that spring day, I thought how more romantic than a fairy tale the realization of her dream would have been.

In the autumn, I was traveling in that region and took a fancy to see Thrushcross Grange again. I found a new house-keeper there, who told me Mrs. Dean was at Wuthering Heights. So, leaving orders for my dinner, I went over to see what had brought about the change. It was moonlight when I arrived; the doors and windows were open.

"*Contrary*," I heard a sweet voice say. "The third time, you dunce! Now read it right, or I'll pull your hair."

"Contrary, then," said a deeper voice. "Now kiss me for minding so well."

Without staying to hear more, I sought Ellen at another door. She was surprised to know that I had not learned of Mr. Heathcliff's death three months previously. He had sent for her to take Zillah's place soon after my departure. She told me with great delight the love-story of her two favorites, Hareton and Catherine.

"You see, Mr. Lockwood, it was easy enough to win Mrs. Heathcliff's heart. But now I'm glad you did not try."

Heathcliff had altered strangely before his death, seeming to have the one fixed idea of going to Catherine and to care for nothing else.

"Nelly," he said to her once, "there is a strange change approaching; I'm in its shadow. Five minutes ago Hareton seemed to me a personification of my youth. His startling likeness to Catherine connected him fearfully with her. But what does not recall her? The entire world is a dreadful collection of memoranda that she did exist and that I have lost her. Hareton's aspect was the ghost of my immortal love, of my wild endeavors to hold my right, my degradation, my pride, my happiness and my anguish—I have a single wish and my whole being and faculties are yearning to attain it. I am swallowed up in the anticipation of its fulfilment. O God! it is a long fight! I wish it were over!"

He died alone, and was buried, as he wished to be, on the other side of Catherine from her husband. I found the three headstones, the middle one gray and half buried in heath; Edgar Linton's with the turf and moss creeping up its foot; Heathcliff's still bare.

I lingered round them under that benign sky, watched the moths fluttering among the heath and harebells, listened to the soft wind breathing through the grass, and wondered how any one could ever imagine unquiet slumbers for the sleepers in that quiet earth.

CHARLES WILLIAM SHIRLEY BROOKS

(England, 1816-1874)

THE GORDIAN KNOT (1868)

This story first appeared as a serial nine years previous to its publication in book form, at which time it was revised and somewhat shortened. A large portion of the story was composed while the author was sojourning in Sussex, in the household of his friends, Helen and Mark Lemon (the latter the editor of Punch), to whom the volume is dedicated.

HE London season was at its height when the manager of the opera-house issued invitations for a *fête* at his beautiful villa on the bank of the Thames. And here it was that Philip Arundel first saw Margaret Spencer.

The gay young Londoner's attention was idly turned in the direction of a bevy of young women engaged in showing their skill at archery, when suddenly a beautiful girl stepped forward and took the bow in hand: the lovely archer's countenance was of a Grecian type, but not too regular for a certain playfulness; she had violet eyes with long lashes; and when she smiled, which she presently did—and did as if smiling were a habit with her—she disclosed exceedingly beautiful teeth. It was also noticeable, as the leathern thimbles and gauntlets were being adjusted to her hands, that they were small and appeared to be soft; and it was equally impossible not to observe that her arms were finely rounded. If ladies do not like to undergo this kind of inspection, they should stay at home; but nobody ought to stay at home who bears such scrutiny so well as could Margaret Spencer.

Charmed with this vision of loveliness, Philip Arundel at once made his way to the side of the fair archer, and by a bit of skilful maneuvering soon succeeded in gaining an introduction to her, and to her large and aggressive aunt, Mrs. Robert Spencer.

Margaret Spencer had but recently come to make her home in London with this scheming and rather unprincipled relative, who endeavored to make her wits do duty to eke out her hen-pecked husband's depleted bank-account.

Margaret's early career had been one of change and adventure. Her father, an officer in the service of the East India Company, whose reputation had been exceedingly shady, had married a flighty young woman, who had deserted her unworthy husband when their small daughter was but four years old, and had run away with a gentleman in the Company's Civil Service.

At this time Captain Armandale Spencer decided to send to England his little girl, to be cared for by his elder brother and his wife, to whom he had previously remitted a good portion of his ill-gotten income.

The child was placed aboard ship with her Eastern nurse, and eventually arrived in England, where a devoted uncle and aunt were presumably awaiting her. Mr. and Mrs. Robert Spencer did not, however, find it convenient to welcome the small charge upon her arrival, as certain business complications made it advisable for them to retire for a time from public notice.

The little Margaret, thus stranded in a strange city, was taken in charge by kind friends, who sought for her relatives and finally placed her in the hands of another aunt, Mrs. Henry Cheriton, who had estranged herself from the members of her family by marrying a country doctor with whom she had found a cheerful, happy home.

In this plain but cultured household Margaret had passed a happy, natural childhood, growing up with her young cousins, and being treated as a daughter of the house. She increased in beauty year by year, and became the idol of many hearts in the country town of St. Oscar's, and at eighteen had blighted the budding hopes of several native swains. She was also deeply beloved by her cousin Alban Cheriton, who had since boyhood looked forward to winning her for his wife.

Into this serene country life had come suddenly a letter to

Margaret from the aunt and uncle who had failed to meet her when as a tiny child she first set foot in England in her lonely plight, urging her to come to them in London, now that more favorable circumstances made it possible for them to welcome her, so that she might see something of society and social life.

Content in her home at St. Oscar's, the young girl would have promptly declined this invitation, but with the letter was an enclosure from her father in India, insisting that she should at once take up her residence with his brother Robert and his wife. That this enclosure came in response to a diplomatic communication written by Mrs. Robert to her brother-in-law across the sea was unknown to Margaret, who with much regret prepared for her trip to London, leaving her cousin Alban with his declaration of love unspoken.

The London home, like its mistress, was very pretentious, but was maintained only by petty economies and by the sub-letting of certain rooms. Mrs. Spencer saw in the introduction into the household of a beautiful niece both a helper and a bait to retain the presence of a generous old friend from whose bounty this wily lady had already extracted all that she felt she could hope to secure single-handed. A lovely young niece would, however, appeal strongly to the old Russian merchant who was ready to bestow his affection upon some young and worthy *protégée*.

In this surmise Mrs. Spencer was correct; this Russian, whose name was Keckling, was at once charmed with Margaret, and set himself the pleasant task of showing her about London. And the invitation to the opera-manager's *fête*, at the villa on the Thames, came indirectly from this Russian friend, who thus became responsible for the presentation of Mr. Philip Arundel. This chance acquaintanceship the young man immediately proceeded to follow up assiduously. He was invited to Gower Street, and went, paying especial attention to the elder lady of the house, who asked him to come again, after which he called there very often.

In short, he had at first sight fallen violently in love with Margaret Spencer,—a fact that was noted with consternation by his friend and partner-at-law, John Claxton, who did his best to dissuade Phillip from plunging recklessly into matrimony with one who had no money and whose social position was not the equal of his own. Was he not better fitted to live the life of a gay bachelor until a desirable heiress should come upon the scene, and had he not already accumulated a fair amount of debts?

But Philip, having made up his mind to marry the lovely Miss Spencer, left nothing undone toward the accomplishment of his desire. He won over his two devoted sisters and frankly stated his pathetic case to his father, who good-naturedly promised to pay outstanding debts and settle something comfortable upon his handsome son. And Margaret, proud of this seemingly brilliant conquest, and with her heart touched for the first time, accepted her ardent lover, regarding him meanwhile as the embodiment of all perfection.

At the close of the London season, Margaret, at the urgent invitation of her self-appointed elderly guardian, Mr. Keckling, visited him at the seashore, and thither came her betrothed to spend many ideal summer days in the society of the young woman of his choice. During this happy period Alban Cheriton made one desperate attempt to express to Margaret his love for her and to warn her regarding the unreliable character of her *fiancé*—a warning that awakened only resentment and caused Alban to be haughtily dismissed, after which he withdrew in desperate mood to busy himself in his medical profession.

While pursuing his practice, this disappointed aspirant for Margaret's hand received a visit from a broken-hearted and vengeful woman, who, having formerly possessed Philip's affection, which had been withdrawn from her at the beginning of his engagement to Margaret, was now longing to prevent his marriage. She thrust into Alban's hands three of Philip's letters, which she implored him to send to Margaret, hoping to destroy her confidence in her *fiancé*; but the somber physician dismissed her and locked the letters in a drawer without glancing at them, though he, too, longed to see the marriage prevented.

Despite these shadows in the background, the wedding-bells pealed out merrily and the Gordian knot was tied; **the lovely** bride was welcomed to the arms of the adoring **bride·**

groom and to the bosom of his admiring family. A charming home was waiting for them, and Margaret and Philip were ideally happy in their new abode.

The first glad year slipped by only too swiftly, and then the married pair were blessed with a son, little Marmaduke Arundel, a lovely child who called forth passionate devotion from his mother, and, in his father's opinion, absorbed too much of her time and interest. Philip resented the fact that he was no longer her one and only love and consoled himself for his loss by more frequent visits to his club. On such occasions he was prone to drink rather too deeply and to reflect upon the pleasures of his old-time freedom.

And now the little cloud upon the horizon of Margaret's happiness seemed gradually to increase, until the whole sky looked dark and ominous.

First came the news that her scapegrace father had suddenly come upon the scene, having returned to London prepared to trade upon his daughter's connection with a well-known family. Margaret, whose knowledge of her parent had been till now of the vaguest description, learned of acts on his part that placed him outside the pale of decent society, and felt that she must face the displeasure of her husband and his family when they learned her father's true character.

While meditating how best to make this confession to her husband, who had seemed somewhat cold of late, an incident occurred that tended to increase the strained relations beginning to exist between the two.

Philip having departed ostensibly on a fishing trip, Margaret, in restless mood, called upon her old friend Mr. Keckling, who insisted that she should stay and dine with him and attend the opera in the evening. Their box being near the stage, someone casually suggested in the course of the evening that it was amusing to take a look behind the scenes; influence was invoked to bring this venture to pass, and the result was an unexpected encounter with Philip, who was gallantly holding a shawl for the leading *danseuse*. The shock that Margaret experienced was so great as almost to cause her to faint, and the whole episode was extremely unpleasant, as the delinquent husband felt that he was being spied upon, and was resentful rather than penitent. He declared that he had intended "going a-fishing," but, having given up the trip, had merely looked in behind the scenes for a bit of careless amusement.

And so the breach widened, though it would probably never have done so had it not been for a certain arch-conspirator who was bending all his energy in the direction of estranging the husband and wife. This was no other than Alban Cheriton, who never had ceased to love his cousin passionately and to hate the man who had won her.

In a hundred insidious ways did this seeming friend exercise his pernicious influence; as the family physician, and one whose advice was continually needed about the child, he was enabled to keep well in touch with all that was going on in the household. He urged Margaret to give closer and more assiduous attention to her small son, and at the same time encouraged the young husband to assert his independence and to drink deeply. It was Alban who spent a certain evening with Philip and brought him home to be seen for the first time by his wife in an intoxicated condition; it was Alban who urged Margaret in her husband's absence to take her son at once into the country for his health; and it was Alban who, on the eve of her departure, left upon her writing-table one of those early endearing letters penned by Philip to the woman of whom he had taken leave after he came to know Margaret. This affectionate epistle, beginning "My dear Maria," did the work that their evil genius desired. For the young wife, keenly sensitive, and smarting from recent neglect, believed that her husband had intentionally left this letter on her desk to apprise her of the fact that she was no longer the sole possessor of his affection.

Following her first impulse to escape, she closed the home, and taking her son hastened into the country without notifying Philip of her whereabouts, being throughout guided by the counsel of Alban, who lost no opportunity of misrepresenting the absent husband.

Having succeeded in separating Margaret from Philip, Alban proceeded to pamper the husband's vanity, and to increase his indignation toward the wife who had fled from him ; moreover, to make matters still more complicated for Margaret, her worthless father suddenly joined her in the country, and made it appear that she had voluntarily taken refuge with one who must reflect discredit upon the distinguished Arundel family.

Alban Cheriton's next card was played when he convinced the unhappy husband that in marrying him Margaret had concealed from him her knowledge of the depravity of both her parents, being merely intent upon making a successful match.

The scheming of the conspirator went still further, for his plan to enmesh Philip included the forlorn woman who had first left the letters with him; she had now become one of his regular patients, and he felt that she was a useful tool, completely in his power. Having prevailed upon her to assume the care of a certain little waif, he determined that when the right moment should come he would represent to Margaret that this child belonged to Philip.

While the plot continued to thicken about Margaret, she yet had two discreet and sensible friends, who believed that her troubles could be satisfactorily adjusted, and who felt sure that some enemy had a hand in the separation of husband and wife; one was the ever-devoted Russian merchant, Keckling, who boldly entered the citadel of which Margaret's father had forcibly taken possession, and ejected the intruder; and the other was John Claxton, who, having taken Philip under his wing, exerted his legal mind to disentangle the bewildering plot in which he found his friend involved.

After a time it became gradually evident to certain persons that the once brilliant intellect of Alban Cheriton was rapidly becoming clouded. His mental balance was undoubtedly impaired, and his conduct grew more and more strange and erratic. In an almost frantic state, he was one day ushered into Margaret's presence, where he deported himself in a way to convince her that he had actually become a madman.

During this interview he cried out that he would kill everyone, her husband, her father, her child, and that they should then go away together. The frightened young mother was greatly relieved to escape from him and to clasp her boy to her heart.

At last the gloomy clouds lifted, and a messenger from

Margaret summoned Philip once more to her side. This message, which he had awaited so eagerly but would not solicit, came through the instrumentality of the poor outcast, Maria, who having come to Margaret in a dying condition, had been by her received and nursed with tender care; she begged to see Philip once more, and Margaret wrote to him, asking him to come.

At the dying girl's bedside the husband and wife again clasped hands, and together did their best to comfort her.

The reunion of Philip and Margaret, so strangely brought about, proved the happiest event of their lives. Philip became a graver and more thoughtful man, and began to discover something of the real beauty and nobleness of the character of her whom he had married only for her attractions and amiability. And as he gradually sobered down, day by day, and learned that the true dignity of married life, as well as its true happiness, is found in wedlock's happy union of a demand for our best energies together with a proffer of our best repose, his views deepened and expanded until he began to conceive something of the meaning of the word Home. That knowledge once gained, the rest was easy; and Margaret, loved and loving, had seldom cause even to murmur into his ear the affectionate remonstrance that was the very strongest argument—save a kiss—that she ever employed to her husband.

RHODA BROUGHTON

(England, 1840)

GOOD-BYE, SWEETHEART! (1872)

This story, published in 1872, belongs to Miss Broughton's earlier group of stories; it called forth much admiration and had many imitators of its piquant and dashing style.

HEN Lenore Herrick learned, one June day at Dinan, from her devoted admirer, Frederick West, that Paul Le Mesurier had declined to be presented to her and her sister Jemima, on the ground that one saw Englishwomen enough at home, a spirit of perversity was roused within her by an indifference she seldom met; and it led her to seek a meeting with him in a manner utterly unconventional, though West had acquainted her with Le Mesurier's unenviable reputation. Thus their acquaintance began with disapproval and distaste on his part, which the influence of her beauty seemed powerless to remove, especially while he was a witness of her rudeness and thoughtlessness toward her sister and their old friend Frederick; and on her part with the determination to change the unfavorable opinion of the ugly, brusque Englishman, whose indifference had roused her interest. Lenore could not bear contradiction; she had never been thwarted, for in her childhood she had been delicate and had been denied nothing, lest in a fit of ill-temper she should burst a blood-vessel; and as she grew up her beauty had brought her the consideration her delicacy had brought her in childhood. She was unable to accept a defeat in anything.

One evening when Lenore had strolled away from the pension, Jemima sent Paul to take her a wrap. He found her in the Place, and gave his message rather stiffly. He was

answered so rudely that he turned to go, but instantly a charming face, with little waves of moonlight rippling over it, smiled
up at him

"I was rude, I suppose. I often am, I fancy."

"Very often."

"It is my way. I do not think it is quite all my fault," she
said almost humbly; "when I was a child, if I said anything
rude they only laughed and thought it clever. I wish they
had not, now."

"So do I." Then after they had been sitting a while in
silence he asked, "What are you thinking of?"

"I am thinking," dreamily, "of how the Rance is looking
now, down at Lehon, as it laps those wild steps where the
monks used to bathe."

"Shall I row you down there to see?" he asked banteringly.

"*Will* you? Ah, no! I see you were only tantalizing me."

"I will take you and welcome, if you wish," he answered
simply.

"If one were fond of her, one would be in the seventh
heaven, I suppose," said Paul cynically to himself as he rowed.

"Stop rowing," cried Lenore suddenly, "I want to gather
some of those lilies."

"What will you do with them?" he asked as she pulled at
the tough stalks.

"You will see," she answered, as she dried a dripping bud
and placed it, closed and sleepy, in her hair. "Do you like it?"

"Yes," he said half angrily. He would have laughed if
anyone had told him that morning that Lenore Herrick would
make his heart beat so.

"Take it, then," said she with a low laugh," as a memento
of the fast girl who *would* go out boating with you at ten o'clock
at night." He reddened.

"You will not have it?" she asked, flinging the blossom far
out into the river.

"How impatient you are!" he cried eagerly, "I did want
it! I will have it yet." He rowed toward it and, unmindful
of the nature of little cockboats, was leaning out to grasp it
when Lenore exclaimed wildly; but in another instant both
were splashing in the moonlit Rance.

An hour later when Paul was scrambling into dry clothes he said to himself:

"A very blessed upset! She was trying her best to make a fool of me, and she had all but succeeded."

A week after this episode Paul succumbed to Frederick's despondent misery and consented to plead his cause with Lenore, urged thereto on the ground that she always listened to him.

"I am so glad you have come!" she said, beginning to talk very fast as she saw his look of grave, critical intentness, under which her great frank eyes paled suddenly and her color changed to tremulous carnation.

"Frederick is going home to-morrow," he began brusquely.

"Is he? I hope he will not cry when he says good-by. It always makes me laugh and that looks so unfeeling."

"You are unfeeling."

"About Frederick? We shall miss him, but you would hardly expect me to go into hysterics over *him*."

"It would be much better for you if you had some one to go into hysterics about. You will not be angry with me, will you? You are one of those women who would be much better and happier married than single. You ought, however, to marry either a tyrant or a slave."

"And which would you recommend?" she asked, lifting her eyes archly, yet with difficulty, to his face.

"In your case, I think, the slave. I do you the justice to believe that a man's looks would not influence you much," proceeded Paul, half wishing he were not a proxy, "and if a fellow had been fond of you ever since he knew you, you would not send him away without hope, even though you do turn him into ridicule now and then, would you?"

Her lips trembled and formed some word, but it was inaudible.

"You will at least listen to him this afternoon?"

"To whom?" asked Lenore in bewilderment.

"Why Frederick, of course."

There was a painful pause; the girl's face grew white and her eyes were dilated in angry surprise.

"I am to understand that you have been taking the trouble

of making love to me off his hands?" she asked in a husky, choked voice. "Tell him to do his own errands next time."

She pointed to the door and Paul hurried out, only to find that he had left his hat in the little salon, where on his return he found Lenore lying on the sofa, her body shaking with violent sobs.

"Lenore! Lenore!" he cried, flinging himself on his knees beside her. "What have I done? Tell me—Lenore! Tell me—darling."

Her lovely eyes were drowned in tears; her cheeks were crimson with weeping—for him—as he felt with irrepressible, passionate exultation.

"What do you mean?" she cried, wrenching herself from him, "I hate you! Go!"

He left her then, but they met soon again at Guingamp during the *pardon* and at Morlaix, where Paul was accompanied by his friend, Charles Scrope, with whom he was making a walking tour. One day Lenore and Paul went to Huelgoat, and as they sat beside the brook near the *pierre tremblante*, Paul sighed for Joshua's gift—that he could with the hope of being obeyed say, "Sun, stand thou still."

"Why should you say so? He will last long enough to light us home and that is all we want him for to-day."

"*To-day!* Yes, but probably he will shine upon us two together at Huelgoat never again."

"He will shine upon us at Morlaix, which will be much the same."

"He will not shine upon us together anywhere long," said Paul, rather crossly, "for I am going back to England the day after to-morrow."

"Going!" she repeated, while a treacherous white spread over her cheeks and lips.

"Yes," answered Paul, his vain man's heart all astir at her change of countenance.

"Lenore," he continued impetuously, "do not you think that we should get on very well together always?"

"I think," said she, trying to laugh, "that we should quarrel a good deal." "I do not know why I am asking you, for I have no business to ask any woman, and yet—tell me, Lenore, am I worth living in a garret with?"

She gave him no speech; he had to read his answer in her eyes that flashed softly through happy tears.

"Paul," she said at length, "you have not yet asked me whether I like you."

"I suppose," he answered gayly, "that I thought actions spoke louder than words."

"You *knew* I was fond of you, you have known it all along! If you had been less sure of me, you would have valued me a hundred times more," said she, with bitter mortification, fixing her solemn, tragic eyes on his face.

"Do not talk such nonsense," he retorted brusquely, the more brusquely from a latent consciousness that there was a grain of truth in her accusation. After another little silence Lenore said:

"Paul, can you swear to me that you like me always, even when you are away from me?"

"Lenore, I will tell you the truth. I would not have loved you if I could have helped it. I feel that you are not a woman that a man will have an easy time with; but now I would not change you for any woman."

"Would not you? I am glad."

"Poor darling, I wish I were better worth being glad of!"

To his disgust, Paul found that his friend would not return with him to England, and the thought of handsome Charles Scrope lying at Lenore's feet reading poetry to her, or succeeding him in moonlight strolls, sent him into a fury of jealousy. His last words when they parted were:

"Be a good girl, Lenore, and do not flirt with Scrope. God bless you, my darling!"

They did not meet again till Christmas, which Paul spent at the home of Lenore's widowed sister, Sylvia Prodgers, where he found that Scrope, an old acquaintance of his hostess, had been for a week. The months of their separation had been spent by Lenore and Jemima at Dinan, whither Scrope had followed them and remained while they did. Paul's jealousy, felt at their parting, was constantly aroused as he saw his friend's unconcealed love for Lenore and their familiarity, evidenced by her cavalier treatment of him. So the time passed with frequent quarrels between the lovers—quarrels based on Scrope's devotion and also on the impression current that Scrope was Lenore's *fiancé*—until the day of the Infirmary Ball. There had been a bitter quarrel the day before, and Lenore demanded of Scrope that he leave her sister's house, where he was causing her so much unhappiness. He recalled to her the long days at Dinan; but she declared that even there she had told him to go.

"Your lips said go," he replied, "but I swear that your eyes said stay."

But at last, by dint of stinging, cutting speeches, she roused him to say that he would go, but not until after the ball and only on condition that she would there waltz with him four times. At first she refused with bitter sneers, but, influenced by his beauty and his uncontrollable love, she relented and promised what he asked.

Paul as a dancer was not a success, and after their first attempt he asked Lenore, as they sat in a secluded nook, to dance with no one else that night. Had he coaxed or entreated her, she might have acquiesced, but he received her first petulant refusal so sullenly, that she left him and waltzed with Scrope, who found her just then. Scrope danced superbly; in Lenore the love of dancing was intense; and during that waltz all feelings were merged in acute, sensuous enjoyment. After their second dance Paul took her aside and said with cold politeness:

"May I ask, Lenore, what is inducing you to make yourself so remarkable with Scrope to-night?"

"What do you mean?"

"I mean," in an imperative tone, "that I distinctly object to your dancing with him."

"That is unfortunate, as I promised him four waltzes on condition that he leaves Sylvia's to-morrow."

"Your promised him!" repeated Paul, "Are you mad, or are you bent on driving me mad? Why, Lenore, why—if you only meant to torment me—why did you not leave me alone?"

'Leave you alone!" she repeated, turning white.

"I mean that you—solely for the gratification of your own vainity as I now see—made me love you against my wish, against my better judgment: it would have been better if we had never met."

"I quite agree with you," she answered, making no sign, though a pain like a knife went through her heart.

Though he believed that if he should marry this woman he would be miserable, he could not give her up without an effort; so he spoke tenderly, pleaded lovingly and had all but melted her, when he used the fatal words, "As long as you are my betrothed wife, I forbid you to dance with Scrope." The word "forbid" maddened her; he made no reply to her jibes, but at length said with a bitter smile:

"To-night has proved to me my egregious conceit. Do you know that for the last six months I have been reproaching myself with the thought that, well and heartily as I loved you, you loved me even better. I am disabused, Lenore; you are incapable of loving anyone but yourself. I have done with you."

Before breakfast next morning he was gone. Lenore, miserable at her loss, wrote to him, and received a reply so cold and cutting that in a fury of despair she engaged herself to Scrope within a week, and threw herself into preparations for a speedy wedding with an ardor more than feminine. The wedding was to be an elaborate one, the feast gay and large, and the house was crammed from attic to cellar; but an hour before the ceremony the bride fell in a faint, from which hours were required to bring her to consciousness. For three days she lay in bed, not ill, not very well; on the third she was dressed and established in Sylvia's boudoir, where Scrope sought her and urged that they be married quietly at once; but she made excuses and declared that he must wait six months or a year.

"A year! That means never. So you have been tricking me! But I have seen it coming. Every day your mouth has said to me, 'I like you—we shall be happy together;' and every day your eyes have said, 'I loathe you!' Has it occurred to you to calculate how many falsehoods you have told me?"

"Stop! You are very bitter to me, but you speak truth. I have told you many lies but I have told them, too, to myself. I have longed and striven with all my strength to care for you.

I tried to wrench away all the love I had given and give it to you instead, but it was too soon. I thought I could forget all in a minute, but I cannot. Do you think I wish to remember? Does one enjoy not sleeping and not eating and being in miserable, uneasy pain all night?"

"I suppose it is all for the best," he said in a tone of somber excitement; "if you had been decently civil to me I should have been happier than any man can be and live. Yet I know that if once I could get you all to myself I could make you love me: you would thwart and hinder me, but I could make you."

"I wish you could," she said sadly.

"Then will you marry me now—at once? Will you marry me to-morrow?"

"Not to-morrow; give me six months."

"I see how it is," he said fiercely. "I have been patient with you and you think I shall be so always. You are mistaken. I will marry you *now* or *never*."

"Then it must be never; you have said it yourself."

"Very well," he answered in a husky whisper, "it shall be never. Good-by, Lenore!"

When June came again it found Lenore with her sisters in the high, cold valley of the Engadine, at Bergun, where they stopped overnight on their way to Pontresina. In the evening Lenore went out beyond the village to the river and walked up the gorge. As she stood on a little bridge that crossed it, she heard steps coming down the path and presently Paul came out of the rock-shadow into the light.

"Lenore!" he cried, looking into her face, pale with the gravity of intense emotion; "who would have thought of seeing you here? Only five minutes ago I was thinking of you, wondering if you had forgiven me. What have you been doing to yourself?" he asked anxiously. "Surely you are thinner than you used to be; are you ill?"

"Not very," she answered with an effort, speaking lightly, "anyone else would have made a trifle of it; but you know I always make the most of things and I have not much of a constitution—so they tell me."

"Lenore," he said after a silence, "I have wondered whether I should have the chance to tell you something. Do you remember that last letter you sent me? I did not believe in it, I thought it only a manuever to get me back and make a fool of me a second time. I hope you burned the answer I sent. I am not proud of it. When it was gone I read your letter over and I came to think there was a true ring in it; and I resolved to ask you to make friends. I had even sat down to write to you."

"Why did not you?" she cried with almost a wail.

"Why? Because at that moment I heard of your engagement to Scrope."

"But I am not engaged now," she cried passionately.

"You are not engaged now?" he repeated.

"Not I."

He turned away with something like a curse.

"Perhaps you will come 'round to him yet," he said, speaking with a white face and a tremor in his voice. "You might do worse."

"You are very good," she said, while a fiery searing pain went through her heart, "but I really do not see what business it is of yours."

"None," he said humbly, "none! Lenore"—impulsively—"before we say anything more I must tell you about my future."

"Well?"

"I am going home—perhaps you have heard it—I am going to be married."

Not much more than the usual interval between question and answer elapsed before she spoke with a stiff little smile.

"To your cousin?"

"To my cousin."

Lenore fought for a voice or a laugh as she thought of the unknown cousin who had caused her so much jealousy during her engagement.

"I never was one to care violently for anybody, but I did care for you beyond measure, only I tried to hide it. But I did love you—I did! Now I love no one beyond measure, I suppose; my affections are well in hand. The other was the pleasanter while it lasted, but no doubt this is the healthier state. If we had married then, how we should have hated each other by now. You would never have given in, neither should I. We should have been miserable."

"Miserable—yes, most miserable," she echoed slowly and mechanically.

"You agree with me," he said sharply, hardly gratified at her acquiescence, "of course. It is better."

"Let me have one good look at you," he cried after a time. "It would be a pity to forget the face of the handsomest woman one ever knew. Good-by, lovely eyes"—in a hoarse whisper—"good-by, lovely lips! You gave me no peace while I had you, but now I wish"—and at last he left her alone beside the thundering torrent, where she lay for hours on the grass.

After Lenore and her sisters had been some time at Pontresina, Jemima, watching her, saw that her sharpened profile was getting a look of pinched and suffering discontent, that its lovely roundness had been slipping quickly away since they left Bergun; and when Scrope came she realized more fully the change in Lenore by its effect on him. One day in passing through the hall Lenore heard a man's voice say, "She is not long for this world." She brooded over the words, believed that he alluded to her, and told her sister and Scrope; the assurances that they made did not deceive her. She was intensely frightened and fright made her ill. Her very fear accelerated what she feared. Two months passed and she had said to Scrope, "When it is all over make them bury me here, in the mountain graveyard, under the west wall, beneath the catchfly and the blown dandelions." One day she sent for him.

"I am going very fast, Charlie. I was never a dawdle. You will get away before the season is over."

"Oh, love, hush!"

"You would do something to oblige me?"

"Anything possible, beloved."

"You know the old story about Paul? I have never seen the notice of his marriage."

"Neither have I."

"Kind, good, patient Charlie," she said after a pause, "I have one more errand to send you on, more difficult than any of the others. When I was well I could not ask him to come back to me; now that I am dying I may send for whom I please. Do you understand? I wish you to go and fetch him."

"And leave you, my darling?"

"What good can you do me?" pettishly. "Can you give me breath or sleep?"

"I will go."

"And you will *certainly* bring him?"

"Yes."

"You think it is love that makes me want to see him. It is not. When one is as sick as I am, one is past love; all night through his face vexes me; I torment myself trying to recall it; I must see whether I have remembered it right; it has been with me every moment in this world, I must take it, distinct and clear, with me into the next."

At length came the day on which Scrope had engaged to return, and at evening he had not come. Lenore lay and with haunted, piteous eyes entreated her sisters to keep her.

"After all—I shall have to go," she said with a low wail, "I cannot wait. Oh, Paul! You might have hurried!"

But finally a carriage rolled up noisily; there was the sound of one step on the stairs and Scrope entered, haggard and travel-stained, alone. He went hastily to the couch and took her gently in his arms.

"My darling, I have broken my promise. He has not come because it was his wedding-day when I got there. Oh, beloved, say you forgive me! You are not going without one word— speak!"

But Lenore had "gone through the straight and dreadful pass of death."

NANCY (1873)

This, generally regarded as one of the best, if not the best of Miss Broughton's novels, was the fifth in the order of publication. It has been used as the foundation of a comedy.

E Greys, six of us, were making taffy in the schoolroom. Barbara, our eldest, was kneeling before the fire and stirring. She was undeniably beautiful; but, alas! we deteriorated in looks as we went downward in age; Algy was not quite as good-looking as Barbara; then with me there was a very decided falling-off, as Algy often candidly told me; the Brat and Bobby carried on the decline in comeliness; and Tou Tou was the climax, having the thinnest legs, the widest mouth, the invisiblest nose, and the over-visiblest ears that ever went to the make-up of a child of twelve.

Our mother entered. "Your father says—"

"Says what? Something unpleasant, of course. Who is it now?" said Bobby.

"Of course it is I," said Algy bitterly. "It is always I."

"It is no one," said mother when she had a chance to be heard. "No one has done anything. Only your father sends word that, as Sir Roger Tempest is coming to-day, he hopes you will make less noise this evening than you did last. He doesn't wish his friend to think he keeps a private lunatic asylum."

I hastened to declare that I should not dine with the visitor that night, as I should be sure to say some of my unfortunate things to father.

"Some of you must dine."

"We will send Barbara and Algy, and he will think we are all equally presentable. It will be more to your credit, mother, than if the rest of us were submitted to the poor old thing's notice."

"What poor old thing? Oh, I understand."

"He must be pretty ancient," said Algy, "as he was at school with father."

"What a grand thing it would be for the family if he were to adopt you, Barbara!" I exclaimed.

"Here he is?" cried Tou Tou from the window. "The dog-cart is turning the corner."

Algy looked out. "Yes, there he is—our future benefactor. Welcome, welcome, good old man!"

My first interview with our guest came after prayers that night. I was hurrying along the passage when I felt a foot on my garment behind and heard the crackling of breaking stitches.

"You beast!" I cried, and turned to strike offending Bobby. "This is the third time—"

What had I done? Called Sir Roger Tempest a beast and raised my hand to cuff him! But then, reassured by the genial laughter in his eyes, I held up my skirt.

"Look! See what you have done and forgive me. But of course I meant it for Bobby."

He took hold of the rent with me and we both examined it.

"How exceedingly clumsy of me! I beg your pardon ten thousand times!"

He was old, despite his straightness and slenderness, and the keenness of his kindly blue eyes. A young man would have said, with the variety and discrimination of to-day, "I am awfully sorry! How awfully stupid of me! What an awful duffer I am!"

Sir Roger walked on with me; as we approached the school-room door, Bobby was heard: "I say, Nancy, who are you colloguing with out there? I believe you've got hold of our future benefac—" His head now appeared around the door and was suddenly withdrawn with an "Oh!" of discomfiture.

"I am keeping you," said Sir Roger, and with a cordial handshake we parted.

A fortnight passed and Sir Roger was still our guest. My friendship with him had advanced rapidly. He had rescued me from the top of the garden wall where Bobby had left me stranded, maliciously carrying off the ladder; and we had had many little walks together. I had confided to him that I should like to marry a rich man, one who could give the boys some shooting and help Algy on in the army and Bobby in the navy; and with a nice house where I could give Barbara a good time and have long visits from mother where she would be away from housekeeping worries, and—I came near saying from father's tyranny, but checked myself, and added that I should like a donkey carriage for Tou Tou, but would not insist upon that.

Other confidences there were; and Sir Roger overheard some of father's remarks when he supposed only his loved ones within hearing that contrasted strongly with the suavity of his address to us in the presence of company. And Sir Roger had spoken of himself to me as "an old wreck"; and I had answered, "Yes, it is rather hard, isn't it?"—one of my "unlucky things," as mother calls them, of which I only became conscious when Bobby crushed me by saying, after I mentioned it in the report I was compelled to give in the schoolroom, "Of course he meant you to contradict him; and from the little I know of you, I am morally certain that you did not—did you, now?"

At the end of the fortnight I returned from a private conference with mother and reported to the incredulous ears of my brethren that Sir Roger had gone away for a week to give me time to consider; for—"Sir Roger wants to—to—to marry me! There!"

"Marry you!" said the Brat. "Why, he was at school with father!"

"I wish to heaven he had never been at school anywhere!" I cried in fury.

"He is forty-seven," said Algy. "Nineteen from forty-seven?"

They were still more astonished when they found I had serious thoughts of saying yes.

"Do you mean to say you are in love with him?" asked Bobby.

"I mean nothing so silly, I am too old for any such nonsense," I said loftily. "It would be such a fine thing for the family," I added.

After a moment's reflection, Bobby mentioned the game at Tempest, and the Brat spoke of a moor in Scotland. Algy wondered if his prospective brother-in-law would give him a mount now and then.

"I would have you all staying with me always!" I said, beginning to dance.

My acceptance, which Sir Roger seemed almost afraid to receive, lest he should be taking advantage of my youth and inexperience to lead me into what I might have future cause to regret, was interspersed with what I afterwards recognized as among my unlucky things; as when he asked if I were not sure that it was for the sake of my brothers and sisters, reminding me of what I had told him of my ambition for them, I said:

"I hope to heaven you did not think I was hinting! I really and truly was not! I was thinking of a young man. I assure you that I had as much idea of marrying you as of marrying father!"

A month later we were married and off for the Continent. Four weeks there, while, to tell the truth, I was lonesome for the clatter of youthful tongues; then a short, blissful visit at home; and then I was alone at Tempest, my new home, and Sir Roger was on his way to Antigua on urgent business connected with some property he owned there.

Not alone long, for Algy and Barbara came; and we had frequent visits from our nearest neighbor, Mr. Frank Musgrave, whom we had met in Dresden, where I had several sharp little quarrels with him. Perhaps I did say a good many of my unlucky things; but he would not have resented them if he had been like the boys I was used to at home, who know how to take chaff good-naturedly. I had an idea, in fact, it had entered my head at Dresden, when I first heard that Musgrave Abbey was opposite my future home—that Barbara might one day be our neighbor at Musgrave Abbey.

On my first Sunday at church I noticed a small, white woman, not remarkable for either youth or beauty, and yet for some reason I looked and looked again at her. When we were going home we were joined by Mr. Musgrave. Presently the lady I had noticed drove by. "Who is she?" I asked.

"You do not know?"

"No; how should I?"

"That is Mrs. Huntley."

"I am not much wiser now."

"Is it possible that you have never heard of her? You must have—Sir Roger has mentioned her to you?"

"No; nor any of the neighbors. Most likely he did not recall her existence."

"Most likely."

"How do you know—what reason have you for thinking he knew there was such a person?"

"I have no reason. I think nothing," with an ostentatious air of reserve.

He took luncheon with us, and on the way to the afternoon service, I asked, trying to speak as if I had but just recalled the subject, "What did you mean about Mrs. Huntley?"

Brushing aside his denials, into which his manner put such a sinister meaning, I insisted upon an explanation, and got it at length: that, according to report, she had once been engaged to General Tempest; but, as he was then only General Tempest, with a healthy elder brother and little else but his pay, she had thrown him over.

"Is she a widow?"

"No; she has a husband somewhere—in the colonies, I believe."

The next day Mrs. Huntley called. Having succeeded in getting little but monosyllables in answer to my attempts at conversation, I was surprised at the change in her manner when Algy came in—the playfulness, the sparkle in it. I found afterward that the presence of a man had always that inspiring effect.

As Christmas drew near I received word that Roger's return would have to be put off still longer. About the same time I made the surprising discovery that Algy was infatuated with Mrs. Huntley and that she was accepting costly gifts from him. I ventured to remonstrate with him, only to make him angry.

"This comes extremely well from you," he said. "How is Musgrave?"

"Is it possible," I thought, "that he does not see the difference? Doesn't he understand that it is Barbara?"

To add to my uneasiness, Frank Musgrave let me know that he had already heard from Mrs. Huntley that Roger's return was postponed. "Roger corresponds with her, then," I thought. And another worry—although Frank and Barbara seemed the best of friends, still he had not "spoken."

When at last Roger was really coming, I was returning through Brindley Wood from a long walk, singing blithely, when I came across Frank sitting on a great stone in a lonely hollow. I told him my good news after making him guess at it, and reproached him for not saying at least that he was glad.

"I am not glad! You have often blamed me for hinting and implying; to-day I will tell you the truth—you know it as well as I—I am not glad!"

I could not answer, but stood staring in horrible astonishment.

"Nancy," he said, coming nearer, "you are not glad either. Speak the truth! There is no one to hear you but me, and I know it already. I have known it from that first evening in Dresden. I was never so sorry for anyone as I have been for you ever since I first caught sight of you—weariness and depression in every line of your face—"

There was a grain of truth in this last assertion that made it sting. At my exclamation of angry astonishment he went on bitterly. Was I going to pretend to be surprised? Why, then, had I made myself the talk of the neighborhood with him? Why had I constantly urged him to visit me?

Why, indeed? I could not give my real reason, even to clear myself. I could not mention Barbara. I could only ask why I should prefer him to Roger. Was he in any way superior? Even if I had not cared for my husband, why should I have chosen him, even to flirt with—him, who never amused me in the least, who had often been a bore to me?

"Is that true? Are you sure that under all your rude words you are not nearer loving me than you think? that, with that barrier between us, you cannot reconcile it to your conscience—"

"Quite sure! it has nothing to say to conscience! If it were right, if it were my duty even, if it were the only way to save

myself from hanging, I never, never could say I was fond of
you! I do not see what there is to be fond of in you! before
God, I do not!"

"There, stop! You will never outdo that!"

The twilight was coming on. In a sudden panic I ran along
the path. He overtook me. "Nancy, we are not going to part
like this? Feeling for you as I do, do you feel absolutely nothing
for me?"

"Feel? I feel as if a slug had crawled over me!"

"Thank you. I am satisfied."

"Stay!" he said as we reached the road, laying his hand
on my arm. "One good wish—Lady Tempest, I hope that
your fidelity will be rewarded as it deserves!"

"I have no doubt of it!" But as I said this, a sharp jealous
pain ran through my heart.

I had just left him when I was passed by a carriage. Its
occupant, Mrs. Huntley, had undoubtedly seen our parting and
my flushed and tear-stained face.

My uppermost thought as I went on was of my own degradation. What had I done? Made myself the talk of the neighborhood, he said. This was, then, the way I had repaid Roger's
boundless trust—brought discredit on his name! Of what avail
that my heart was clean? And Barbara—how should I tell her?
"I will not," I resolved. "I will never tell anyone. No! I
will wade knee-deep in falsehood before anyone shall know
of my disgrace."

Barbara, I thought, would learn gradually, when he ceased
to come, of the baselessness of her hopes. But she learned it
the next day from a cold little note saying he was starting for
London and Paris and offering to undertake any commissions
for her.

While I was watching for the dog-cart that was to bring
Roger from the station, I was surprised to see the groom drive
in alone and turn to the stables.

"Why did not the groom wait for the next train?" I asked
the footman that answered my ring.

"If you please, my lady, Sir Roger is walking up."

"What! all the way from Bishopsthorpe?"

"No, my lady; only from Mrs. Huntley's. She was at

the gate, and Sir Roger got out to speak to her and bade
James drive on and tell your ladyship he would be here
directly."

So our first meeting after his eight months of absence was
clouded by the shadow that Frank Musgrave's fate had thrown
over my happiness. But though it was but half dispelled by
his explanation that "the poor little thing" was at the gate so
eager to hear from her husband, that he had not the heart to
keep her waiting, and though I threw out several ugly hints,
yet the day could not be entirely spoiled, and sunshine came
back after every passing cloud.

The next was a bright February morning and I proposed a
walk in the grounds. "Come, let us go—at once!"

"At once? Well, I don't know—duty before pleasure. Had
I not better go to Zephine Huntley's first and get it over?"

"To Zephine Huntley's? Again?"

"Yes, again; why not? I have a whole sheaf of letters and
papers for her."

"Let John or William carry them. Don't go, Roger. Stay
with me this one first day. I will ring for John."

"No, no; they will not do. I have to go through many of
these papers with her. We are trying to make an arrangement
with her husband's creditors so that he can come home."

At length it was settled that I should walk to Mrs. Huntley's
with him, but not go in, as she might not care to go into her
husband's liabilities before a third person, and come back in an
hour and a half to walk home with him. I was there at the
minute, but he was late; not only late, but changed, unaccount-
ably changed to me. I thought of Algy—Algy as he used to be,
Algy as he was now, soured, sulky, unloving, his very beauty
dimmed by discontent and passion. Was this the beginning of
a like change in Roger?

I thought so. I thought the contrast between the crude
gawkiness of the girl he had married and the mature and subtle
grace, the fine and low-voiced sweetness of the woman he had
lost, had struck him with keen force on seeing her once more.
But later I found that his silence and constraint had another
cause. She had told him of the parting she had seen between
me and Musgrave. And when he asked me if it was true and I

told him it was false, he turned away; and I knew that I had lied in vain!

Some time afterward a longing seized me to go to him and tell him the truth even yet; but when I was with him I could not; for he never gave me an opening; and if I could, the thought would come, would he believe me? He would say, "If you were innocent, why did you lie? And how do I know that you are not lying now?"

So the days passed and the constraint between us grew—without unkindness or even neglect—and yet what a chill there was in all his friendly words, in all his kindly, considerate actions! We went to London for the season; and Mrs. Huntley was there too in her little apartment with stacks of cut flowers, with her brougham and her opera-boxes. The season over, we went back to the same old unhappiness.

September came and with it a letter from Barbara—"It has all come right! I am going to marry Frank after all!" Engaged to Musgrave! Was Brindley Wood a dream, or was this a dream? Roger's surprise was as great as mine, and now his questions gave me an opportunity to make my confession; but I turned them off with perverse flippancy, and with another of my gibing hints at his devotion to Mrs. Huntley, hints that gave me one of the few pleasures I had left.

"Nancy," he said after one of them, "if the idea had been less unspeakably absurd, it would have occurred to me many times that you are jealous of Zephine and me! You jealous of me! Who has put such notions into your head? I am sure they did not come of themselves—by whom you best know, and whether his words or mine are worthy of most credit!"

Some days later, Roger came in greatly disturbed with an open note in his hand. It was from Mrs. Huntley, to the effect that Algy Grey had come there, much against her will, and had been taken with what seemed the low fever that was about. She would wish to stay and nurse him; but her knowledge of the world's sharp tongue and consideration for Mr. Huntley forbade it, and she was leaving at once.

"Is it possible," I said, "that after having decoyed him there she is leaving him to die alone?"

"So it seems," he answered indignantly, "I could not have believed it of her."

"He will die!" I said, "I know he will! We were too prosperous. None of us has ever gone! And I said yesterday that I liked him the least of all the boys. Oh, I wish, I wish I had not said it!"

But he did not die. Barbara, Roger and I went to him, and Barbara pulled him through the weary weeks; for it was always Barbara for whom he called when he was not raving about Zephine.

He was saved; but the fever laid hold of Barbara, and she slipped quietly out of life, her hand in Musgrave's, trusting him to the last, but willing to go and confident of the future.

When all was over I went home for a while, to be where Barbara was known and loved. I stood alone in the empty schoolroom, I only of all the noisy six. The old carpet was still discolored with the stains of our cookery; there was the black splash on the wall made by the inkstand I dodged when Bobby threw it at me. I went into the village to the poor she had loved; they were sorry, certainly, but it was more what they had lost by her than herself that they deplored; and I found more consolation in retracing alone the walks I had taken with her. In time a sort of peace came to me; and as I looked back over the months before she died, I recalled with dazed wonder that even then I regarded myself as unfortunate, overwhelmed with sorrow. And why? My jealousy, a living, biting, stinging thing then; how dead it was now!

I would begin all over again; and so I told Roger when I was back at Tempest.

"I shall be so different that you will not know me for the same, and if—if—you still go on liking her best, and thinking her prettier and pleasanter to talk to—well, it will not be your fault, and I will try not to mind!"

"Are you still harping on that worn-out string, child?"

"Is it worn out? If you say so I will believe it. But when you were engaged to her—"

"Engaged to her?"

"Were you not?"

"Never to anyone but you. Her father was my friend and

when he was dying he asked my promise to do what I could for her; I was fond of her and willing to help her in any way—but marry her—be engaged to her—"

And then I told him the story of Brindley Wood.

"And is that all? Are you sure that you did not a little regret that it must be so, that you did not feel it hard to be forever tied to my gray hair, my eight-and-forty years?"

"Hush! I will not listen to you! What do I care if you were a hundred, two hundred? What is it to me? I love you— love you—how stupid you have been not to see it all along!"

And so we are happy, though I can never be as boisterously gay as before the grave closed over Barbara. Only I wish that Roger were not nine-and-twenty years older than I.

CHRISTINE CHAPLIN BRUSH

(United States, 1842-1892)

THE COLONEL'S OPERA-CLOAK (1879)

This book was published anonymously in the No Name Series, and immediately gained a wide popularity, owing to its lively humor and clever delineation of Southern characteristics. It was its author's first book and also her most important one, as her later works did not equal this in interest or in literary value.

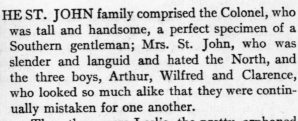

HE ST. JOHN family comprised the Colonel, who was tall and handsome, a perfect specimen of a Southern gentleman; Mrs. St. John, who was slender and languid and hated the North, and the three boys, Arthur, Wilfred and Clarence, who looked so much alike that they were continually mistaken for one another.

Then there were Leslie, the pretty, orphaned niece of the Colonel; Pomp, a faithful old slave, who had clung to his master's family through thick and thin; Jasper, his grandson; and last, but not least in importance, the Colonel's opera-cloak.

This beloved object, which had often warmed and clothed the St. John family, and had been with them, by day and by night, in pleasure and in sorrow, having neither eaten their food nor spent their money, should certainly not be omitted from the category.

Mrs. Douglas, the doctor's wife, had her introduction to this interesting family when she went to call upon Mrs. St. John. Her son, Ned Douglas, had made the acquaintance of the St. John boys in Sunday school, and had brought home to his mother such wonderful accounts of their manners and doings that her interest became thoroughly aroused.

Through Ned Mrs. Douglas learned that the boys, though poor, were "splendid;" that there were three white and one black, and that they had lived previously in the South, where they had been as "rich as kings and had owned lots of slaves." Ned also informed her that Arthur, the oldest boy, had told him that his mother was sick and would be pleased to have Mrs. Douglas call upon her, as she had not seen a real lady for a year. Accordingly Mrs. Douglas set out for this visit with missionary intent, but when she reached the specified street and number she was convinced that she had made a mistake, as she was confronted by a handsome residence in a fashionable part of the city. However, she saw two dirty white boys and a black one, who was a trifle cleaner, playing on the doorsteps, so she inquired whether Mrs. St. John lived there, and was informed that she did.

Mrs. Douglas then announced her identity, and finally secured entrance into the house after much difficulty, as the knob had parted company with the door-bell and it took repeated efforts on the part of Jasper, the colored boy, to force open the front door, which was apparently unaccustomed to such a process.

Upon entering, Mrs. Douglas was greeted by a black man who was just ascending the basement stairs and who bowed respectfully, in response to her inquiry as to whether she could see Mrs. St. John.

"Yes, Missus, if yer will have de goodness to wait one moment whiles I opens de parlor do'. De knob, I sees, is off." He said this as calmly as if it were quite usual for knobs to step out on business.

He vanished into the back parlor, where a murmuring conversation was soon heard.

The sliding-door groaned, and evidently ran off its track. Then, with a flourish, as if he had that instant heard of the arrival there, Pomp opened the front-parlor door.

Such a parlor! The shades were drawn to the highest point, the lace curtains were tied in knots.

There were a pair of cavalry boots under the piano, and a pan of molasses candy on top of it. A bowl of broth stood on the center table. The chair which Mrs. Douglas took refused to hold her; and the sofa was as comfortable as a seat in a coal-bin, the springs being broken and twisted.

Pomp retired into the back parlor to inform "Missus" that the lady was in the other room.

The rustle of silk was now heard, and the beating of pillows. No word was spoken; but Mrs. Douglas was conscious of the pantomime which was directing Pomp as he squeaked about the apartment.

At last he appeared at the sliding-door, which had refused to close behind him, and asked her in, saying: "Mrs. Douglas— Mrs. St. John."

On a bed, in one corner of the finely furnished room, Mrs. St. John half-sat, half-lay. She motioned Mrs. Douglas to a chair, which the poor lady tested with her hand before seating herself.

Mrs. St. John was a young and very handsome woman. She wore a lilac silk waist, with a lace shawl thrown over her shoulders, fastened with a diamond pin.

"You can't tell how glad I am to see someone who has lived South," she said, in a low, drawling voice. "These Northerner are so ill-bred. I hate to have my boys associate with them— it's so bad for their manners. I see the difference in them already. I believe it's in the air. The war made things very hard for the Colonel. He fought and fought; and the Northerners stole everything they could lay their hands on. The Colonel lost all his slaves, and I lost all mine, except Pomp: he knew what was good for him. The ungrateful things—to clear out, after we had fed and clothed them for generations.

"The Colonel brought us all here, and then went out to his old mines. I'm so much younger than he, he ought to stay at home and look after me. I was only sixteen when I was married.

"I never am very well," she continued. "I like to lie down— it's so much easier than to sit up. It's so cold here that I never can keep warm out of bed, and hardly in it. Pomp! Pomp!"

Mrs. Douglas had seen Pomp through the door, nodding in one of the red satin chairs. He started on hearing his name.

"Pomp, my feet are cold! Bring me the Colonel's opera-cloak."

Pomp began a search. He looked in the closet and behind

the chairs, and finally went on all-fours under the bed, whence he triumphantly emerged with a large blue cape, lined with scarlet, with shining gilt clasps at the neck.

After Pomp had tucked the cloak about his mistress's feet and settled himself for another nap, Mrs. St. John continued her remarks. She discoursed for a while about the Colonel's niece, her lack of prospects, and her Spanish admirer named Cavello, and then called Pomp and ordered him to summon Miss Leslie into their presence. Pomp opened the door into the hall, when instantly there was a scampering and scuffling.

"Yer unmannered boys, hain't yer got no 'ligion, to make yer act like gent'men? Don't yer know de Bible—'Member yer fader an' moder to keep 'em holy'? Peekin' fro' de do' at de strange lady, actin' as ef yer was raised Norf!"

Leslie St. John, having been summoned by Pomp, came shyly into the room, and Mrs. Douglas was pleased with her at once.

"This is the Colonel's niece, that I was telling you about," said Mrs. St. John. "She's an orphan, and hasn't a cent. Well, I hope the Northerners are satisfied, when they see the poor starved orphans they made." Mrs. St. John looked severely at Mrs. Douglas, as if she had personally been upon the war-path. Leslie, who did not fancy being exhibited as a representative Southern orphan, was somewhat mortified by her aunt's introduction, but the scene was soon interrupted by the entrance of the boys, who demanded the purchase of a new football at once.

An animated discussion, to which Pomp added his protesting voice, immediately ensued, the excited participants forming about Mrs. St. John a group which closely resembled the death-bed of Luther.

After listening to the parleying for some time, Mrs. St. John said fretfully, "Oh, dear, do go away! you want to kill me, I know. Here, Arthur, take this twenty-dollar bill, spend five dollars for all of you, and bring me back the change."

Before long, the black boy, Jasper, returned, and laid a bill on the bed.

"I want—I want—let me see," said Mrs. St. John, "why, I want fifteen dollars, and here's only five."

"Why," said Jasper, his eyes bulging white and round, "yer said how't every one on 'em was to have five dollars. Massa Arthur an' Massa Wilfrid dey got footballs an' knives an' heaps o' things, an' Massa Clar'nce kicked 'em in de store, an' hollered, an' dey had to buy him things."

"That's just the way those boys act since they came North," said the poor lady, feebly shaking her head.

Pomp had been nodding again in the satin chair. He roused himself at Jasper's voice, and came into the room.

"I'se gwine to market now, Miss Marie," said he to Mrs. St. John, "an' I wants five dollars, ef yer pleases. Ef I don't go now, I specs yer'll give Massa Cavello a football next, an' den dere won't be no mouf-balls for to eat when de dinner-time comes."

Mrs. St. John handed him the money.

"Now you've got the last cent, Pomp, and I hope you're satisfied!" she said.

"Ef I could ever git de fust an' de middle an' de last," said Pomp to himself, "I reckon things wouldn't go so cont'ry as dey does now in dis house."

Mrs. Douglas finally took leave of her new acquaintances, filled with astonishment at the surprising scenes she had witnessed, and immediately wrote to a friend who knew them, inquiring what sort of people these were.

She described their elegantly furnished house, which looked as if it had been struck by an earthquake, and continued: "They apparently walk on the ceiling; the colored servant sleeps in the red satin chairs; they spill broth over the moquette carpets, and leave molasses candy pans on the piano. Everything is done that ought not to be done, and nothing is done that ought to be done."

In response Mrs. Douglas learned that the St. Johns belonged to one of the first Southern families, that they had been impoverished by the war, and that the Colonel, in his red-lined opera-cloak, was a most picturesque figure.

Mrs. Douglas followed her visit by an invitation to Leslie to take tea at her house, and the young woman joyfully accepted, the only drawback to her pleasure being the fact she had no proper raiment. However, when the appointed night came, she was dressed in her aunt's lilac silk, pinned over to fit her more slender form, and with the Colonel's opera-cloak about her shoulders she was guided on her way by the faithful Pomp.

Leslie, in spite of her lack of fashionable clothes, made a favorable impression upon the Douglas family and especially upon Tom, the doctor's son, who immediately fell victim to her charms.

But the pleasant evening was suddenly interrupted by the arrival of Mr. Cavello, Leslie's Spanish admirer, who appeared upon the scene with the announcement that he had come to escort Miss Leslie home. The lady, however, did not agree to this arrangement and flatly refused to accept his companionship. Soon the doorbell rang furiously, and the hall was filled with boys' voices; the little St. Johns had arrived in full force. Their advent was closely followed by the arrival of Jasper, who, like the others, had come to take Leslie home.

Mr. Cavello endeavored to dismiss the boys, but they refused to give up their ground, so the Douglas party was enlarged by several additional members. Later in the evening young Jasper, who had been napping in the hall, suddenly awakened, and seeing the opera-cloak hanging near him decided to don the familiar garment and depart for home.

Mr. Cavello caught a glimpse of the cloak as it flitted through the door, and, thinking that Leslie had succeeded in eluding him, made a hasty exit and started in pursuit. His sudden departure caused much amusement to the assembled company, and someone suggested that this was an example of taking "Spanish leave" such as was not often witnessed.

Mr. Cavello's disappearance gave Tom an opportunity to see Leslie home, which proved to be a very satisfactory arrangement for both the young people.

The experiences of the opera-cloak were many and varied. "O. C. St. John," as it was facetiously dubbed by the Douglas family, figured in one dramatic episode after another.

One day Clarence disappeared, and to the consternation of his family no trace of him could be found. The following morning an item appeared in a paper to the effect that a boy had been discovered nearly drowned from having fallen through the ice, but his escape from death was due to his having on a military cape, which buoyed him up, and prevented such a catastrophe.

Leslie, with Tom for an escort, immediately hastened to the hospital, where Clarence had been taken, and found him in bed with the opera-cloak hanging by him, giving the effect of a guardian angel hovering near.

The next adventure in which "O. C. St. John" participated was of a more enjoyable character ; Tom took Leslie for a ride into the country and of course the opera-cloak formed one of the party. The excursion proved truly delightful, and all went well until a storm arose, which prevented their return until late in the evening.

On their way home, Tom collided with another team owing to the darkness of the road, and during the confusion the opera-cloak was lost out of the carriage.

Pomp was greatly exercised when Leslie returned without this beloved article, and overjoyed when it was found and restored to him some days later. As the cloak was somewhat soiled from having lain in the mud, Pomp decided to have it cleaned, and for that purpose took it to a neighboring China-man.

While hanging by the Chinaman's door it caught the eye of the boy Jasper, who, recognizing this old friend and thinking it had been stolen, immediately decided to take possession of it.

Accordingly he proceeded to accomplish his purpose, but in so doing he did not reckon on the resistance of the China-man, who discovered him in the act. A tussle ensued, which ended in poor Jasper's being captured by a policeman and brought into court to answer to the charge of assault and battery.

Here Tom discovered him the following morning and suc-ceeded in compassing his release by explaining matters to the judge, and the opera-cloak, which had been an important witness in the case, was once more restored to its owners.

Not long after this episode little Jasper was taken with a sudden and fatal illness, and Dr. Douglas was called in the middle of the night to render what assistance he could.

He found the little sufferer beyond the help of human aid, lying on the parlor sofa surrounded by the weeping family.

After the doctor had done what he could for his patient, he was drawn into a corner by Pomp, who was anxious to tell him about his little grandson's case.

"Doctor," said he, "I must tell yer de symptims. John Jasper ain't never dreffle strong—his const'tution ain't good. He's had de consum'tion twice, an' times an' times he'd a perished ef I hadn't ben a-lookin' after him. Yes'day aft'noon he fell down on his side—de side what's had de fits into it before; an' wid his sore froat an' all, I know he's gwine fur to die.

"When de death-cravin' come on, says I to me, He's a-gwine to die. Fust, he axed fur some tripe, an' I cooked it fur him, an' he eat it all up. Den he axed fur some watermillion—pore boy—but I couldn't git him none, 'cause 'tain't de time fur watermillions. Den he axed fur some pie, an' I giv him dat, an' he eat it all up; an' den he axed fur some fish, an' I got dat, an' cook it an' giv it to him, an' he eat it all up. I couldn't git no pigs' feet fur him, so he axed fur liver, an' I got it an' cook it, an', don't yer b'lieve, he never eat one mou'ful of it! Den I fought, he's gwine to die right away, dis aft'noon.

"After dat, he got better, an' spoke up smart an' peart, an' I fought p'r'aps we could bring him round; but now, Massa, he's gwine—I've seen heaps of 'em gwine, an' I knows de looks."

"I am afraid he is, my poor fellow," said the Doctor.

His verdict was only too true, for in a short time little Jasper breathed his last, wrapped in the Colonel's opera-cloak, in accordance with his dying request.

After this sad event, which brought genuine sorrow to the family, it was decided by Mrs. St. John that it was time to make arrangements for the summer.

The warm weather came that year all at once. Mrs. St. John bloomed into life with the flowers, and left her bed when they arose from theirs.

The Colonel had sent home more money lately, and they had been able to have new clothes and a better table, and had paid fewer bills. Mrs. St. John sent the doctor an elegant dressing-gown—he had two already—and to Mrs. Douglas fresh flowers every day, but took no more notice of the doctor's bill than if it had never been sent. One May morning the sun poured down as hot as in July; and, cheerful and amiable and handsome, Mrs. St. John announced that she was going out of town with Pomp, to engage summer board.

Mrs. St. John decided on rooms at a fashionable hotel at the seashore and transported her family there, where Leslie's prettiness and charm, enhanced by her dainty clothes, made her an acknowledged belle.

Tom, on running down for a visit, was taken aback at the change which had come over his shy little Southern girl, and was made quite jealous by the attentions which the other men lavished upon her. He left, however, without having declared himself to Leslie, much to the disgust of Mrs. St. John, who vented her feelings by saying: "Well, I declare, and after all the pains I have taken to keep those boys away, and invite him here, he didn't care to face me, after such dishonorable conduct. I reckon he'd have done differently if the Colonel had been here. I wish he'd just met up with him."

Leslie said nothing.

"Why don't you speak?" said Mrs. St. John, displeased at her silence. "Perhaps Mr. Douglas didn't have time, you will say. How long would it take him to ask, 'Will you marry me?'"

"I don't know," said Leslie, crying.

"Well, I do," said her aunt: "about half a minute; and he had twenty-four hours for it."

Leslie felt as if she had a sum to do: if a man can offer himself in a half minute, how many times can he offer himself in twenty-four hours? She was utterly miserable.

In course of time word came from Colonel St. John that he wished his family to join him in the South, and Mrs. St. John proceeded to carry out his wishes without delay. She immediately gave up the rooms at the hotel, in spite of the protestations of the landlord that she had engaged them for the season, and returned to town at once.

In leaving the furnished house that she had hired, Mrs. St. John discovered that various articles of her own had accumulated which she did not care to transport, and accordingly decided to dispose of them by auction. Pomp was despatched to hire an auctioneer, and the sale was arranged for the following day.

When the appointed hour arrived Mrs. St. John seated herself at a front window, where she inspected the people who came up the steps, and when anyone appeared whose looks did not please her, she immediately called to Pomp and told him not to admit the person.

When the bidding finally began, much amusement was afforded the would-be purchasers, as this auction was unique in every way.

Articles were offered and then withdrawn, according to the whim of the owner, and many mistakes were made regarding her property.

After several sales the auctioneer took up a clock and offered it thus: "Well, here is a clock. Who will bid on this? It is an elegant French clock—runs a week."

"It runs two, if you run with it," said Wilfred; and he and Arthur laughed.

"I'll give you five dollars," said a man.

"Five-fifty," said another.

"Six dollars."

Mrs. St. John beckoned to Pomp.

"Nobody can't buy dat," Pomp called out, in a loud voice, "'cause it doesn't b'long to us. We forgot. Dat's de lan'lord's clock."

Everyone laughed. Soon after this a vase was being taken away when Mrs. St. John suddenly remembered that it was not hers.

"The pink pair are mine—on the mantelpiece," she called through the crack of the door behind which she was sitting.

The woman who bought the large vase was very angry.

"Why do you have an auction," she asked, "if you haven't anything to sell?"

"We have," replied Mrs. St. John, through the crack.

"Why don't you sell it, then, and know your own mind?"

"Why don't you buy the things we own, and not the things which belong to the landlord?" replied again the invisible proprietress.

After a number of ludicrous episodes, during which the auctioneer hardly knew how to conduct himself, the climax was reached when he held up a military cloak with red lining and brass buttons.

"Here is a fine cloak—a military cloak, I should say. It is of fine—"

"Oh! Nobody mustn't make no bid on dat," called Pomp, in a loud voice. "Dat can't be sold, nohow; dat b'longs to de Colonel, an' wa'n't never meant to be sold. Massy gracious! Why, don't you know! Dat's de Colonel's op'ra-cloak—Colonel St. John's."

"No, don't sell that!" cried Mrs. St. John, through the crack. "Of course that can't be sold; anybody might have known that. We are not second-hand clothes men."

"What did you put it here for, if it wasn't to be sold?" asked the auctioneer, in a little temper.

"I didn't put it dar," said Pomp. "It hed to be somewhar or 'noder, didn't it? I don't 'spect yer to sell yer own clo'es, jes' 'cause dey happens to be in dis house."

When the auction was at last over and the people had dispersed, Mrs. St. John sank into an easy chair completely exhausted, and cried: "I declare! I am almost tired to death. I was never so sick of anybody in my life as I was of that auctioneer. I thought he would never get off till he had sold every one of us; and you'd think, to hear him go on about things, that he owned them all. I pity his wife, if his tongue runs that way all the time."

Their worldly goods being satisfactorily disposed of, the St. Johns folded their tents and quietly slipped away without leaving behind them any address or any clue to their whereabouts.

Tom Douglas was filled with consternation when he learned what had occurred, and set out on a search for Leslie, who had disappeared without leaving any word of explanation.

One day in a Southern city he caught sight of a familiar object, and, recognizing the opera-cloak, he immediately accosted the wearer and found it was veritably Colonel St. John.

That gentleman received Tom's explanations cordially and took him at once to the hotel where he and his family were staying, and Leslie's greeting settled all doubts in Tom's mind regarding her indifference to him.

Tom persuaded Leslie to agree to an immediate marriage, and the event was solemnized with little delay, much to the satisfaction of the St. Johns and the faithful Pomp. The opera-cloak did not accompany the bridal couple on their journey North, but was sent in an express package by the thoughtful Pomp and reached the Douglas home in advance of Tom and his bride.

It was there to greet them upon their arrival, much to the surprise of Leslie, who had not known it was to be included in her wedding outfit, and who could not fail to look upon it as an important factor in her affairs.

The opera-cloak was hung in the lower hall awaiting its return to the Colonel, which all deemed advisable, when it suddenly disappeared and never was seen again.

Whether it was stolen, or whether it saw that its mission to the St. John family was accomplished, and went off on an errand of mercy in some other field of labor, never was known. But this we do know: somewhere, somehow, it still exists. And if you ever happen to meet a blue cloak, lined with red with "brass knobs" at the neck—no matter where it is or on whom it is, look on it with respect. You know its story. It is The Colonel's Opera-Cloak.

ROBERT BUCHANAN

(Scotland, 1841-1901)

GOD AND THE MAN (1881)

This tale of elemental passions was dramatized for the English stage soon after its appearance in book form.

FEUD of many generations had existed between the Orchardson and the Christianson families, during which the former had risen much in wealth and importance. Robert Christianson, owner of the Fen farm, and the father of two children, Christian and Kate, was finally induced to place a mortgage on his estate, negotiated with his hereditary enemy, Squire Orchardson. When the farmer died, oppressed with debt, the Squire, not at first disposed to press foreclosure, had his latent dislike fanned into fury by an altercation between his only son, Richard Orchardson, and Christian Christianson in which a blow passed.

The two young men were totally different in person and temperament. Christian, with the robust beauty and vigor of his Norse ancestry, was the type of the magnificent English yeoman. Richard, of slight frame, somewhat crippled, with greater refinement of person and manner, carried in his face suggestions of sensuality and craft. The mutual hatred became further heightened by rivalry in love, the object of their common affection being Priscilla Sefton, the daughter of a blind evangelist, a follower of John Wesley, who was then propagating the new Methodist cult in that neighborhood. Priscilla shrank from the addresses of both her lovers, when she realized the

327

acrimony of their grudge, which she sought to soften; but her heart inclined almost without self knowledge toward the young yeoman.

Richard Orchardson was agreeably surprised to find that his father approved his suit. The Squire had learned that Mr. Sefton was entitled to much higher social consideration than appeared. His large wealth had been placed in the hands of trustees, with its income diverted to religious and philanthropic uses, that the owner might live the simplest life in his religious propagandism. The culmination of Christian's hate was reached in his discovery of his sister's shame, which had been secretly wrought by the wiles of Richard Orchardson.

After a time the Seftons returned to London, and Christian's rival, Richard, also disappeared. Christian's mother, stricken to the heart by the terrible blow of her daughter's disgrace, died suddenly. The maddened son rushed to The Willows, the country seat of the Orchardsons, and compelled the Squire to return with him to look on the corpse of one who had been indirectly his victim, as well as that of his son.

"Your son," said Christian, "hath betrayed my sister and killed my mother, who lieth yonder. No matter where he is hiding, I shall find him. No matter how long I may have to wait, I shall kill him; and I should kill you this night for the wrong you did my father, if I did not wish you to live to see my vengeance on your son—to see him lying dead before you, killed by my hand."

The old man at once wrote to his son Richard, warning him of Christian's fierce threats and adjuring him to stay away, and in every way to guard himself against so desperate an enemy. To remain longer in the place of his birth was poison to Christian Christianson, and he prepared to shake its dust from his feet. All his inquiries as to the whereabouts of Richard failed, but he resolved to hunt him till he died. He was no less firmly bent, too, on finding Priscilla Sefton, the only vision of beauty and goodness he ever had beheld on this dark earth.

In the autumn of that year the good ship *Miles Standish* of Boston, Captain Ezekiel Higginbotham, master, lay one day in Southampton Roads waiting for a few more hands to complete the crew. She was laden with goods for the American

market, and had on board also a large party of religious emi-
grants, to whose spiritual wants ministered Richard Sefton,
accompanied by his devoted daughter, Priscilla. They were
sitting on the deck, when a boat hailed the ship, and from it a
passenger debarked, in whose eager face Priscilla recognized,
not entirely with pleasure, young Orchardson. He told them
that he had come with his father's approval to help the good
cause, and promptly paid his passage-money to the willing
skipper. When this rich suitor told Priscilla that he would
undergo any chances of life and death to be with her and serve
her she could not but believe his sincerity, much as she had
distrusted him. The skipper was afraid that they must sail
short-handed, when the bark was boarded by a stout country-
man, who was engaged as a last resort. As the newcomer
stood in the forecastle, he heard in the distant cabin a sweet
voice singing hymns.

"I was right after all," he muttered, "she is here—he hath
followed her; I have only to watch and to wait."

A few days after leaving port John Dyson—such was Christian's pseudonym—was lying along a lofty yard striving to reef
the bellying folds of a sail, when a sudden lurch precipitated
him into the deep. He was rescued, but his shipmates noted
that he had lost his heavy beard; and the next morning his
features were marked by disfigurements that had not been
there before. Captain Higginbotham came to regard him with
great suspicion, especially as he had caught him crouching
near the cabin several times, eagerly peering through the sky-
light. There was something in John Dyson's appearance
and figure that irresistibly reminded Richard Orchardson,
with a quake of dread, of his indomitable enemy, but of course
he concealed the suspicion from Priscilla. He mistrusted that
the maiden, deep down in her heart, carried a vivid image of
Christian. She herself was becoming more and more conscious
of the secret inmate of her bosom. She could still hear his
voice quivering with the words: "Priscilla, I love you!" She
was sure of that, and now she acknowledged to herself what
she never had dared to confess aloud—that that love had awakened a response.

One night she stood with Richard Orchardson looking at

the foaming crests and their exultant beauty—she half *distraite* with the vivid sea spectacle, he pouring into her ears his importunate suit, in which a subtle depreciation of his rival and his motives, and of the character of his family, bore a large part. An iron hand suddenly leaped out of the shadows, clutching the slanderer by the throat, and Christian's voice rang, "Liar!" as he stood before them, wrapped in his sailor's rags, livid with passion.

At the shriek for help, the Captain and his mates rushed across the deck but could hardly release the victim, who demanded that his assailant should be put in irons for attempted murder. The skipper perceived that Priscilla knew the offender and, at her intercession, would have refrained from punishment, if the man would pledge himself to refrain from further violence. But the savage rejoinder was, "I came to kill him, and I shall kill him!"

Priscilla swooned on the deck, when the skipper took the only alternative. She obtained permission, however, to go into the foul-smelling den, where the sullen man lay handcuffed, and after a while he broke his silence. He told her everything, and justified his set purpose of vengeance on the villain who, with his father, had wrought such a sequence of woes on him and his. Richard Orchardson felt the cold aloofness of Priscilla after this, which was verified by words when he reproached her. Furthermore he suspected, what indeed was the truth, as Priscilla continued to visit the prisoner, that she had fully outspoken her love for the unfortunate yet fortunate Christian.

The man's nature grew diabolical in his war of jealousy, despair, and fear. Wicked schemes flitted through his brain, until at last he was ready to risk even his own destruction, if thereby he could compass that of his hated enemy. The most deadly of sea-alarms aroused the ship one night—that which thrills the sailor's heart with something akin to despair. The ship was afire, and it soon became evident after strenuous effort that it was doomed.

"Christian—is safe? He was down there," cried Priscilla in passionate accents. Higginbotham and a gigantic negro plunged down into the raging furnace of flames, and barely succeeded in extricating the unconscious man. The pas-

sengers and crew took to the boats, and the irons were soon
knocked off the prisoner, who even then tried to spring at his
enemy. The skipper sternly threatened to throw him overboard
if he attempted any further assault. As strong hands held
Christian back, he pointed to the cowering Orchardson, saying,
"Speak to him; ask *him* who set your ship on fire."

The accused man vehemently denied the imputation,
asserting that it was prompted by the malice of a mortal foe.
For two days the shipwrecked were exposed to the terrors of
the open sea with all its unknown vicissitudes, and hope began
to languish. Good fortune, however, brought rescue in the shape
of a Dutch ship bound from Amsterdam to Halifax, though
the crowded vessel gave them little more than a bare refuge.

Christian's spirit, which not even the assurance of Priscilla's
love could cure of its rancor, was still more corroded with the
gall of bitterness by his certainty that it was Richard Orchardson who had fired the ship. Yet the honest Captain, after
hearing the defense of the accused again, came to believe that
the charge was a malignant lie, when reiterated by Christian,
who solemnly averred that he had recognized the dim figure
of the incendiary and his peculiar walk in the gloom of the
hold. Hungry as he might be for Priscilla's love and her divine
compassion, all that his morbid soul could then crave from
God was that the Divine Judge would give this wicked wretch
into his hands to do with according to the evil he had wrought.

Further perils of the sea were in store for the unfortunate
ones. A terrible storm, in which the Dutch skipper kept his
obese carcass saturated with gin and proved himself in every
way incompetent, well-nigh sent them to the bottom of the ocean.
It was only the skill of Captain Higginbotham, and the discipline of his men superseding chaos, that brought the ship through
her travail.

Observations showed that they had gone far north in their
storm-drift. The dense, chilling fog warned them of icebergs,
and they began to pass these shining monsters in such number
as filled all with apprehension. Narrowly they escaped destruction more than once, when "land ahead" sounded from the
masthead. Soon the frowning bastions of precipice stretching
or miles, abutting on a vast ice-floe, came into vision. Huge

bergs, tossing all around them on a turbulent sea, fretted by half a gale, made the situation one of imminent peril. They anchored to the floe, but that was hardly less dangerous. To find refuge ashore seemed the only resort, and they began to pass stores and necessaries over the side. Richard clambered down and joined the working throng, but soon a storm of blinding snow smote them, obscuring all outlines, and the ice under foot quivered as if to break up. He turned back in terror, but missed the ship, and there, looming up before him, was a full white face from whose lips came the words: "At last!" He recognized Christian, before whom he fled in mad panic. A race of life and death ensued, but Christian's shedding of blood was saved him by an opening in the floe, which caught and swallowed the human victim in a second. Alone the survivor stood, and, in a cessation of the storm, he caught a glimpse of the ship drifting out to sea through the open water, driven by the fierce white squall.

In Christian Christianson's journal appears the following record:

"God had given me vengeance, even if I myself were to die of cold and starvation. But I would not perish if I could live; for I had strong hope that the ship with its precious freight would be saved. Picking my way shoreward, I scrambled up the huge cliffs and reached the summit of the desolate island, pinched with hunger. Then I remembered that stores and provisions had been landed before the ship had drifted away. I hid myself from the cold wind in a fissure of the rocks, and in the morning went down to the water's edge, where I found a goodly portion of the stores. These, consisting of flour, ship-biscuit, cheeses, a keg of rum, blankets, loose planks, flint and steel, lamp-oil, and a carpenter's ax, were my salvation. I toiled hard in conveying them to a well-sheltered cave, and thus I was assured at least for a time in the bare necessities of life. I soon created for myself a livable shelter, and learned how to kill and skin seals, which abounded on the island, thus securing additional food and protection from the rigors of the season.

"It was not long before the conviction seized me— from a sound like the tramp of feet and heavy breathing at the top of the cave—that I was not alone and that the disturbance was not that of beasts. Greatly perplexed, a few days later I found my precious ax stolen from the spot where I had laid it by the carcass of a slaughtered seal, which I had left to go after my knife. Horrible dreams afflicted me one night; I opened my eyes and saw in the red ray of the fire a face peering through the partly open aperture. It was that of Richard Orchardson, white and horrible of aspect, but I dismissed the vision as a nightmare. The next day brought him, ax in hand, face to face with me as I ascended the hillside. At first I shrank in horror, and then grappled with the hideous figure, wresting the ax from him and raising it to brain him. He moaned, begged for his life, said he was already dying, and cried piteously for food and for shelter from the icy cold. My heart and tongue only gave back mockery, as he lay writhing on the frozen earth, and I said to myself: 'Yea, God is just!'

"Then between us two deadly foes arose a strange experience. The starving wretch continually threw himself in my way begging with importunate cries for relief, asking as a mercy that I would either kill him or help him. My heart, frozen in its bitterness, was marble. I began to doubt God, however. Why had He not finished the affair without making me spectator of the long and torturing process? At last I was conscious of the feeble birth of pity in an obdurate breast, as I witnessed his sufferings, heard his half insane ejaculations, and looked on his spectral figure. I told him to take half of everything and go away by himself, never crossing my path. The wretch was too feeble to obey, so it ended in his remaining in my cave, but without being permitted to speak, though I fed and sheltered him. I even saved him at the risk of my own life from a great white bear, whose paw was uplifted to strike.

"So the weeks and months passed in this strange companionship. He grew weaker and weaker, till he was barely able to crawl, and the hand of death lay surely on him. Then a new horror affrighted me. No succor had come; it might never come! What could I do in this land of frozen desolation without companionship—even that of my enemy—but go mad in my very loneliness?

"One night, as I listened to his faint breathing and broken

delirium, I prayed to God, who had answered my former blasphemous petition with such dreadful irony of consent: 'Spare him, O God! Of all living things, he is the sole creature that remains to me, and if he goes where shall I look for the light of a human face, the touch of a human hand? He has shared my shelter, eaten my substance, and his sorrow has been harder to bear than mine. Spare him, O God! Leave me not utterly alone.'

"He awoke, called me softly by name, and, as I stroked his cold hand, he gave me a message for his father. Then, as I prayed with him, he said, ' 'Twas I that fired the ship.' Clutching my hand despairingly, he implored: 'Have you nothing to say to me—can you forgive me now?'

"Then the cloud of my old hate passed forever, as I replied, 'May God forgive us both! He hath dealt with us as we deserved.'

"I buried Richard Orchardson in an icy barrow and raised a rude cross with his carven name over the grave. That night the sky auroral, with its prismatic splendors, had a new meaning of peace and good-will, for my soul was washed clean."

Captain John MacIntosh, master of a Scotch whaler, reported his rescue of a half-dazed castaway, clothed in skins, and told how he brought him back to civilization. Christian Christianson found himself at last in a seaman's hospital in the town of Tynemouth, Yorkshire, slowly recovering his broken strength. One day he heard a silvery voice singing a hymn. He asked with streaming eyes who it was that sang so like an angel. "A young missionary from London," was the answer.

Priscilla Sefton came to him, but did not at first recognize that gaunt and stricken countenance. What the grave had given up she took to her own heart and life with tender solicitude, saying she had no one now but him, for her father had gone home. Mr. John Wesley himself came down from London to marry the much-tried lovers at the old Fen farm. But before their hands were joined, Christian went to The Willows and gave the old Squire his son's dying message; and it came to pass that the Orchardsons and the Christiansons were united at last by the marriage tie. The family feud of centuries had been quenched on that ice-bound coast of Labrador.

EDWARD GEORGE EARLE BULWER-LYTTON

(England, 1803-1873)

FALKLAND (1827)

This novel was a frank imitation of Byron's characters and philosophy, and was the first prose work of the author, who had, however, written a good deal of verse.

N May, 1822, Erasmus Falkland, Esq., after an absence of many years abroad, had taken up his residence in one of the least valuable of his English possessions. In writing to a friend he said: "The place is a ruin rather than a house. I have chosen it for my retreat, because here I am personally unknown and therefore little likely to be disturbed." His past life had left him sated with worldly pleasures, and he wished to lead the life of a recluse.

About a mile from Mr. Falkland's home was the beautiful villa of Mr. Mandeville, situated in the midst of a large park, where, during the absence of the family, Mr. Falkland delighted to wander, alone with his thoughts. Lady Emily Mandeville, married at sixteen to an unimaginative man with political ambitions, had spent four years in London society. Her health had suffered from this dissipation, and her physician ordered her to spend the summer at her country home. Accordingly she came hither, accompanied by two friends and her young son.

On the third day after their arrival, one of the friends announced that she had a relative in the neighborhood, a Mr. Falkland, and begged that he might be invited to dine with them. Lady Emily readily granted her request, and then left her friends to stroll about the grounds with her little boy. During the walk they came upon a man asleep on the bank of the lake, with a book in his hand. The stern, mournful face impressed Lady Emily and haunted her like a dream. She said nothing of her discovery to her friends, and the next day, when Mr. Falkland came in response to the invitation, she recognized in him the person she had seen the day before. Though the guest departed early, he left a most favorable impression with his hostess, and the effect upon him of her pensive nature and gentle manner was no less marked.

In his relationship to her guest Falkland found an excuse for frequent visits at her house. Day after day he made excursions with Lady Emily, and in the still summer twilights their hearts first went out to each other.

Emily wrote frankly of her new acquaintance to her friend, Mrs. St. John, and rather alarmed that lady, who had some knowledge of Falkland. Before her marriage, unknown to Falkland, she had conceived a strong attachment for him, and was well aware of his peculiar fascination for and power over women. Therefore Mrs. St. John wrote to her friend an impassioned caution, actuated by affection, and perhaps also by smothered jealousy.

The relation between Emily and Falkland was growing ever closer, when one day the family formed a little party to visit a celebrated cliff some miles distant on the seashore. Falkland acted as guide, and was most reluctant to go on with the other ladies when, Emily's strength failing, she was obliged to stop and rest awhile on the sands. While the others were examining the cliff, they suddenly became aware of the approaching tide. Falkland, having despatched a man for a boat, rushed to Emily's assistance. With the waves approaching and the booming waters ringing in his ears, he bore her to a hollow; but soon the water girt them in, and he saw that death was inevitable. In that moment, with her form pressed in his arms, he declared his mad love and held her in one passionate embrace. As the spray broke over their feet, they saw a boat approaching, and thus escaped the death that would have united them.

After the adventure on the sands Falkland implored Emily to fly with him, but, borne up by virtue and the love of her child, she resisted, and remained utterly desolate, while he returned to London.

They had meant to make the separation final, but letters kept up the ardor of both, and finally Mr. Mandeville, bringing down a Spanish uncle for Falkland as a guest, must invite that gentleman as well. Mrs. St. John also was of the party this time, and to her Emily confided all her suffering.

During a dinner, Mrs. St. John learned that Falkland's uncle desired to interest him in the Spanish cause, and, looking toward Emily and Falkland whispering together, she said: "See you not that while he has such attractions to detain him your hopes are in vain?" From that time the two worked together to break this tie.

Falkland continued to urge Emily to elope with him, and at times she was almost consenting. One evening when they were entertaining a few guests, Mrs. St. John sang a touching song, which she said had been sent anonymously to a certain well-known woman on the eve of her elopement. Emily was so overcome by the words that, with one look of anguish directed toward Falkland, she left the room. A moment later they heard her fall, and found her apparently lifeless, having broken a blood-vessel. As soon as she was sufficiently recovered Falkland wrote begging an interview, which was granted. After this meeting he wrote:

"I have seen you, Emily, and for the last time. You did not conceal from me that I was not sufficient to constitute all your world. In two weeks I shall leave England. I have another country still more dear to me, from its afflictions and humiliation." This letter was too much for Emily. She replied: "Oh, Falkland! You have conquered! I am yours, yours only, wholly, and forever. I will fly with you anywhere, everywhere."

Falkland came at once from London, where he had gone preparatory to carrying out his threat. Emily, fearful that her husband was already suspicious, did not dare see him at the house. Falkland wrote to arrange a meeting, but Mrs. St. John, having observed his servant waiting to deliver the note, intercepted Emily's reply. Carefully reading the note before giving it to the messenger, she disclosed its contents to Mr.

Mandeville. He was roused from his wonted apathy to a paroxysm of indignation, and thanked her again and again for what he imagined was solely an act of friendship.

That evening Emily stole out of the house and met Falkland on the edge of the lake. He clasped her to his bosom and her lips answered to his own. They remained long under the dark sky, and when they separated their love had a meaning it never had had before. Emily's senses were bewildered and her conscience was dulled.

"To-morrow, then," said Falkland, "we will fly hence forever. Meet me at daybreak. The carriage shall be in attendance."

One more kiss, one last embrace, and they parted.

Falkland returned to his home with gloomy foreboding. He gave all the necessary orders for the morrow, and went to his room, but not to sleep. The clock struck the half hour after midnight. At this moment he started in wild terror; at the far end of the room stood a dim, slight shape, which gradually became clearer and clearer. He saw at length the features of Emily; but how changed! sunken and colorless, and set in death. Falkland sat at the window the remainder of the night, and by giving himself up to his new hopes he partially overcame the ghastly impression of the nocturnal vision.

At dawn he awaited Emily at the appointed place, but she was not there. Time glided on, the sun rose, and she had not come. When he could bear the suspense no longer, he went to her house. He found all in confusion. He saw Mrs. St. John. "Good God! why are *you* here?" she exclaimed. No one would answer his wild questioning. He pressed on to her room. Two women were bending over her bed. She was dead! He pressed one long kiss on her lips and left the house. Two hours later he was found senseless on the spot where he had met Emily the night before. For weeks he lay in a delirium, and when he came forth his doom was—*never to forget*.

Shortly after Emily had reached home that fatal night, her husband had entered her room, bringing Falkland's letters, which he had found in her desk. When he accused her, she sank back gasping for breath. Mandeville seized her by the arm and flung her from him, and as she fell, the blood gushed in torrents from her lips. She was a corpse. At that instant the clock struck half-past twelve. Thus the grave closed upon her erring heart with its guiltiest secret unrevealed.

Falkland joined his uncle in Spain and fought with the Constitutionalists in their lost cause. When they were surrounded, and only flight was left, he fled into the mountains with one of the staunchest leaders, but on this man's head a price was set. The peasant who harbored them learned of this and betrayed them. When Falkland saw the soldiers coming toward them, he moved, in defiance of his captor. The peasant shot at him, and Falkland, staggering for a few minutes, clove him with one blow from skull to jaw and fell to the floor with his lifeless victim. Falkland's wound was serious and recovery was hopeless. On the last night of his life, he asked to be left alone. As the hand of the clock pointed to the half hour after midnight, the attendants heard a faint cry and rushed hastily into the chamber. His hand still pressed a locket of dark hair against his breast, but on his countenance was the seal of death.

PELHAM; OR, ADVENTURES OF A
GENTLEMAN (1827)

This is the second of Bulwer's novels, the scene of which is laid in England, in the beginning of the last century. It appeared anonymously, and reached a second edition in 1829. It was elaborately burlesqued by William M. Thackeray in his *Adventures of Barry Lyndon*.

 AM an only child. My father was the younger son of one of our oldest earls, my mother the dowerless daughter of a Scotch peer. I went to Eton; the second day I had been there I was half-killed for refusing, with all the pride of a Pelham, to wash teacups. I was rescued by a boy not much bigger than myself, but reckoned the best fighter, for his size, in the school. His name was Reginald Glanville; from that period we became inseparable, and our friendship lasted while he stayed at Eton. His father, a baronet, was of an ancient and wealthy family; his mother, a woman of some talent and more ambition, made her house one of the most attractive in London.

"It is an excellent connection," said my mother, "and will be of more use to you than many of greater apparent consequence."

Notwithstanding my mother's instructions, very few prudential considerations were mingled with my friendship for Reginald Glanville. I loved him with a warmth of attachment which has since surprised even myself. He was of a very singular character; he used to wander by the river in the bright days of summer, without any companion but his own thoughts, which were tinged, even at that early age, with a deep and impassioned melancholy. Yet to those he loved no one could be more open and warm, more watchful to gratify others, more indifferent to gratification for himself; an utter absence of all selfishness and an eager and active benevolence were indeed the distinguishing traits of his character.

From Eton I was transplanted to Cambridge, where at the end of two years (being of royal descent) I became entitled to an honorary degree. When I left there I was not in good health, and as nobody had yet come to London, I accepted the invitation of Sir Lionel Garrett to visit him at his country-seat. There, among others, I found Lady Roseville. My mother had written me to be particularly attentive to her. "In London, she is so much surrounded by all that she is quite inaccessible to one. Nothing, my dear son, is like a *liaison* (quite innocent, of course) with a woman of celebrity in the world." I took particular pains to ingratiate myself with her, and so far as acquaintance went had no reason to be dissatisfied with my success. But anything else, I soon discovered, notwithstanding my vanity, was quite out of the question. We had not one thought or opinion in common; she was like a being of another world than myself.

Not caring for the "sporty" men who made up Sir Lionel's visitors, I was accustomed to take long walks in the neighborhood. One night my way led me through the churchyard of ——. The night was clear, and I paused a moment to admire the old church, which stood alone and gray, in the rude simplicity of the earliest form of Gothic architecture. As I was about to renew my walk a tall figure, wrapped like myself in a large French cloak, passed slowly from the other side of the church and paused a moment; then flung himself upon the earth and sobbed audibly. I was in doubt whether to remain still or to proceed, but, my curiosity being excited, I walked slowly onward. I had not gone three paces when the figure arose and stood erect before me. His hat had fallen off and the moon shone full upon his countenance. As his eyes met mine I started back and felt my heart stand still. Notwithstanding the fearful ravages graven in that countenance, I recognized the noble and striking features of Reginald Glanville. He turned hastily, but I put my hand upon his arm and drew him toward me.

"Glanville!" I exclaimed, "it is I! it is your old friend, Henry Pelham. Good Heavens! have I met you at last, and in such a scene?"

Glanville looked at me, as if fully to recognize me, and then, throwing himself in my arms, wept like a child. His weakness lasted but a few minutes. He rose suddenly and his whole expression changed, his proud, stern countenance seeming to deny the feelings which his almost feminine weakness had betrayed.

"Pelham," he said, "*you* have seen me thus; I had hoped that no living eye would—this is the last time that I shall indulge this folly. God bless you!—we shall meet again—and this night shall then seem to you like a dream."

Before I could answer he turned swiftly away and disappeared.

A few weeks later found me in Paris, where I soon had the *entrée* to the best society, and in company with an English friend, Lord Vincent, visited many places which might be called questionable. One evening, when alone, I had the curiosity to see one of the smaller cafés. I went into one of the meanest of them near the Palais Royal and was insulted by a Frenchman who, with several companions, sat at the next table.

"If I walk away," I thought, "they will probably think me a coward and follow me to the street;" so I raised my hand and —quietly knocked him down.

"*Sortons*," he said, as he rose, "a Frenchman never forgives a blow!"

An Englishman, who had been sitting in an obscure corner, came up and took me aside. "Sir," said he, "don't think of fighting the man; he is a tradesman of the Rue Saint Honoré."

"Sir," I replied, "I thank you for your information, but fight I must. Perhaps you will be my second."

"With pleasure," said he.

We went forthwith to a retired spot in the Bois de Boulogne. We joined swords, the Frenchman made a desperate lunge; I struck his sword from his hand, caught it instantly, and presented it to him. We left the spot with the greatest professions of amity and reëntered our respective fiacres.

"Let me thank you," I said to my second, "most cordially for your assistance. I lodge at the Hotel de ——, Rue de Rivoli; my name is Pelham. Yours is—"

"Thornton," he replied. "I will lose no time in profiting by an offer of acquaintance which does me so much honor."

One night, not long after this, I strolled into one of the gambling-houses near the Palais Royal. While looking on at the *rouge et noir* table, I was struck with the expression of painful anxiety in the face of one of the players, a man of about forty years. His complexion was dark and sallow, his features were prominent and even handsome; but there was a certain sinister expression in his eyes and mouth which rendered his physiognomy rather disagreeable than prepossessing. At a small distance from him, playing with a carelessness and nonchalance in remarkable contrast to the anxiety of the other, sat my late second, Mr. Thornton. Standing directly opposite the seat of the swarthy stranger was another Englishman, in a rough great-coat, with his hat slouched over his eyes. I shall never forget the stern and ferocious expression with which he watched the gambler opposite. He neither played, nor spoke, nor moved, and appeared utterly insensible of every feeling in common with those around.

The gambler took from an old purse a few napoleons and set them all at one hazard on the *rouge*. He hung over the table with a trembling lip, his hands tightly clasped, his nerves strained, while the countenance of the man opposite took on an expression of joy at once malignant and fiendish. A moment more—the fortune was to the *noir*. The stranger did not utter a word, but rising left the room. The other Englishman uttered a low laugh, heard perhaps only by myself, and strode quickly to the door. I felt relieved when he was gone.

A few days after this I was sipping a glass of lemonade in a cabaret near the Jardin des Plantes, when a couple took a seat on a bench under the window where I was sitting. The pair were the Englishman in the rough coat and a woman companion.

"Is this absolutely the very last remnant of his property?" the man asked.

"The last. When these two hundred pounds are gone, there will be nothing between him and beggary."

The man laughed and then said in an altered tone, "Then will this parching thirst be quenched at last. My whole soul has been melted down into one burning thought. Feel this hand—ay, you may well start—but what is the fever of the frame to that within?"

"But poor Tyrrell—you will not suffer him to starve, to die of actual want, abandoned and alone!"

"Alone! no!" cried he fiercely. "When the last agonies shall be upon that man—when, sick with weariness, pain, disease, hunger, he lies down to die—when remembrance peoples the chamber with Hell, and his cowardice would falter forth its dastard recantation to Heaven—then—may I be there!"

Mr. Thornton and I had called on each other twice, but neither had been at home. But the interest I took in the mysterious person of the gambling-house and of the Jardin des Plantes, and his acquaintance with him, induced me to make another attempt. I found him up several pairs of unclean stairs, in a room separated from the *chambre à coucher* by a half-drawn faded blue curtain, which did not conceal the unmade bed within. On a table were a cracked bowl, reeking with the lees of gin punch, two bottles half full, a mouldy cheese, and a salad dish; and on the floor beneath it two books and a woman's bonnet. At another table, spread with breakfast appliances, mingled with a pack of cards and dice, sat Thornton beside a consumptive fire. Everything bore testimony of low debauchery.

He rose, with an air half careless, half abashed, and expressed his pleasure at seeing me after so many failures. "I have but a small tenement," said he, smiling; "but, thank Heaven, in Paris a man is not made by his lodgings. Small house, small care."

After a somewhat desultory conversation, I said: "I have seen you once or twice with a tall, handsome man, in a loose great-coat. Pray, if not impertinent, who is he? I am sure I have seen him in England."

Thornton changed color and answered my gaze with a quick glance from his small, glittering eyes before he answered.

"I hardly know whom you mean, my acquaintance is so large in Paris."

"He has a pale complexion, light eyes, and very black hair, moustachios, and whiskers. I saw him with you once in the Bois de Boulogne, and once in a hell in the Palais Royal."

"Oh! that man; I have known him but a short time. Let me see—what *is* his name? War—Warbur—I have it—Warburton—is it the one you supposed, Mr. Pelham?"

"No," I said, "I was mistaken "

The surest way to make a dupe, I thought, as I left his apartment, is to let your victim suppose you are his.

Not long after this I was summoned back to England, my mother writing that my uncle wished me to stand for one of the parliamentary seats in his borough. On the night before departure I went to the hotel in the Rue St. Honoré in hope of seeing the person called Warburton again. While I was talking with one of the fair decoys of the place, my ear caught the sound of an English voice, and turning, I saw Thornton in close conversation with a man whose back was turned, but whom I rightly conjectured to be Tyrrell.

"Oh! he'll be here soon," said Thornton, "and we'll bleed him regularly to-night."

Tyrrell replied in an inaudible tone, and a minute afterward Warburton entered, and went directly to Thornton and his companion. Presently the trio went into an adjoining room and the door closed behind them. Time passed; the hour grew late, and most of the guests had gone before the door, which I had anxiously watched, again opened. Tyrrell came out, his countenance hueless, his cheek sunken and hollow. I observed that his teeth were set and his hands clenched. Warburton and Thornton followed him, the latter with his usual air of reckless indifference. He nodded to me with his wonted impudence and ease; Warburton passed on, like Tyrrell, without noticing or heeding anyone. I quitted the salon and followed, reaching the staircase before the two had descended. I heard Tyrrell say, in a tone of deep anguish: "I am an utter beggar—I have no expectation but to starve."

"Have you no hope—is beggary your absolute and only possible resource from famine?" asked his companion.

They were just descending into the courtyard, where the moon shone. Warburton, but one step behind Tyrrell, laid his hand upon him, as he made no answer. "Turn," he cried suddenly, "your cup is not yet full—look upon me—and *remember!*"

The light shone full on the face of the speaker, his dark hair was gone, and I recognized, what I had suspected, the bright locks of Reginald Glanville.

Tyrrell uttered one low cry and sank lifeless on the earth.

I knocked up the porter, procured some cold water and bathed his temples several moments before he recovered. "Gone—gone—what did he here at such a moment? Vengeance? I do not fear; I defy his malice." With these words, Tyrrell sprang to his feet.

"Can I assist you to your home?" I asked.

"Who speaks to *me*," he said, staring wildly, "the lost—the guilty—the ruined—in the accents of kindness?"

I took his arm and led him into the street. As he persisted in declining my services to see him to his home, I bade him good-night, saying, "I trust we shall meet again under auspices better calculated for improving acquaintance."

Tyrrell bowed, pressed my hand, and we parted. When I had walked on a while, I looked back. He was still standing where I had left him.

The next time I saw Tyrrell was at Cheltenham. I was talking with Lady Harriet Garrett when I saw a dark man in deep mourning enter the room. "Is it possible," I said, "can that be Tyrrell?"

"Yes, it is Sir John Tyrrell," replied Lady Harriet. "His is a very singular history."

"What is it?" said I, eagerly.

"He was the only son of a younger branch of the Tyrrells, a very old family. He was in a certain *roué* set for some years, and noted for his gallantries. When his fortune declined he took to gambling, and lost the remains of his property. He led a precarious and degraded existence in low gambling-houses in Paris till about three months ago, when two persons who stood between him and the title and estates of the family died, and he succeeded most unexpectedly to both. They say he was found in the utmost penury and distress in a cellar in Paris; however that may be, he is now Sir John Tyrrell, with a very large income."

At this instant Tyrrell passed us. As he caught my eye, he stopped short, and colored violently; then returned my salutation, expressed himself delighted to meet me, and said he should certainly call upon me.

The next day I fell in with an old friend, Lord Vincent, whom I had left in Paris. As we sauntered down the street, I saw a vision of loveliness standing by a corner shop. "Good heavens! Vincent, what a beautiful girl!" I said. "*O Dea certe,*" he murmured, and stopped.

She was apparently about twenty; her hair was of the richest chestnut, her eyes of light hazel, shaded by long and dark lashes. Her complexion was so clear, so pure, that the blood blushed beneath it, like roses under a clear stream. She was somewhat taller than the ordinary height, and her figure united all the freshness and youth of girlhood with the more luxuriant graces of the woman. The girl turned abruptly, as she saw us looking, and entered the stationer's. "Let us go in," said Vincent. "I want some sealing-wax." The girl was leaning on the arm of an old lady. She blushed deeply when she saw us enter; and presently, the old lady having concluded her purchases, the two went out. All the remainder of that day I was absent and reserved.

The next day I saw Tyrrell, who lodged in the same hotel. After dinner, in conversation, I mentioned Glanville. His countenance fell, but recovering himself, he said: "Oh, you mean the *soi-disant* Warburton. I knew him some years back—a poor silly youth, half mad, I believe, and particularly hostile to me. I believe I was more fortunate than he in a certain intrigue. Poor Glanville is a little romantic, you know."

On my return to London, I called on Lady Roseville, to pick up the newest scandal of the day. Hearing that Glanville was in London, and that he was now Sir Richard Glanville in consequence of the death of his father, I went at once to see him. Our meeting was cordial in the extreme. Though still pale and thin, he appeared in much better spirits than I had seen him since our boyhood. In speaking of his family, he said: "To my mother I am particularly anxious to introduce you; of my sister I say nothing; I expect you to be surprised with her."

While we were driving in the Park, Lady Roseville passed. We both bowed to her, and I was struck by the deep blush which overspread her countenance. "That can't be for me," I thought.

"Do you know Lady Roseville well?" I asked.

"Very," answered Glanville, laconically.

As we were passing through Cumberland Gate, a voice

loud, harsh, and vulgar, called Glanville by name. I turned and saw Thornton.

"For Heaven's sake, Pelham, drive on," cried Glanville. "Let me, for once, escape that atrocious plebeian."

Not long after this, at Lady Roseville's, Glanville remembered his promise to introduce me to his sister. I followed him into the next room, and to my inexpressible astonishment and delight, discovered in her the beautiful, never-to-be-forgotten girl I had seen at Cheltenham. For once in my life I was embarrassed; but a few moments sufficed to recover me, and I strained every nerve to be as agreeable as possible. There was nothing about Ellen Glanville like a heroine, but, thank Heaven, *she was alive!* She had great sense, but the playfulness of a child; if she laughed, all her countenance, lips, eyes, forehead, cheeks, laughed too; if she looked grave, it was with such a lofty and upward, yet sweet and gentle gravity, that you might have supposed her one of a new order of angels between the Cherubim and Seraphim, the angels of Love and Wisdom. I went home intoxicated with a subtle spirit of enjoyment that gave a new zest and freshness to life.

Glanville was in Parliament and was much occupied with his duties, entering into the leading debates and making telling speeches that marked him as one of the most promising of the junior members. He lived in an almost ascetic seclusion, but I saw him frequently. One day he spoke of Thornton: "He was useful to me abroad, and I rewarded him well for his services. He has since applied to me several times for money, which is spent at the gambling-house. I believe him to be leagued with a gang of sharpers. He is a mean, mercenary rascal, who would scruple at no enormity, if he were paid for it."

Glanville paused a moment and then said, "You remember Mr. Tyrrell, at Paris?"

"Yes," I said, "he is at present in London."

Glanville started as if he had been shot. "No, no," he exclaimed wildly, "he died at Paris, from want—from starvation."

"You are mistaken," I said, "he is now Sir John Tyrrell, and possessed of considerable property. I saw him three weeks ago."

Glanville's cheek grew more ghastly and livid at every moment. Just then the door opened and Mr. Thornton was announced. Glanville sprang toward him, and seized him by the throat.

"Dog!" he cried, "you have deceived me—Tyrrell lives!"

"Hands off!" cried the gamester, "or you shall have gripe for gripe!"

"Wretch," said Glanville, "do you dare to threaten me?" And he threw him against the opposite wall. The gambler rose slowly and, wiping the blood from his face, fixed his malignant eye on Glanville with an expression of collected hate and vengeance that made my blood creep.

"It is not my day *now*," he said in a calm, quiet, cold voice.

I was dining with Lord Guloseton, when a note from Glanville asking me to come to him immediately was handed me. I arose instantly and went out. Glanville was awaiting me in the street.

"I want you to take immediately," said he, "a challenge from me to Sir John Tyrrell. I have been hunting him ever since I saw you. He leaves town to-morrow, so there is no time to lose. You have only to hand him this paper. I have left it open for you to read."

"You are my earliest friend," I said when I had read the note, "and I will not flinch from the place you assign me, though I would sooner cut off my hand than suffer it to give this to Sir John Tyrrell." But I did as he wished me to do.

Tyrrell made no reply for some moments when he read the note; then he raised his head with a haughty air of defiance and, tearing the paper deliberately through and through, stamped his foot upon the atoms.

"Tell your principal," said he, "that I retort upon him the foul and false words he has uttered; and that before this hour to-morrow I will confront him to death as through life. I cannot name my second till the morning. Leave your address and you shall hear from me before you are stirring."

Next morning at breakfast I received a packet from Tyrrell containing a sealed letter to Glanville and a brief note to myself saying that there were circumstances to forbid his meeting Sir Reginald, and that he should leave town before the delivery of the packet. I sent the packet to Glanville, with a note saying I would call in an hour. When I went I was informed that Glanville had gone out, leaving word that he should be gone the whole day. The next day I had from him a brief note saying he had left London in pursuit of Tyrrell and that he would not rest until he had brought him to account.

Sometime after this I was on my way to Chester Park, Suffolk, the seat of the Marquis of Chester. At an inn on the way, while my horses were changing, I heard a familiar voice, and looking out saw Thornton in the stable yard. "Ah! Mr. Pelham, going to Newmarket? Bound there myself."

"I'm not going to Newmarket," I replied, "I never attend races."

"Indeed!" answered Thornton. "If I was as rich as you, I'd soon make or spend a fortune on the race course. Seen Sir John Tyrrell? No? He is to be there. Good day, Mr. Pelham"—this last as my post-boy started and released me from my *bête noire.*

I spent several days at Chester Park. During my visit occurred the great day at Newmarket, and, our whole party being bound for the race-course, I was with great reluctance pressed into the service. As we were not many miles from the course, we rode across country mostly by an intricate series of cross-roads. About six miles from Chester Park we passed an old brick house with new Venetian windows, and I saw Thornton and another man ride out from behind it. We had not gone far before they overtook us. Thornton, nothing abashed by the slightness of my bow, said smilingly: "Sure I should have the pleasure of seeing you, though you kept it so snug. You're a sly one. I'm staying at that nice-looking house you passed. Belongs to Dawson, an old friend of mine—shall be happy to introduce you!"

"Sir," said I abruptly, "you are too good. Please rejoin your friend Mr. Dawson.

"Well, as my mare is none of the best, I'll wish you good-morning."

As I took no interest in the races, I visited a friend in the neighborhood. Unfortunately, when I returned to the course the races were ended and I had to ride back alone. I had pro-

ceeded about three miles on the way when I was overtaken
by a horseman who proved to be Sir John Tyrrell. He informed
me that he had accepted an invitation to visit Chester Park,
but had been detained at Newmarket by a rascally fellow
named Dawson, who had lost a considerable wager to him and
had failed to keep his appointment to pay the money.

"I cannot sympathize with you," said I, "since I am bene--
fited by your misfortunes; though I fear my horse can scarcely
keep up with yours."

"It is cursed unlucky you should be so badly mounted, and
we shall have a pelting shower presently."

I tried to push my horse, but he soon went lame. We both
dismounted, in hope that it might be caused by a pebble between
the shoe and the hoof, when two men overtook us. "By
Heaven!" said Tyrrell, in a low tone, "it's that dog Dawson,
and his worthy coadjutor, Tom Thornton."

Thornton dismounted, felt my horse's leg, pronounced it a
severe strain, and said the best I could do was to walk the animal home. He also suggested that Tyrrell, if anxious to reach
Chester Park, should ride on with Dawson and himself. Tyrrell, who was in a vile humor, declined, and the two rode on.

"I'm sorry you rejected his offer," I said.

"To say truth," answered Tyrrell, "I have so bad an
opinion of him that I was afraid to trust myself with him on so
lonely a road. He knows that I have nearly two thousand
pounds about me, for I was fortunate in my betting-book
to-day.

"I had a d——d fellow dodging me all day, and yesterday
too; wherever I go I'm sure to see him. He's wrapt up in a
long horseman's cloak, so one can't get a sight at his face."

Rain began now to fall and Tyrrell, who had long been
impatient, at last put spurs to his horse and rode on. About
five minutes later a horseman passed me at a sharp pace. A
thrill of fear crept over me as I saw that he was enveloped in a
horseman's cloak. Further on I met a riderless horse, which
turned and paused beside a tree. In the distance I saw, by
the light of the moon, which had now burst through the clouds,
a horseman in a long cloak galloping across the waste. Something like a human figure lay beside a pool near the roadside.

It was the body of Sir John Tyrrell, the face and throat wet with blood.

Dawson's house was not far away, and I went thither and tried to arouse the inmates. A window above was finally opened and a blunderbuss run out, with a threat to shoot if I did not instantly leave. I at last got the information that "Master and Squire Thornton are not returned from Newmarket, and we cannot let any one in till they come home." I accordingly made the best of my way to Chester Park, where I procured a fresh mount and, accompanied by four horsemen, rode back to Dawson's. Thornton opened to us. "How shocking!" he said, "we are only just returned from the spot."

"Where is Dawson?" I asked.

"Within," he answered. "Poor fellow, he was so shocked by the sight that he is all in a panic. Besides, he is half drunk. I'll call him."

I looked narrowly at Dawson. He was evidently intoxicated, and appeared nervous and frightened. We found that Tyrrell had been struck by some blunt instrument, but also stabbed with a knife, the broken blade of which was still in the wound. While the others were examining the body, Thornton and I searched the ground around. At a distance of several feet from the corpse I picked up a miniature. I was about to cry out, when Thornton whispered—"Hush! I know the picture; it is as I suspected!" I cleansed the picture of blood, with which it was covered, and tried to make out the initials. "I know them," whispered Thornton in a tone of savage exultation; "they are G. D. and R. G. They are the initials of Gertrude Douglas and Reginald Glanville."

I grasped his hand—our eyes met—he understood me. "Put it up," he said, "we will keep the secret."

On the way home Chester said to me: "That fellow Dawson looked devilish uneasy. Don't you suspect him and his friend?"

"I do not!" I answered emphatically.

I returned to London sad and dispirited. What was ambition henceforth to me! My earliest friend a murderer, whom the chance of an instant might convict; and she, the only woman I ever really loved—the sister of an assassin. To save a criminal, in whose safety I was selfishly concerned, I had tampered with my honor and paltered with the truth; and my heart swelled proudly and bitterly against the miniature which I still concealed in my bosom.

I met Glanville and his sister only casually after this and never called on them. One day Glanville came to my rooms. The miniature was lying on my table and I threw my handkerchief over it.

"You have lately changed toward me," he said, "I have come to demand the reason."

"Can Sir Reginald Glanville's memory supply him with no probable cause?" I asked.

"It can," replied he, "but I would not trust only to that. Sit down, Pelham, and listen to me. My days are approaching their end. I have made up my accounts with others; I would do so with you. I have, moreover, a dearer interest than my own to consult in this wish; for my sister's sake, if not for my own, you will hear me."

As he paused, I raised the handkerchief and pushed the miniature toward him. "Do you remember this?" I asked.

With a wild cry Glanville seized it and gazed intently on it with a flushed cheek and heaving breast. "Where got you this—where?" he cried, "answer, for mercy's sake?"

"I found it on the spot where Tyrrell was murdered."

"True—true," he answered. Then, in a low, exulting tone,—"was it red with his blood?"

"Wretch!" I exclaimed, "do you glory in your guilt?"

"Hold!" said Glanville, rising, with a haughty air. "It is not to your accusations that I am now to listen. Come to me at ten o'clock to-night and you shall know all."

Glanville told me his whole story. After leaving school he fell in love with Gertrude Douglas, who was no match for himself, either in family or fortune, and in an evil hour fled with her, but not to the altar. They traveled extensively, never staying long in one place. At Spa he became acquainted with Tyrrell, who had not at that time dissipated his fortune and, having traveled much, was an agreeable companion. While Glanville was absent, having been recalled to England by the sudden illness of his mother, Tyrrell forced Gertrude to accede to his wishes, and when she went mad sent her to an asylum. Glanville had great difficulty in finding her, on his return, and she had received such treatment that she soon died. It was at her grave, in the lonely churchyard, that I had seen Glanville at midnight.

"Nearly mad, I vowed deep, endless, implacable revenge, and determined that he should suffer everything that I had suffered. I followed him to Paris, and employed Thornton to beggar him, if possible—to reduce him, step by step, to the lowest abyss of poverty, to watch him through all the stages of starvation, and then reveal myself to gloat over him and point him the way to hell. Thornton led me to think him dead, and I returned to England. When he reappeared here, I sent him a challenge, as you know. He left town and I followed him around with two pistols to force him to fight. I found no opportunity at Newmarket, and followed him on the road. Two men passed me and stopped to assist you. After they had gone on, I followed you and Tyrrell until he left you, when I rode on past you. As I picked my way down a steep hill I heard a shrill, sharp cry. When I reached the foot of the hill, Tyrrell's riderless horse passed me. I pushed hastily forward, hoping to find my enemy. A dark object lay by the side of the pond— merciful God! he had escaped my hand, and lay in death before me!"

"What!" I exclaimed, "it was not by *you* then that Tyrrell fell?" I burst into tears of gratitude and joy. Reginald Glanville was innocent; Ellen was not the sister of an assassin.

There is little more to tell. Thornton blackmailed Glanville with threats, until the latter determined to leave England, when the gambler had him arrested and charged with the crime. I, in the light of Glanville's story, believed that Thornton himself was the guilty one. After a long search I succeeded in finding Dawson, who turned state's evidence, and Thornton was convicted and executed for the murder. A month after Reginald's release from prison Ellen and I were married; and the very day that witnessed our happiness saw his final release from earthly cares

THE DISOWNED (1828)

This, the third novel published by Bulwer, was written when he was twenty-five years old. It is a story of the eighteenth century and was intended, according to the author's preface, to contain "scenes of more exciting interest and vivid coloring, and a more sensible and pervading moral influence" than were found in the preceding ones.

 YOUNG man, disowned by his father, set out on foot, under the assumed name of Clarence Linden, to battle with the world. Arrived at the inn in the town of W——, he found there his luggage and a letter from his father addressed to "C. L.," the latter enclosing an order for £1000, payable in London. Carefully securing the money, he tore the letter into fragments and went out into the stable-yard, where a horseman, called by the landlord Mr. Mordaunt, had just ridden in. Meditating on plans for the future, he passed too near the heels of the horse, and a moment later fell stunned and motionless against the stable door. He had received a severe kick in the right shoulder. The few days in which he was laid up with this injury secured him the acquaintance of Squire Mordaunt, who sent him medical aid, called on him frequently, and invited him to visit him at his house, five miles distant.

Linden found Mordaunt Court in a wild and extensive park, filled with forest glades through which a brawling rivulet made its way, where deer lay half concealed in the ferns, and rooks cawed about the ancient mansion. The interior was filled with relics of the past, but there was much also to indicate present poverty. When the young man congratulated his host on the possession of so noble a home, Mordaunt told him that he feared it would not long be his, and that a quibble of law would soon transfer into other hands that which he was foolish enough to value the more from his inability properly to maintain it. Mordaunt followed his guest to the door on his departure, and many years passed before they met again. The next morning Clarence Linden set out for London.

He obtained lodgings in a villa near Paddington with a Mrs. Copperas, whose husband was a stock-jobber in the city. Next door was the brick mansion of Mr. Talbot, an old gentleman of means, who occasionally visited his neighbor. Mr. Talbot, struck by Clarence's appearance and conversation, invited him to visit him, and in time the two became intimate.

Clarence was instrumental in saving Talbot's life from burglars, and the result was that the old gentleman, who had no heirs, adopted him after he had told him his whole story under promise of secrecy. Clarence removed to Mr. Talbot's mansion, and his new-found father obtained for him the appointment of *attaché* to a foreign legation and settled upon him money to pay his expenses.

Meanwhile Mr. Mordaunt's fears had been realized. Mr. Vavasour Mordaunt, a distant relative who had lent money to Mordaunt's father, pushed his claims and succeeded in getting possession of the estate, and the young man was turned loose upon the world without means of livelihood. Some time previous to this Mordaunt had become engaged to a penniless orphan, Isabel St. Leger, a daughter of a captain in the army, who had died when his child was in her infancy. She lived with a relative, Major General Cornelius St. Leger, who had made a fortune in the Indies. His temper was as hot as his curries, and when he heard of Mordaunt's loss of property he forbade him his house. But the lovers were true to each other and fled together to London, where they were married.

After four years' residence in a foreign country, Clarence Linden was again in London. He had become interested in Lady Flora Ardenne, daughter of Lady Westborough, whom he had met on the Continent. At an entertainment one evening, Lady Flora asked him, "How long shall you stay in England?"

"It rests with the ministers, not me," replied Clarence. "If Lord Aspeden obtains another appointment, I am promised the office of Secretary of Legation. Do you remember I told you, when we last parted, that it was **not as** an unknown adventurer that I would claim the hand **of her** whose heart, as an adventurer, I had won?"

Lady Flora raised her eyes and meeting his instantly dropped them.

"The time is not yet come," he continued, "for the fulfilment of this promise; but may I—dare I hope that when it does I shall not be—"

"Flora, my love," said Lady Westborough, who had been making some anxious enquiries about Clarence's lineage and means, "let me introduce to you Lord Borodaile."

Lady Flora turned, but after returning Lord Borodaile's address, glanced again at Clarence. His complexion was deadly pale, and his eyes were fixed with a searching and unaccountable meaning on the face of the young nobleman. As soon as he saw that he was observed, he rose and quickly walked away.

Lord Borodaile, son and heir of the powerful Earl of Ulswater, was about thirty, small, slight, and rather handsome. His complexion was dark and sallow, and a very aquiline nose gave a stern and somewhat severe air to his countenance. He had served abroad in the Russian army with the Earl of Effingham in the war with the Turks, and on his return to England had obtained the command of a cavalry regiment. His manners were cold, haughty, and self-possessed, and his conversation was that of a man who has cultivated his intellect rather in the world than in the closet.

"How very disagreeable Lord Borodaile is!" said Lady Flora, when he had turned away. "Disagreeable!" said Lady Westborough. "I think him charming. How true his remarks on the world are!"

Shortly after this, at a ball at Lady T——'s, Clarence saw, on entering, Lord Borodaile in close conversation with Lady Flora. As he drew near, he caught her eye, advanced, and was introduced to Lord Borodaile. The Viscount, who had drawn himself up very stiffly as Clarence approached, returned much more stiffly and haughtily, but with old-fashioned courtesy, Clarence's bow.

"Are you engaged?" said Clarence to Flora.

"I am, at present, to Lord Borodaile."

"After him, may I hope?"

Lady Flora nodded assent; and disappeared with Lord Borodaile.

A few nights later Clarence, in going home from a party at Lady Westborough's, noticed a man before him walking with an agitated step and eccentric gestures. He passed and, looking back, recognized him as one Wolfe, a violent republican whom he had seen several years before. Presently a gentleman, coming in the other direction, met Wolfe and turned to take the wall, though not entitled to it by street courtesy. Wolfe resented this and doggedly kept his way. The stranger contemptuously tried to push him aside, an altercation ensued, and the result was that Wolfe threw his antagonist to the pavement and placed his foot on his breast.

"So shall it be with all of you," he cried. "Lie there! If you stir limb or muscle, I will crush the breath from your body."

Clarence rushed to him. "Look you," said he, "you have received an insult, and you have done justice yourself. Remove your foot or—"

"What?" shouted Wolfe fiercely.

"Or I will hinder you from committing murder," said Clarence calmly.

Just then the watchman's voice was heard approaching, and Wolfe strode haughtily away. Clarence, who had recognized in the man's antagonist Lord Borodaile, assisted the prostrate man to arise, saying, "You are not severely hurt, my lord, I trust?"

"Well, quite well," cried Borodaile. "Mr. Linden, I think? I thank you cordially for your assistance; but the dog— the rascal—where is he?"

"Which way did he go?" asked the watchman. "I warrant I'll nab him."

"No—no," said Lord Borodaile haughtily. "I leave my quarrels to no man. Mr. Linden, excuse me, but I can walk very well without your polite assistance."

With these words, the proud patrician bowed with extreme courtesy to Clarence, again thanked him, and walked on unaided.

"He is worthy his name," thought Clarence; "though he was in the wrong, my heart yearns to him."

From that night Clarence appeared to have formed a sudden

attachment for Lord Borodaile, and took every opportunity of cultivating his intimacy. But his advances were ineffectual in conquering Borodaile's coldness and reserve. To have been seen in a humiliating and degrading position made the proud man hate the spectator. Though always ceremoniously civil, he was immovably distant, and avoided, as well as he was able, Clarence's insinuating approaches.

"Insolent intruder!" thought Lord Borodaile. "A man whom nobody knows to make such advances to *me!*"

Circumstances drove the rivals farther and farther apart and at last, at a dinner-party given by Lord St. George, Borodaile insulted Clarence so pointedly and egregiously that it was impossible to avoid challenging him. Borodaile refused all apology for his words, and the two met on the field of honor. Clarence was shot in the side, fired his own pistol in the air, and fell into the arms of the surgeon. Borodaile, touched at a forbearance he had so little right to expect, hastened to him.

"Thank God," said Clarence faintly, "that *you* were not the victim!" and fell back insensible.

Clarence's wound, though not mortal, was dangerous, and he had a lingering recovery. During this, he was incensed because no inquiry had come from the Westboroughs concerning him, and a letter written by him had been returned unopened.

Soon after this Mr. Talbot, his benefactor, died and left him a large fortune.

"Now," thought he, "I have at least no unworthy pretensions even to the hand of Lady Flora Ardenne. If she can love me for myself, if she can trust to my honor, then this wealth will be welcome to me, and the disguised name, which has cost me so many mortifications, become grateful, since she will not disdain to share it."

With these thoughts pressing on his mind, he determined to seek an interview with Lady Flora, and, if necessary, disclose to her his whole history. With this object he rode down to Westborough Park, but only once succeeded in getting a glimpse of her, and then amid a large party. So he wrote her a note, entreating her to give him a meeting, which he entrusted to the daughter of the lodge-keeper, with directions to give it only to Lady Flora. Several hours later, Linden received a letter written by Lord Westborough, in which he spoke of his "extraordinary request for a clandestine meeting," and added: "If you intend to confer upon my daughter the honor of a matrimonial proposal, she fully concurs with me and her mother in the negative which I feel necessitated to put upon your obliging offer."

"Insufferable arrogance!" Linden muttered. "I will live to repay it. I will accept Aspedon's offer, and hey for Italy!"

About three years later a gentleman in deep mourning rode up to the door of the Golden Fleece, in W—— and asked for accommodation for the night. As he was without an attendant, he was consigned to a minor room. An hour afterward a carriage and four drove up to the door, and landlord, landlady, and daughters flocked out to greet arriving guests. A valet took from out the carriage a desk, and said: "My master's here, ma'am, I think—rode on before!"

"And who is your master?" asked Mrs. Merrylack, with a thrill of alarm.

"Who!" said the valet, "why, Clarence Talbot Linden, Esq., of Scarsdale Park, county of York, late Secretary of Legation at the Court of ——, now M.P., and one of his Majesty's under Secretaries of State."

"Mercy upon us!" cried the landlady. "Run, John, light a fire in the Elephant, Number Sixteen, beg the gentleman's pardon, say it was occupied till now, and ask what he'll have for supper."

During these three years of Linden's absence from England, Lord Borodaile, now Lord Ulswater from the death of his father, had fixed himself in the train of Lady Flora Ardenne, determined to win her. Thrice he had been refused, but he gave out that he was her affianced, forced himself near her at all parties, unheeding alike her frowns or indifference, and kept from her the less arrogant and hardy pretenders to her favor. The father he had served financially and the mother he had won. He had at last succeeded in his quest, and the wedding-day was set.

During this time changes had come in the fortunes of Mr. Mordaunt, who, dispossessed of his ancestral estates, was left to battle with the world with a young wife who had accepted his portionless lot. Under the assumed name of Glendower, the pair went into poor lodgings in London, where they struggled with poverty until the wife died of destitution, leaving him a daughter, Isabel. When on the borders of despair, Mordaunt received word that the only son and heir of Vavasour Mordaunt, who had despoiled him of his property, had died. Vavasour, who had spent much money on the old house, invited him, as legal heir to the estates, to return thither, as he preferred to live in London; and Linden found him once more in the home of his fathers, to which he had returned under most favorable auspices, Mr. Vavasour Mordaunt having settled a large sum on him. He had also been elected to Parliament.

A letter from the Duke of Haverfield, who had married Lady Flora's bosom friend, led Clarence to revive his hopes. "She still cherishes your memory," he wrote, "though I do not advise you to run away with Lady Flora—gentlemen don't run away with the daughters of gentlemen; but, without running away, you may win your betrothed and Lord Ulswater's intended."

Clarence was like a man transformed on reading this, and a burning and intense desire, which for years he had not permitted himself to form, arose within him. On the next morning he rode to Westborough Park and, watching his opportunity, saw Lady Flora alone. She acknowledged that she had been deceived, but asserted through her tears that it was too late, that she had given her pledge and must become Lord Ulswater's wife in two months.

"Never!" cried Clarence. "Who is he that claims you? I am his equal in birth—in the world's name—and oh, by what worlds his superior in love! I will advance my claim to you in his very teeth!"

"Be it so, sir!" cried a voice behind, and Clarence turned and beheld Lord Ulswater, his dark countenance flushed with rage. "It is not the first time we shall have met, if not as rivals, as foes."

Lady Westborough just then entered the pavilion and, Clarence, ignoring Ulswater, appealed to her. Lord Ulswater arrogantly interfered and insisted that none but himself, Lady Flora's legitimate defender, should answer the intruder.

"Man!" cried Clarence, "beware how you incense me to pollute my soul with the blood of a—"

"What!" exclaimed Lord Ulswater.

Clarence whispered one word in his ear. Lord Ulswater staggered back, his face paled, and he stood with eyes dilated and fixed on Clarence's face.

Linden did not wait for him to recover, but hurried after Lady Westborough and her daughter. He had scarcely spoken to them when Lord Ulswater came up, laid his hand on Linden's shoulder, and said calmly, "Are you furnished with proof to support the word you uttered?"

"I am," replied Clarence haughtily.

"And will you favor me with it?"

"When and where you please."

"So be it. I will meet you here on Wednesday next at twelve o'clock. I have military business to detain me on Tuesday."

Clarence Linden was at Westborough Park at the appointed hour, but Lord Ulswater did not come. The full hour passed, one o'clock struck, and still he did not appear. Clarence, to whom the situation had become awkward, said to Lady Westborough; "I do not see the necessity of delaying the explanation I have to offer to your ladyship till my Lord Ulswater deems it suitable to appear. Now—"

He was interrupted by a commotion and loud voices in the hall. Clarence threw open the door and Lady Westborough, who had followed him, uttered a shriek of horror and fainted. Men were bringing in the bleeding body of Lord Ulswater.

A socialist meeting had been held in —— the day before, at which Wolfe and other prominent radicals had taken part. Lord Ulswater, who had been sent thither with part of his regiment to keep the peace, had acted with his usual haughtiness, had insulted Mr. Mordaunt and angrily threatened Wolfe with imprisonment. Wolfe's fierce spirit was in arms on the instant, and but for his friends would have committed some impudent act. He eyed Lord Ulswater's retreating figure with a menacing look, and muttered: "The time may yet come when I shall have license to retaliate on the upstart."

Thanks to the efforts of Mordaunt, the meeting passed off

without trouble, and Lord Ulswater set out the next morning
to keep his appointment at Westborough Park. He was joined
on the road by Mr. Glumford, a gentleman who had sided with
him at the meeting. When about two miles from Westborough
Park, Lord Ulswater took a narrow footpath over the hill
instead of the main road. Glumford warned him that the soil
was crumbling and the descent to the road steep, but Lord
Ulswater replied that he thought himself capable of guiding
his horse on so good a road.

"Ha!" cried Glumford, "look yonder, there is Wolfe, gesticu-
lating to himself. Excuse me, my lord, but you had better
come down—it is not wide enough for two—the d——d rascal
would not get out of the way for the devil himself."

"I do not understand, Mr. Glumford," remarked Lord
Ulswater, "what peculiarities of temper you are pleased to
impute to me or from what you deduce the supposition that
I shall move out of my way for such a person."

Wolfe, hearing them coming, turned quickly and, recognizing Lord Ulswater, took the middle of the path. Ulswater,
now close upon him, arrogantly ordered him to stand aside
for him to pass. Wolfe turned on him. "Poor and proud fool,"
he said in a voice of biting scorn, "do you think that your
privileges have reached so pleasant a pitch that you may ride
over men like dust?"

Without deigning any reply, Lord Ulswater spurred his
horse upon him. Wolfe stepped aside and seized the bridle
with a powerful grasp. The fated nobleman, enraged, struck
him with his whip, and the next instant horse and rider were
rolling over each other down the hill.

Lord Ulswater was senseless when Wolfe reached his side.
One arm was crushed and his head was covered with blood.
A passing carriage was hailed by Glumford, and, with the
assistance of the traveler, Lord Ulswater was placed in it and
conveyed to Westborough Park.

When Lord Ulswater opened his eyes, they rested upon
Clarence, beside whom stood Wardour, an old servant of his
family, whom Clarence had bought to substantiate his claim.

"My brother—my brother!" cried Clarence in anguish,
"is it thus that you have come to—"

Lord Ulswater looked at Wardour, seeming to ask the truth of Clarence's claim.

"It is—it is, my honored lord," exclaimed the old servitor, "it is your brother—your long-lost brother, Clinton L'Estrange."

Clarence felt the damp chill hand press his own and knew by the smile of the dying man that the disowned was at last recognized and the long-broken ties again united.

When Lady Flora came to his bedside, he took her hand and gave it to Clarence, saying, "Let this—my—brother—atone —for——" and fell back on his pillow.

The old Earl of Ulswater was twice married. By his first wife he had three children, of whom only the youngest, Francis, Lord Borodaile, survived. When Francis was six years old his mother died, and a year later Lord Ulswater married a Miss Talbot, daughter of Colonel Talbot and niece of Squire Talbot of Scarsdale Park, who brought him one son, Clinton.

Francis was educated in Germany and was abroad many years, during which the Earl learned to love his younger son more and more. When Clinton was about eighteen years old, a cousin of Lady Ulswater's, Sir Clinton Manners, a constant visitor at the house, eloped with her, and letters left behind showed that the two had long been lovers and that she had accepted Lord Ulswater in a momentary passion with Sir Clinton, after whom she had named her child. Lord Ulswater's love for Clinton now turned to hatred. He declared that he was not his son, and turned him adrift in the world. Years afterward when the mother, dying in a convent in Italy, wrote him that he was mistaken, that Clinton was really his son, he relented and would have gladly welcomed him back, if he had known where he was; and on his death-bed he enjoined Wardour to tell him that his best comfort in departing was the hope of his forgiveness.

Lord Ulswater's death made Clarence, or Clinton, as he was called henceforth, Earl of Ulswater. But Lady Flora, who soon became his bride, always insisted on calling him Clarence, the name under which she had first become acquainted with the Disowned.

DEVEREUX (1829)

This novel, the fourth of Bulwer's romances, is in the form of an auto-biography, and while dealing with events in the life of Count Morton Devereux, introduces many celebrities of the eighteenth century, as Lord Bolingbroke, the Regent Orléans, and Peter the Great, of Russia.

Y grandfather, Sir Arthur Devereux, had two sons. At his death, my father, the younger, bade adieu to the old hall and his brother, and went to France to join as a volunteer the armies of Louis, afterward surnamed *le Grand*. My uncle went up to court, as his ancestors had gone before him, was knighted by Charles II, took to Sedley and champagne, flirted with Nell Gwynne, wrote a comedy, and married a wife. The wife brought him a child six months after marriage, the same day the comedy was acted; and, luckily for the honor of our house, both died as soon as they were born. Six weeks after her confinement the wife eloped with a gentleman of the court, and my uncle retired to the country in a fit of disgust and gout. Good old man! he was too honest and too simple to shine in that galaxy of prostituted genius. In retirement he was no longer the same person; and I do not think the elements of human nature could have furnished forth a more amiable character than Sir William Devereux.

My father never left the service of Louis Quatorze, and the great King repaid him with orders and decorations without number. He died of wounds received in battle, a count and a marshal, full of renown, and destitute of money. He had married twice: his first wife, of the noble house of La Tremouille, died without issue; his second, our mother, was of a younger branch of the English race of Howard. On his death she hastened to return with her children to England, where my uncle was unaffectedly rejoiced to receive us. To say

365

nothing of the pride he felt at the honors my father had won for our ancient house, the good gentleman was well pleased to get four new listeners for his garrulous stories, out of whom he hoped to select one for his heir, and he soon grew as fond of us as we were of him. At the time of our new settlement, I, Morton, had attained the age of twelve; my twin brother Gerald was born an hour after me; my other brother Aubrey was about fifteen months younger.

I never had been a favorite; my brothers, especially the youngest, were handsomer, and my mind was considered as much inferior to theirs as my body. I was idle and dull, sullen and haughty; the only wit I ever displayed was in sneering at my friends, and the only spirit, in quarrelling with my twin brother. But, to the astonishment of myself and my relatives, I became Sir William's favorite and the object of his preëminent attachment. We were constantly together; I loved to listen to his stories of courts and courtiers, and he was ever ready to defend me when my vanity or my recklessness led me into trouble.

Another member of our family was the Abbé Montreuil, a Jesuit priest who had followed us from France as our preceptor. He had been educated at St. Omer, and possessed a great variety and depth of learning besides a knowledge of the principal European languages. He was of low origin, though his address and appearance did not betray it; and while his age did not exceed twenty-eight years he impressed the beholder with the idea of one more advanced in life. Through his influence we were sent to an academy for three years.

My twin brother Gerald was tall, strong, and handsome, and had extraordinary quickness of ability; but he was indolent and had a certain vein of irresolution which rendered it easy for a cool and determined mind to awe or persuade him. With him I had a deadly and irreconcilable feud. There is nothing in human passion like a good brotherly hatred. But he was considered a genius in the family, and I believe we were sent off to school to prevent my uncle deciding everything in my favor. My brother Aubrey was of a very different disposition of mind and frame of body: thoughtful, gentle, susceptible, acute; with an uncertain bravery, like a woman's, and a taste for reading that varied with the caprice of every hour. He was very handsome, and my mother's favorite. I had always loved Aubrey, but they had not suffered him to love me.

Montreuil, on his entrance into our family, had not only fallen in with, but favored and fostered, the reigning humor against me; he also fomented the dissensions and widened the breach between my brothers and myself. He especially favored Gerald, who showed great assiduity in his studies, in his instruction, and when a prize was offered for the most proficient at a very severe examination, the Abbé counted certainly on the success of the "genius" of the family. But my uncle told me I could win if I chose, and I promised him faithfully to try.

The Abbé came with Aubrey to my room a few hours before the examination, with the professed desire of giving me a few preparatory hints, but I would not admit them.

" Go," said I bitterly through my locked door, "you are both my foes and slanderers—you come to insult my disgrace beforehand: but perhaps you will yet be disappointed.'

Every boy passed the examination, but I was the victor of the day—I was more—I was one hundred marks before Gerald. My uncle was overjoyed, and Aubrey, coming to my room, threw his arms around me and kissed me in silence. Then the Abbé entered, extending his hand. "Morton," said he, "I have wronged you, I own it—here is my hand; Aubrey, let all but early love, and the present promise of excellence which your brother displays, be forgotten."

With these words the priest joined our hands. I looked on my brother, and my heart melted. I flung myself into his arms and wept.

The Abbé was now particularly courteous to me. He made Gerald and myself breakfast with him, and told us nothing was so amiable as friendship among brothers. We became at last civil but distant, and avoided each other. The Abbé had obtained a wonderful hold over Aubrey, and made the poor boy think so much of the next world that he lost all relish for this. For me he seemed to have carved out a more worldly career.

"Morton," he said, grasping my arm, "you know me not—for many years I have not known you—that time is past. Let us henceforth be more to each other than we have been—let us be friends. I, insignificant as I appear, can, in every path through life, be more useful to your desires than you can ever be to mine. I offer you my friendship. Do you accept my offer?"

"Can you doubt?" said I, with eagerness. "I do embrace it, and with rapture."

"But," he continued, "all alliances have their conditions—I require implicit confidence, and, for some years, obedience. Name any wish you may form for worldly advancement—and I will pledge myself to carry that wish into effect. What say you?"

"That I think I will agree to the bond; but, I must have time to consider."

"Be it so. To-morrow I depart for France. I shall return in a few months, but perhaps not until the expiration of a year. I leave you until then to decide. Meanwhile, name some commission in France which you wish me to execute."

"I can think of none—yet stay—I would like to know if my father's name has become an unknown sound at the court of the Great King."

As he closed, I muttered to myself, "Well, well, my sage ecclesiastic, let us see if, at sixteen, we cannot shuffle cards and play tricks with the gamester of thirty."

About eight miles from my uncle's house was a seaport town, and near it a cottage in the midst of a garden. Its tenant, Don Diego d'Alvarez, was a Spaniard of high birth who, for participation in an insurrection, had been obliged to flee his country, and lived here in seclusion with his motherless daughter, Isora. After making the recluse's acquaintance I had become interested in the daughter, and made frequent visits to the cottage. One evening, when Don Diego and I were conversing, with Isora sitting near, the Don asked, "How comes it that you have never met our friend, Señor Bar—Bar—how is he called, Isora?"

"Mr. Barnard," replied Isora, with evident confusion and downcast eyes, "Mr. Barnard, I believe you mean."

"Right, my love," said the father;" "a handsome youth, but shy and over-modest."

"How comes it indeed," I asked, with a piercing look at Isora, "that I have not met him? Is he a friend of long standing?"

"Nay—perhaps some six weeks earlier than you. I pressed him this morning to tarry your coming, but he is diffident, poor youth!"

Isora looked up, blushed as she met my gaze, and rising went into the house. As she did not return, I took my farewell for the night.

Day after day I renewed my visits to the Spaniard's cottage, yet I had not told Isora of my love. I was inexpressibly jealous of this Barnard, whose name she never heard without visible confusion. One day, when Don Diego had gone to a neighboring town, I sought Isora in the garden, and found her, apparently lifeless, on the ground. I raised her form in my arms, and while I pressed kisses on her lips, she slowly recovered consciousness. As her eyes met my ardent gaze the blood rushed to her cheek, and as suddenly departed, leaving it hueless as before, while anguish was depicted on every feature. A pang shot through me.

"I see all," I cried, "you love another—you love him!"

From her lips came a single word that thrilled my heart like fire—"No!"

"Who is this Barnard?" I demanded. "Who or what is he?"

"Listen to me!" she said. "You profess to love me—I am not worthy of your love, Count Devereux. I will not wrong you by encouraging hopes which I may not and I dare not fulfil. I can never be yours, and when you ask me to be so you know not what you ask, nor what perils you incur. Be this our last meeting—our very last—God bless you, Morton!" She tore herself from me, and I was alone.

On my way home along the cliffs I saw Alvarez on the beach below apparently waiting for a boat that was coming shoreward. As the boat came nearer, I recognized Gerald in it. He gave the Spaniard a letter and the two conversed nearly an hour, when they parted.

"My enemy! my rival! my brother! my twin brother!"
I muttered bitterly, as I watched the boat push out toward
the islet. For several days I was confined to my bed with a
fever. As soon as I got out I rode to the Spaniard's house.
He and his daughter had gone, none knew whither.

The next evening the Abbé Montreuil suddenly entered
my room and, after a paternal embrace, presented me with a
splendid sword, the hilt sparkling with jewels. Attached was
a label inscribed: "To the son of Marshal Devereux, the
soldier of France, and the friend of Louis XIV."

Before I recovered from my surprise, the Abbé said, "I
received this from the King's own hand, and I have authority
to inform you that if you ever wield it in the service of France
it will be accompanied by a post worthy of your name."

"The service of France," I said, "is at present the service of
an enemy."

"An enemy only to a *part* of England!" replied the Abbé
emphatically. "The friendship of the court of France may
be synonymous with the friendship of the true sovereign of
England."

There was no mistaking the purport of this speech, and I
drew back alarmed, for I recognized in him an agent of the
exiled royal family whose intrigues had brought so much
trouble to the kingdom. The Abbé noted my change of countenance and artfully turned the conversation.

On the following morning a letter was brought to me by a
small, dark man, who requested that no one should be allowed
to see it but myself. When I broke the seal the first thing
that met my eyes was a letter in the Abbé's own handwriting.
At that instant the Abbé himself rushed into the hall, cast a
hasty look at the messenger, then grasped my hand, and cried,
"Do not read it—not a word—there is poison in it."

"Pardon me, Father—when I have read it you shall have
that pleasure—not till then," and glancing at the letter I saw
my own name written in two places.

"Boy," said the Abbé, gasping, "give me that letter
instantly."

"You forget yourself, sir," said I. "If you have not yet
learned the respect due to my station, it is time you should."

He then turned from anger to supplication, said there was a secret in the letter which imperiled his personal safety, and humbly begged it of me.

"Will you swear," said I, "that this letter does not concern me? That I am not even mentioned in it?"

"Solemnly," answered he raising his eyes, "upon peril of my soul, I will."

"Liar—traitor—perjured blasphemer." I cried, in a rage, "Look here, and here!"

"Count Devereux, I warn you not to push my patience too far. Give me the letter, or you will find me now and forever your most deadly foe—deadly—deadly!" His look was so malignant that I drew back and laid my hand on my sword.

Montreuil was much better dressed than usual and wore a rapier. He quickly drew his weapon and made a rapid and fierce thrust at me, which I parried. The moment our swords crossed I found him far more adroit than myself in the art of offense; and it might have fared ill with me if the servants, hearing the noise, had not rushed in. I turned the affair off with a laugh, and, at Montreuil's request, led the way to a secluded place where we could finish our quarrel. But, to my surprise, he came without his sword. He expressed repentance for his rashness, and gave so plausible an explanation of the letter, appealing to my honor, that I finally handed it to him with the remark, "Never shall it be said that Morton Devereux hazarded his honor to secure his safety. But the tie between us is broken now and forever."

After this the Abbé disappeared, and his name was seldom mentioned in the family. I told my uncle of the affair, and he was troubled by it for a time, and especially at my receiving a sword from the King of France, with whom we were then at war. Soon after this I went up to London, where I lived the life of a young man of the time, meeting many celebrated men and becoming intimate with many women, some of whom were not so celebrated. My uncle and Aubrey wrote me occasionally, so that I was kept in touch with events at home, and I supplied them in turn with the scandal of the town.

In one of my uncle's letters I received information which led me to believe that Montreuil was still in the neighborhood and that he had Gerald in his toils. I did not doubt but that the two were engaged in some intrigue for the exiled Stuart family. But, eager alike in my hatred and my love, I said to myself, "What matters it whether Gerald win fame or death in the perilous game he has engaged in?"

During my stay in London I had become intimate with Mr. St. John, afterward Lord Bolingbroke. One day I met two men coming from his rooms; one I did not know, but the second one I recognized as Montreuil, who passed me without recognition. St. John received me with his usual gayety, but when I referred to his late visitor, he said coolly, "I wish to receive no information concerning him." As my host intimated that this was a state secret and sought to turn the conversation, I soon rose to depart. St. John asked me to ride with him in the afternoon to Spring Gardens, on "a mission of charity to a poor foreigner, Don Diego d'Alvarez—but heavens! Devereux—you seem ill."

"No, no! Have you ever seen this man?"

"Never."

This reply caused me a thrill of joy, for I knew St. John's fame for gallantry. "I know this Spaniard," I said, "know him intimately. Could you not commission me to do your errand?"

St. John gave me the address and I hastened thither. It was a humble but not absolutely wretched abode. A woman, who opened the door, said the foreign gentleman was so ill that he could see no one—even Mr. Barnard had been denied admission. I was shocked and stunned, but I thought this no time for any jealous or selfish emotion.

"I am an old friend of the family," I said, as I slipped some money into her hand. She took me to the second floor and, pointing to the door, said simply, "There!"

I cannot describe my meeting with Isora. When I proposed the removal of her father to a better lodging, she said, "I accept your kindness. *You* will not deceive us—from *him* I rejected the same offer."

"Him—this Barnard, or rather—I know him!"

"Know him!" she cried, "You do not—you cannot!"

"Tell me, Isora, do you love him?"

"Love—O God, no! But I fear for *you!*"

"Me!" I cried scornfully. "I do not fear this masked rival—my own brother!"

Isora quailed beneath my gaze, her face paled, and took an expression of keen anguish, but she made no answer.

Alvarez bore the removal without signs of fatigue. I established him and his daughter in comfortable lodgings, and procured him the best of medical attendance, but he died before many days. The day after Don Diego's funeral, I went to see Isora.

"She has been very ill," said the servant who admitted me, "ever since the strange gentleman left her."

Convinced from her description that Gerald had been the intruder, I hastened upstairs. Isora endeavored to conceal the traces of her tears.

"Morton, dear Morton," she said, "I was alarmed, but it was only for you. 'The moment,' he said, 'Morton Devereux discovers who is his rival, that moment his death-warrant is sealed.'"

"Arrogant boaster!" I cried. "I will seek him this moment, and dare him to do his worst."

"Do so," said Isora calmly, "and I swear by that crucifix that I will never be yours."

Three months after this we were married privately by a priest, St. John and an old lady who had been my father's godmother being the sole witnesses. I took a small house in the environs of London, and furnished it with every luxury wealth could procure. Thither, under an assumed name, I brought my bride, and there the greater part of my time was spent.

Not long after this my uncle was taken ill and I was sent for. I arrived in time to receive his blessing and to see him die. His will was read in the little room where he had been accustomed to sit. Gerald and my mother, Oswald, the attorney, and myself were the only persons present, Aubrey having gone away. I had always supposed that my uncle intended to make me his heir. What, then, was my astonishment when the whole bulk of the property was bequeathed to Gerald; to Aubrey forty thousand pounds and to myself twenty thousand were given. I suspected foul practice and I said so, looking at Gerald.

"You cannot, Morton," exclaimed Gerald, "you dare not insinuate that I have been base enough to forge this will?"

"The case, sir," I answered coldly, "stands thus: my uncle could not have made this will. Fraud has been practised, how, I know not! by whom I do know."

"Morton, this is insufferable—I cannot bear such charges, even from a brother."

"Charges!—your conscience speaks, sir—not I; no one benefits by this fraud but you."

I returned to London, sold off my horses and equipages, jewels and plate, and found, when I had paid my debts, that I had only about fifteen thousand pounds left. My best plan for the future seemed to be to offer my services to some foreign court, and to that end I was anxious to announce my marriage by a second or public nuptials, purposing to leave the country within a week afterward.

On the evening of the day set for this ceremony, a man called on me and announced himself as Marie Oswald, the half-brother of the Oswald that drew my uncle's will. "My poor brother is just dead; I am charged with a packet for you, given me by him on his deathbed. You shall have it on two conditions—"

"Which are—"

"First, to pay me five thousand pounds if through it you become possessed of the Devereux estates now enjoyed by your brother Gerald; second, to promise not to open the packet for seven days."

"The devil! and why?"

"One of the papers in the packet is my brother's written confession; it will criminate one I love and who, I am resolved, shall have a chance to escape."

"Who is that one? Montreuil?"

"No—but I cannot tell you more. The promise, Count, is indispensable."

"The reward shall be double, if I succeed," said I.

Oswald then gave me the packet, which I placed in my bosom and then I returned to my guests. After all had departed I consigned the packet to one of the drawers of my escritoire.

As I was locking it, my valet Desmarais came to ask leave to go and visit a friend.

"There are five guineas," I said, "go and get drunk with your friend, and be merry instead of wise."

It was past midnight when Isora asked me whether I did not hear a noise below. I heard nothing, and we both went to sleep. Some time later I awoke and saw a masked man in a long cloak standing near the bed. Before my escritoire, where I had put the packet, stood another man, similarly disguised. He had the packet in his hand. I tore myself loose from Isora's arms, and reached for my sword—it was gone! I sprang from bed and upon the man who held the packet. He tried to shake me off, and when I had nearly succeeded in unmasking him, he stabbed me in the side with a poniard. With a piercing cry, Isora sprang from the bed and flung herself before the uplifted blade and arrested his arm. His companion now came forward, brandishing a similar poniard.

"Spare him! Oh, mercy, mercy!" Isora cried.

I made an effort to rise—the blade descended—Isora threw herself before it—her blood gushed over me—I saw and felt no more.

Months passed before my senses returned. I arose from a bed of suffering, altered but tranquil. All efforts to discover the murderers were in vain. The packet was gone, and when I was able to tell of its loss, suspicion naturally rested on Gerald. But he came forward publicly and proved that he had not stirred from home during the whole week in which the event had occurred. However, I could not rest until I had told him what I thought of him. I rode to Devereux Court, leaving behind my sword lest I should be tempted to use it, and told him to enjoy while he might the fortune acquired by fraud and the conscience he had stained with murder.

"But know," I said, "that the day will come when the blood that cries from earth shall be heard in Heaven, and your blood shall appease it."

I left him stunned and horror-stricken. Once he wrote to me. I returned the letter unopened.

About a year after the murder of Isora, my mother informed me of the death of Aubrey, of consumption. Montreuil had

been with him in Ireland, where he died, and wrote most
glowingly of his devotion in the last months of his life. On
receipt of this news, my mother retired to a convent of ladies
of our faith, a step she had long contemplated.

When Lord Bolingbroke fled to France I accompanied
him, and for many years I lived abroad in the service of the
Regent of France and later of the Czar Peter in Russia. I won
honors and wealth, and, after transferring my immense fortune
to England, set out for home, with the intention of visiting
Italy on the way. Near a small village at the foot of the Apen-
nines I heard of a recluse in the neighborhood, called the Hermit
of the Well, whom I visited. When he heard I had come from
St. Petersburg, he asked whether I had ever met the Count
Devereux.

"I have both seen and known the man," I said calmly.

"Ha! and where is he at present?"

"That, Father, is a difficult question. He was ambassador
at the court of —— just before I left it."

To shorten my story, he entrusted me with a packet
addressed to myself, which I read that very night. The hermit
was no other than my brother Aubrey. The manuscript told
me that he was the guilty one—not Gerald. His motive was
pure jealousy. Montreuil was a Jacobite agent pledged to the
restoration of the House of Stuart. He obtained a mysterious
and pervading power over both Gerald and Aubrey, and to
secure Sir William Devereux's wealth for the cause, changed
his will in favor of Gerald. The agent in effecting the change
was my valet Desmarais, an accomplished penman, who was a
spy of Montreuil's. Aubrey, who had taken the name of
Barnard in his intrigues with Don Diego, who was also an
agent of the Stuarts, fell in love with Isora, who did not return
his passion. To secure a hold on her, he threatened my life
and warned her against uniting herself to me. Montreuil
learned from Desmarais of the receipt of the packet from
Oswald, and he and Aubrey were the masked villains who
entered my chamber. After Isora's death Aubrey nearly went
mad, and Montreuil removed him from England and finally
spread the report of his death.

I read the manuscript, which was full of agonized and

bitter self-accusation and humiliation, to the end, without one thought of anger or vengeance. His conscience had avenged me. I went at once to my brother, took him by the hand, revealed myself to him and gave him my forgiveness. He looked at me with wild eyes, his lips quivered, and I heard the death-rattle in his throat.

When I returned to England, I found Gerald at first haughty and sullen. He expected reproaches and defiance; he was not prepared for my prayers for friendship and my grief for our past enmity, and he melted at once. I endeavored to arouse in him some sympathy with my own indignation against Montreuil. As I knew the priest to be still deeply involved in schemes of treason, I obtained a warrant for his apprehension. That night he endeavored to escape to a French privateer that lay off the coast, but was intercepted. In the combat that ensued between the officers of the law and the French sailors that had come to meet him, I had the satisfaction of passing my sword twice through his body. He was not the only victim: several of the pirates and their pursuers perished, and among the bodies we found my brother Gerald. By a sort of retribution, he was killed by a shot fired by the villain Desmarais, who had followed Montreuil's fortunes, and who unfortunately succeeded in escaping. Thus I, at the age of thirty-four, succeeded, by the death of my brother, to the Devereux estates, which should justly have been mine long before.

PAUL CLIFFORD (1830)

To use the author's own words, "this story is the *only one* in which a robber has been made the hero." It was written, first, to draw attention to two errors in Great Britain's penal institutions—a vicious prison discipline and a sanguinary criminal code; and second, to show that there is nothing essentially different between vulgar vice and fashionable "fast life."

AUL CLIFFORD was present at the death of his mother in an upper room of an obscure ale-house named "The Mug," in Thames Court, London, the resort of thieves and pickpockets. The only persons present were Dummie Dunnaker, a small, thin man, with a yellow, cunning face, and Mrs. Margery Lobkins, familiarly called Peggy or Piggy Lob, the hostess. The child, about three years old, who thus became the ward of Mrs. Lobkins, was named by her Paul after her grandfather, who had been thrice transported and finally hanged. He grew up to be a sturdy and handsome boy, a pet of the frequenters of "The Mug," whose pockets he learned to rifle, though rather for the love of frolic than a desire for profit, and an adept in the use of keys in all locks but the right one. Mrs. Lobkins, who loved the boy, desired that he should have a better education than those he met, and agreed with Mr. Peter MacGrawler, a canny Scotchman, editor of a periodical called *The Asinæum*, to teach him two hours daily, in consideration of such meat and drink as "The Mug" afforded and two and sixpence weekly.

One morning Paul met in the apartment of MacGrawler Mr. Augustus Tomlinson, a young man of promise, whose business was the chronicling in a certain leading newspaper of "horrid murders," "enormous melons," and "remarkable circumstances." This gentleman, Paul's senior by several

378

years, dressed smartly, quoted Latin with remarkable grace, and exhibited such a spirit and ease of demeanor as to captivate our hero.   Tomlinson reproved him for using flash expressions and vulgar language, and told him he should have a nobler spirit, a loftier emulation than that which distinguishes the ragamuffins of the street.   "Genius and learning," said he, "carry everything before them; and, if you behave yourself properly, you may one day be as high in the world as myself."

Paul took this to heart, went home and consigned the memoirs of Dick Turpin to the flames, and from that day he used choicer words, assumed a more refined air of dignity, and paid more attention to MacGrawler's lessons.   While his progress in the learned languages was not astonishing, he gained, by reading novels, plays, and poetry, a tolerable knowledge of his mother tongue and a certain refinement of taste. They aroused also an ambition to see something of the gay life depicted in them and gave his temper a tone of enterprise and of generosity which contributed to counteract the evil influences to which his youth was subjected.

One evening, when Paul was sixteen years old and a fine, handsome lad, he met at a ball several people noted for living handsomely on their own brains and those of other people. Among them was a tall gentleman with a remarkably fine head of hair, Mr. Edward Pepper, commonly called Long Ned, who introduced him to a certain club in Fish Lane.   From that time Paul became a regular visitor to the club, and shortly became a gentleman of three outs—out of pocket, out of elbows, and out of credit.   Dummie Dunnaker, who was a ragman and knew the world, cautioned Paul to shun the acquaintance of Long Ned, as "of very dangerous morals, and not by no manner of means a fit 'sociate for a young gemman of c'racter."

Soon after this, in consequence of the refusal of Mrs. Lobkins to furnish him with money enough to support himself like a gentleman, Paul announced his intention to throw himself on the world and seek his own fortune.

Dame Lobkins, enraged at this assertion of a desire for independence, replied: "I'feaks, Master Pride-in-duds! seek your fortune yourself, will you?   This comes of my bringing you up, and letting you eat the bread of idleness and charity, you toad! Take that and be d——d to you!" With this she took her pipe from her mouth and threw it with such good aim that it grazed Paul's cheek.

Paul cast one look at the scarlet face of the old woman, who had drunk more than usual that day, and turned slowly and in silence to the door.

"I will eat the bread of idleness and charity no longer," said he, sullenly. "Good-by—and if ever I can pay you what I have cost you, I will!"

Paul at first called on MacGrawler, for whom he worked on *The Asinæum* until he had saved five guineas and four shillings, when he left him to seek other employment. One evening while leaning on the parapet of London Bridge, he was accosted by a gentleman booted and spurred, with his hat cocked on one side, and a military cloak thrown over his shoulder. He had a riding-whip in one hand and a cigar in his mouth. To his surprise he recognized in this gentleman Ned Pepper, who, Dummie Dunnaker had told him, had "gone on the road."

"I am glad to meet you," said Paul, "but I hope what I heard of you is not true."

"Hist!" said Ned, "never talk of what you hear of gentlemen. Come with me; there's a tavern hard by. But you look cursed seedy. Follow me—I can't walk with you."

Paul, at first disposed to resent his words, put his pride in his pocket and followed Ned, who fitted him with a second-hand suit of clothes and took him to the theater. The two occupied seats in the dress tier, for Ned was a gentleman who would never condescend to appear anywhere but in the boxes. In the next box to them sat a gentleman and a young lady, the latter so uncommonly beautiful that Paul could scarcely keep his eyes from her. While Paul was feeding his eyes on her charms, Long Ned had found an object no less fascinating in a large gold watch which the gentleman ever and anon brought to his eye as if weary of the performance on the stage. When the two went out Paul and his companion followed them, but with very different motives. Long Ned brushed by the gentleman in passing, a voice cried, "Stop thief!" and Ned, saying to Paul, "Shift for yourself—run!" vanished in a twinkling.

Before Paul could recover his senses he found himself seized by the collar, and saw the dark face of the young lady's companion.

"Rascal!" cried the gentleman, "my watch!"

The next minute he was marched off between two watchmen. On the following morning Mr. Brandon, the loser of the watch, a barrister of reputation, appeared in court against him, and Paul Lobkins was convicted as an accomplice and sentenced for three months to Bridewell. He did not stay there long. Among the prisoners he found Mr. Augustus Tomlinson, and three weeks after Paul's incarceration the two escaped. After reaching the country safely and getting a good sleep under a haystack, Tomlinson introduced our hero to an inn near Finchley Common, called the Jolly Angler, kept by one Gentleman George, where, among other choice spirits, he found Long Ned.

About fifty miles from London, on the banks of one of England's fairest rivers, stands Warlock Hall, an ancient building showing many signs of former magnificence, and surrounded by a large tract of waste land bearing evidences of being a dismantled chase or park. This place, the home of a family of high antiquity, and once of considerable note, had gradually decayed with the fortunes of the race, while its owner now had held no higher rank than that of a small country squire. Joseph Brandon, the present proprietor, was a widower of about fifty years of age, with one child, Lucy. William, his younger brother, passed his boyhood on the estate; but when thirteen was sent to school, where he showed remarkable talents, and when nineteen bore off at the university two of the highest honors. From the university he went on the "grand tour" with a young nobleman, whose friendship he had won, and after two years abroad settled down to the profession of the law. Through the influence of the same nobleman he obtained a seat in the House of Commons, and he was regarded as a man of rising fortunes.

Meanwhile, the elder brother resided in the paternal mansion with his daughter Lucy in undisturbed obscurity, the discreditable character and habits of the preceding lords of Warlock having rendered the surrounding gentry little anxious

to cultivate the intimacy of the present proprietor. Lucy
Brandon was lovely at nineteen. She had a silvery, joyous
laugh, and all her movements seemed to keep time to it. While
little can be said for her intellectual attainments, she could
spell indifferently well and wrote a tolerable hand. She had
some skill on the spinet, and the power of singing old
songs in the richest and sweetest voice that ever made one's
heart beat faster.

One afternoon Squire Brandon, who was reading his newspaper, said to Lucy, "I see that Lord Mauleverer has been
made our Lord Lieutenant. Since he is such a good friend of
William's, I hope he will be a little more attentive to us than
Lord —— was."

"He was very polite when he dined with us in London six
years ago—the time uncle took me to the play and lost his
watch," remarked Lucy.

"By the way," continued the Squire, "Pillum is coming
to play a rubber at backgammon. If you would like to walk to
the parson's, I will send John for you at nine o'clock with the
lantern."

When Lucy arrived at the rectory the parson's wife
exclaimed: "Oh, my dear Miss Brandon! Which way did
you come? Such an accident to poor, dear Slopperton—stopped
on the king's highway and robbed. If it had not been for that
dear, good young man, I might have been a disconsolate widow
by this time!"

Lucy, glancing round the room, saw the round, oily little
person of Dr. Slopperton, with a face of miserable pallor,
collapsed in an arm-chair, and beside him a young man, who
had risen at her entrance, and was now gazing at her intently.
Blushing involuntarily, she turned her eyes hastily away, and
made inquiry of the doctor concerning the matter.

The doctor narrated the incident at length, giving great
credit to the young man, who sprang over the gate, crying
"Hold, villain!" on which the scoundrels had taken to their
heels. "His act," continued he, "will no doubt be remembered
at the Great Day!"

As Lucy, looking at the stranger, said something in compliment, she observed a vague and covert smile upon his

countenance which, as if by sympathy, conjured one to her own.

"Mention it not, madam! I were unworthy of the name of Briton and a man, could I pass the highway without relieving the distress of a fellow-creature. Methinks it were sufficient reward to receive the thanks of a lady, whom I might reasonably take for one of those celestial beings of whom we have been piously taught that the Church is especially the care!"

This high-flown compliment, coming from the mouth of one whom Lucy thought the very handsomest person she had ever seen, appeared to her anything but absurd, and she long remembered how the cheek of the speaker had glowed and his voice had trembled as he spoke it.

When Miss Brandon's servant came, the young man gallantly assisted her with her cloak and hood. "By what name shall I pray for the gentleman to whom I am so much indebted?" asked the doctor.

"You are very kind," said the stranger; "my name is Clifford. Madame" (to Lucy), "may I offer my hand down the stairs?"

As they passed through the fields, with the servant in advance carrying the lantern, Clifford asked, "Is Miss Brandon related to the celebrated barrister of her name?"

"He is my uncle," said Lucy; "do you know him?"

"Your uncle?" replied Clifford; "I feared—I thought he might have been a nearer relation. Miss Brandon, I think I had the honor of seeing you at the theater in London several years ago."

"I was there only once," said Lucy; "an unpleasant circumstance makes me remember it—my uncle had his watch stolen."

"Was the thief caught?" asked Clifford.

"Yes, and sent to Bridewell. I was foolish enough to beg my uncle to intercede for him, but he said he was quite hardened."

"You will come in, of course!" said Lucy, as they reached the door.

Clifford hesitated a moment, then said in a quick tone, "No! many—many thanks. Will Miss Brandon accept my gratitude for her condescension in permitting the attendance of one unknown to her?" And Clifford bowed profoundly over her hand as he took his leave.

The next day Lucy heard that Lord Mauleverer had been stopped on the road by three highwaymen, while on his way to his country seat, and robbed of a considerable amount. Not long afterward Miss Brandon had an unexpected stroke of good fortune in the bequest of sixty thousand pounds from a Mrs. Warner, a distant relative in London. As soon as this became known, the surrounding gentry made a simultaneous discovery of the merits and great good sense of Mr. Joseph Brandon, and coaches, chariots, chaises, and horses began to arrive at Warlock Hall in the most friendly manner. Among those to call was Lord Mauleverer who, after a dissolute youthful life, was now, in his mature years, credited with matrimonial designs.

A fortnight later Joseph Brandon received a letter from his brother William informing him that the doctors had advised him to take a rest, and asking him and Lucy to become his guests at Bath. In a postscript William wrote: "Ah, Miss Lucy, Miss Lucy! are you going to conquer him whom all London has, for years more than I care to tell (yet not many, for Mauleverer is still young), assailed in vain? Answer me!" William Brandon was an ambitious man. "With me," he thought, "perishes the last male of Brandon. But the light shall not go out under a bushel. Lucy must go as another score to the fortunes of William Brandon. After all, who suffers? Not she. She will have wealth, rank, honor: I shall suffer, to yield so pretty and pure a gem to the coronet of—faugh! How I despise that dog! but how I could hate, crush, mangle him, could I believe that he despised me!"

Brandon had been promised a judgeship. "What," said Mauleverer, "forsake your brilliant career for so petty a dignity? You jest!"

"Not at all," replied Brandon. "It is proposed that I should retire, with the pledged promise of the first vacancy among the chiefs. The place of chief justice or chief baron is the only fair remuneration for my surrender of the gains of my profession. The title, which will of course be attached to it, might go to the eldest son of my niece, in case she married a commoner; or her second son, in case she married a peer."

"Ha—true!" said Mauleverer, as if struck by some sudden thought; "and your charming niece, Brandon, would be worthy of an honor either to her children or herself."

"I can't laugh at that man," thought Mauleverer, after he had gone to bed, "though he has much that I should laugh at in another; and, faith, there is one little matter I might well scorn him for, if I were not a philosopher. 'Tis a pretty girl, his niece, and with proper instruction might do one credit; besides she has sixty thousand pounds ready money, while I have not a shilling for my own pleasure, though I have, or alas! had, fifty thousand a year for that of my establishment. She will be the lawyer's heiress. Moreover, if he rise to the peerage? and the second son—Well! it will not be a bad match!"

On the evening of a ball at Bath, Brandon dined with Lord Mauleverer. When the two entered the ballroom and looked for Lucy, they found that she was engaged for the first two dances to a certain Captain Clifford. Mauleverer watched them awhile as they danced, and then asked the master of ceremonies who "that young—*man* is, now dancing with Miss Brandon?"

"Captain Clifford, my lord! a very fine young man, my lord! Has your lordship never met him?"

"Never! Who is he?"

"I scarcely know. He came to-night for the first time."

In three weeks from his arrival, Captain Clifford was the most admired man in Bath. He found many opportunities of meeting Lucy, all of which he improved, and even won the heart of her father. Mauleverer, who became jealous, watched the motions and looks of the pair, wherever he met them, and soon became convinced that Lucy was attached to Clifford. Once, in talking with her, his anger got the better of him, and he took the liberty of warning her against the attentions of the "young man calling himself Captain Clifford"; but Lucy, with glowing cheeks, showed so much resentment that he hastened to apologize. But he immediately wrote to William Brandon, who had been recalled to London, and told him of his fears.

Brandon smiled bitterly when he read Mauleverer's letter. "If," said he to himself, "I can effect this object, and Mauleverer marry the girl, why so much the better that she has a fairer and a more welcome lover. It would be to me more sweet than fame—ay, or even than power—to see this fine-spun lord a gibe in the mouths of men—a cuckold—a cuckold!" But before he went to bed he wrote a politic letter to Mauleverer, and affectionate ones to his brother and niece. He advised his brother to drop Clifford and accept Mauleverer, and appealed to Lucy not to waste her affections on one whom the family could never receive as a suitor for her hand. The squire was disconcerted at William's letter. He disliked Mauleverer, and never felt at home in his society. For Clifford he had a great liking, and he saw no reason why so agreeable a companion should not be an agreeable son-in-law. "If he be poor," thought the squire, "though he does not seem so, Lucy is rich." Nevertheless, as William had great influence over him, he resolved reluctantly to follow his advice. As for Lucy, her uncle's letter made her wretched. She shut herself up and consumed the time in tears and struggles with her own heart. At one time she resolved that it was her duty to forswear her lover; but the night undid the labor of the day; for every night her lover's voice, accompanied by music, melted away her resolution.

One night Lord Mauleverer's coach had been attacked on the highway, overturned into the ditch, its contents rifled, and the peer left to find his way on foot to the nearest town. The three masked men, Captain Lovett or Clifford, Tomlinson, and Pepper, who had accomplished this robbery, rode across country to a secluded dell where, overgrown with bushes, they found the entrance of the Red Cave, their secret and favorite resort. Within the cavern, which was large enough to provide stabling for their horses as well as accommodation for themselves, they found a bright fire and a meal cooking under the care of our old friend Peter MacGrawler. Clifford sat looking gloomily on while Tomlinson and Long Ned divided the spoil into three parts. When MacGrawler suggested that a share was due him, Ned cried: "You have a share in what you never took! Mind your business, Mr. Scot, and fork nothing but the beefsteaks."

Clifford, seeing MacGrawler's eager look, shoved ten guineas of his own share toward his quondam tutor.

"Nay, nay," grunted MacGrawler, "I scorn such dross." But he pocketed the coins before returning to his cooking.

That night, as soon as sleep had overcome the three highwaymen, MacGrawler let himself out of the barred door, and hastening to Reading returned about daylight with Mr. Nabbem of Bow Street and four armed men. Taken by surprise, Ned and Tomlinson were soon captured, but Clifford escaped through a secret door into the wood behind.

A few days later Clifford, disguised as a farmer, rescued Tomlinson and Pepper from the hand of Nabbem, but was shot in the side while mounting his horse and captured.

Meanwhile, Squire Brandon hardly reached home after his visit to Bath, when he was stricken with paralysis, and before his brother could reach Warlock Hall, was dead. "I will be your father now," said William, "and you—the last of our race—shall be to me as a daughter."

William Brandon and Lord Mauleverer had been long acquainted. They had been intimate at the university and had been boon companions and associates in many licentious intrigues in Italy, and elsewhere. After Brandon became a solicitor, he made the acquaintance of the daughter of a retired tradesman, married her secretly under the name of Welford, and settled in an obscure town in ——shire. Their manner of life bespoke poverty, they had no visitors, and never received any letters. Whispers were circulated through the town that the pair lived unhappily, but there was a mystery about them that no one seemed able to penetrate.

One morning a gentleman was thrown from his horse in front of Welford's house. When Welford himself came out, the rider, whose right leg was broken, exclaimed, "Heavens! is that—"

"Hist, my lord!" said Welford, interrupting him while a dark blush overspread his sullen features. "But you are hurt— will you enter my house?"

Lord Mauleverer was detained under Welford's roof more than a month. During that time he resumed his old habits and made love to the wife of his friend. Welford, who had watched the growing intimacy, said to himself: "She has been my ruin, and would now be my disgrace; but, instead of my disgrace, I will make her my footstool to honor and wealth. And, then, to the devil with the footstool! Two years I have borne this, and now will I have my revenge;—I will sell her—sell her! God! I will sell her like the commonest beast of a market! But I will make market of a mistress, not a *wife*. The fool shall believe my marriage was a forged one, an ingenious piece of gallantry. My son's legitimacy may be convenient to me hereafter. I will have his 'honor' thereon, and will guard the proofs."

Three weeks later Mrs. Welford eloped with the nobleman, and on the morning following the husband and his child disappeared from the town. When he resumed his own name, as no one, not even his brother, knew that he had been married, he gave out that the child was the orphan of a dear friend whom he had known abroad. Brandon idolized this child and built great hopes on him; but when he was about three years old he was stolen, and he could never find trace of him.

Brandon, now Sir William and a judge, had kept from Lucy all knowledge of her lover's ignominious situation, for the identity of Lovett with Clifford had not yet even been rumored. Mauleverer, who had not given up hopes of winning Lucy, aided him in this, for her health had not been good that winter.

In his capacity of judge Brandon was called to preside at the trial of Lovett in the town of ——. While getting ready to go to court, he was handed a letter with an official seal informing him of his elevation to the dignity of Chief Baron, with the title of Lord Warlock. "Aha!" he said, "this letter is a cordial and gives me a new lease of life. Minister—Peer—Warlock— My son, my son! would to God that I could find thee!"

Another note from Mauleverer said: "A dinner waits you at Mauleverer Park, only three miles hence. Lord —— and the Bishop of —— will meet you. Make haste and hang this poor fellow, that I may see you the sooner."

The trial of Clifford was short. MacGrawler appeared as chief witness against him and the jury returned a verdict of "Guilty, with a recommendation to mercy." While the jury were out, a paper was handed up to the judge containing a few words, written by Long Ned and signed "Dummie Dunnaker," which plainly informed him that the prisoner at the bar was his own son. The Judge's head was observed to droop suddenly, as if by a spasm, as he read this, but he quickly recovered himself, and asked the prisoner if he had anything to say why sentence of death should not be pronounced against him. He listened attentively while Clifford spoke, attributing his downfall largely to Sir William's own act in having him committed to Bridewell for a theft which he did not commit. "You, my lord, who will now pass my doom, you were the cause of my crimes."

Minutes elapsed before Brandon drew on the black cap, and twice his voice failed him. But at a third effort he spoke clearly and unfalteringly, although in a strange and hollow tone, condemning the prisoner to be hanged. "The recommendation to mercy shall be forwarded to the supreme power, but I cannot flatter you with much hope of its success."

Later, Brandon was long closeted with Dummie Dunnaker and Long Ned, the latter assured of immunity, until he had wrung from them all they could tell him. When they had done, he said: "I have heard you, and am convinced you are liars and impostors. There is money; quit this town instantly; if you are found here two hours hence, your blood be on your own heads!"

They left in hasty confusion, and Brandon exclaimed, "I may—yes, yes—I *may* yet conceal this disgrace to my name!"

He ordered his carriage and went to Mauleverer Park. When the carriage door was opened he did not alight. "Why does he not get out?" asked Mauleverer, who had come to greet him. They found Brandon in a corner of the carriage—a corpse.

From Dummie Dunnaker's paper found on Brandon's body, Mauleverer learned the identity of Clifford with Brandon's son, and through his efforts the death sentence was commuted to transportation for life. Before the ship sailed the cousins met in the convict's cell. Their conference was low, for the jailer stood within hearing; and it was broken by Lucy's convulsive sobs. But she left her lover with a steady and resolute hope, and returned home with a firm step.

After Clifford had been sent to the place of his punishment,

Lucy took up her residence in an obscure town by the seaside. She had succeeded to the great wealth of her uncle, and as soon as she attained her majority, she sold her estates in England and transferred all her property to France. Twenty years after her departure from England, there resided in a certain town in America a man held in high and universal respect, not only for the rectitude of his conduct, but for the energies of his mind and the purposes to which these energies were directed. He was seconded in his projects and undertakings by a wife over whose surpassing loveliness time had flown with a gentle and charming wing. With a happy home and growing children, Clifford looked from his windows at the public benefits he had created and at his own pleasant surroundings, and said to his wife, with glistening eyes and subdued voice—" I owe all these to thee !"

EUGENE ARAM (1832)

Bulwer intended originally to adapt the story of *Eugene Aram* to the stage. He changed that plan when it was more than half completed. In the preface to the edition of 1840 he wrote: "The strange history of Eugene Aram had excited my interest and wonder long before the present work was composed or conceived. It so happened that, during Aram's residence at Lynn, his reputation for learning had attracted the notice of my grandfather—a country gentleman living in the same county, and of more intelligence and accomplishments than, at that day, usually characterized his class. Aram frequently visited at Heydon (my grandfather's house), and gave lessons, probably in no very elevated branches of erudition, to the younger members of the family. This I chanced to hear when I was on a visit in Norfolk, some two years before this novel was published, and it tended to increase the interest with which I had previously speculated on the phenomena of a trial which, take it altogether, is perhaps the most remarkable in the register of English crime. I endeavored to collect such anecdotes of Aram's life and manners as tradition and hearsay still kept afloat. These anecdotes were so far uniform that they all concurred in representing him as a person who, till the detection of the crime for which he was sentenced, had appeared of the mildest character and most unexceptionable morals." Aram was credited with the discovery of the affinity of the Celtic to other European tongues. His arrest was the subject of a poem by Thomas Hood, *The Dream of Eugene Aram;* and a play (founded on Bulwer's novel) by W. G. Wills, entitled *Eugene Aram*, was produced by the late Henry Irving in London in 1873.

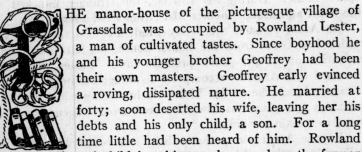HE manor-house of the picturesque village of Grassdale was occupied by Rowland Lester, a man of cultivated tastes. Since boyhood he and his younger brother Geoffrey had been their own masters. Geoffrey early evinced a roving, dissipated nature. He married at forty; soon deserted his wife, leaving her his debts and his only child, a son. For a long time little had been heard of him. Rowland took the wife and child into his own home, where the former soon died, the boy growing up with Rowland's two motherless daughters. At this time, Madeline, the elder, was eighteen, the beauty and boast of the county. Ellinor in her way was equally lovely. Their cousin Walter, Geoffrey's son, was twenty-one, high-spirited, bold, restless.

One evening a rather unprepossessing stranger came to the village. He learned from the landlord of the Spotted Dog that the most noticeable man at Grassdale was the great and respected scholar—Eugene Aram. At this name the stranger sprang from his seat and muttered, "What!—Aram!— did you say Aram? Great God, how strange!" To the astonished landlord he explained that Eugene Aram had been an early and an intimate acquaintance of his. Further conversation was delayed by the passing of Madeline Lester and her sister, who, frightened by the malignant expression of the stranger's face, hurried on. Ellinor had noticed the barrel of a pistol in the man's pocket and was much alarmed, but Madeline reassured her, and they continued their walk. Suddenly, at a desolate spot, they saw the same man approaching them. Terrified, they quickened their steps. Fortunately, a turn soon brought them to a broad plain, and the abode of the solitary student and recluse, Eugene Aram. Just then Madeline struck her foot and fell to the ground, with her ankle badly sprained. There was nothing to be done but to intrude upon Mr. Aram. The pale student answered the bell, and at once showed the liveliest sympathy. Leaving the young ladies with his old domestic, Aram set out to find assistance at the manor-house. During his absence, the stranger knocked at the door, and asked whether Mr. Aram lived there.

As Aram assisted the lovely Madeline into the carriage, which had come from the manor-house, he felt that vague sensation of delight which preludes love. Lester, who had returned with Aram to accompany his daughters home, begged Aram to break the ice for friendship by dining with them the next day. A glance at Madeline conquered Eugene's resolutions to remain a recluse.

Eugene Aram was perhaps thirty-five years old. He was tall, thin, and well-knit. His cheek and brow were pale with the delicacy of thought. There was a singular calmness about him that betokened one who had lived in contemplation. "He was one of those earnest and high-wrought enthusiasts who now are almost extinct upon earth, and whom romance has not hitherto attempted to portray; men not uncommon in the last century, who were devoted to knowledge, yet dis-

dainful of its fame; who lived for nothing else than to learn."
He was kind to all animals, and were anyone in danger he
would have hazarded his own life to save him, but in his heart
he despised men. From almost every college in Europe people
came to consult with him. He received them courteously;
gave freely of his lore; but he proffered no hospitality and
shrank from friendship. He had lived two years in his present
retreat. Unsocial as he was, everybody loved him; his reserve
was considered to arise from a painful excess of modesty.

The clock struck eleven. Aram had been absorbed in
thought since the departure of his visitors. He was now aroused
by a loud summons at the door. Who at that hour could be
demanding admittance? Suddenly his cheek blanched, and
he felt for his pistols. After a moment of irresolution, he slowly
unbarred the door, and beheld the ill-omened traveler.

The next day Aram kept his engagement at Lester's.
Though habitually reserved, he seemed unusually gloomy.
But at times his conversation sparkled with incident and
description, and all were fascinated save Walter, who looked
at Aram suspiciously, angry that he monopolized the conversation, and that his cousins so evidently admired him. A few
days later, Walter came suddenly upon Aram, who was muttering to himself. Thus interrupted, a fierce change came over
Aram's face, and his eyes flashed with anger. With a ghostly
smile, he accused Walter of eavesdropping, and was visibly
relieved when the latter sarcastically answered that he had
heard nothing. With instant contrition Aram said: "Pardon
me, I am a poor, half-crazed man; much study has unnerved
me; I should never live but with my own thoughts." This
touched Walter, who gave Aram his hand, which Aram pressed,
his eyes filling with tears.

Aram had long admired Madeline, and the evident kindness
which she showed him was awakening in him an irresistible
and growing attachment. Fate insisted upon bringing them
together. Aram's words had softened Walter, and Lester
earnestly desired to win his solitary neighbor. By degrees
Aram relaxed from his unsociability. After a time, few evenings passed without his presence at the manor-house. Ellinor,
eager to study botany, begged him to teach her its principles,

and Madeline shared these lessons, which brought the lovers closer. Lester perceived this attachment with satisfaction. He confided this to Walter, intimating that he hoped Walter in turn might care for Ellinor. Walter replied bitterly that he did not see why the plainer and less brilliant of the sisters should be selected for him. Furthermore, he longed to travel. Hurt, but with affection, Lester told Walter that his wish was a natural one, and that he could go whenever he wished. Then a painful thought occurred to Lester. "Walter! Have you ever felt for Madeline more tenderly than for a sister?" Walter trembled. Lester grasped his nephew's hand.

"God comfort thee, my poor boy! I never dreamt of this."

It was this long-nourished attachment which at first made Walter dislike Aram. His only wish now was to leave the scene which had become hateful to him. It did not help matters to have Bunting, an old corporal, who was to accompany him on his travels, say that he did not quite like "this larned man— something queer about him." Bunting had noticed Master Aram get into a sudden passion with himself. Moreover, it puzzled him how that vagabond who had once scared the young ladies could boast of a friendship with Aram, and pass a night at his house. "Birds of a feather flock together—augh!—sir!"

The same day Aram saw Walter at a distance, and hastened to join him. He tried to overcome the coldness of the young man, whose irritation finally led him to say: "Men may shun the world from another motive than that of philosophy." With a menacing look, Aram answered: "Boy, were there meaning in your words, I should (mark me!) avenge the insult; as it is I despise it. Go!"

Ashamed, and wishing to redeem his weakness, Walter dared Aram to fulfil his threat. But Aram, in calm words, brought Walter to humility, and the unhappy youth then blurted out his confession of unrequited love.

The eve before his departure, Walter sought Madeline, and begged her to permit him to speak as a brother. He then told her that he could not help entertaining some doubts about Aram: he could not think him altogether the calm and pure being he appeared. Would she not *observe* him! Madeline bitterly rebuked him, and, pale with anger, Walter left her.

But before he set out on his travels she asked his forgiveness for her hasty words. The chief motive in Walter's desire to travel was to ascertain the fate of his long-missing father, and his uncle besought him to spare no pains to do so.

It was now the middle of September, and it was arranged that by the end of the next month the wedding should be celebrated. Since Walter's departure Aram had almost lived at the manor-house; and no two lovers were ever more ardently and romantically in love.

Meantime Walter and Bunting proceeded on their way. At a small town a riding-whip in a saddler's shop attracted Walter's attention. He found his own crest on its handle; then he discovered the initials G. L.—his father's initials! He questioned the saddler, who told him that fourteen years before a gentleman passing with Squire Courtland had left the whip to be mended, and never had called for it. Walter at once inquired the way to Squire Courtland's. From the old gentleman he gathered that fourteen years before his father had ridden at full speed to the Greyhound Inn. For the sake of Rowland Lester, whom the Squire knew, he invited Geoffrey Lester to stay with him. Geoffrey had just returned from India, and while there he had saved the life of an old Colonel, who shortly afterward returned to England, settling in Yorkshire. Geoffrey, also returning later, learned that the Colonel had died, leaving him a handsome legacy and the Yorkshire house, and he was then on his way to claim his property. He purposed to seek out his brother Rowland, and perhaps settle down. He left the next day, and Mr. Courtland had heard nothing more of him. As Geoffrey had looked so prematurely old, the Squire imagined that he had died. Geoffrey had not told the Squire the name of the Colonel who had been so generous to him, but fortunately one clue had been left by his saying that in his adventures he had been favorably known under the name of Clarke.

To return to Grassdale: One evening Aram and Madeline learned from the innkeeper that two neighboring houses had been robbed. She entreated Aram to stay that night at the manor-house. His brow darkened as he replied that it would be time enough to take precaution when the grounds for alarm had been sifted. "Meanwhile," he continued, "do not blame me if in your presence I cannot admit fear. Formerly, dark and boding apprehensions were wont to lie heavy at my heart. But now I can see nothing but hope."

"And yet, Eugene—yet—"

"Yet what, my Madeline?"

"There are still moments when you mutter to yourself feelings in which I have no share, and which seem to steal the consciousness from your eye and the color from your lip."

"Ah, indeed!" said Aram quickly; "What! you watch me so closely?" Then, almost fiercely: "I cannot bear too nice a scrutiny. Mark, I pray you, whenever, in spite of myself, these moods you refer to darken over me, heed not, listen not— *leave me!*"

Madeline promised this, and they walked on more cheerfully. Suddenly Madeline shrieked—the same ominous stranger confronted them. He greeted Aram, who left Madeline for a moment's conference with him. The stranger then disappeared into the bushes, and Aram explained to Madeline that he had known him, then in better circumstances, fourteen years before. The stranger had accidentally learned Aram's residence and had sought him for aid, and had now returned for that same purpose. He had told the man to be at his house in an hour. After saying this Aram was abstracted the rest of the way to the manor-house. He left Madeline and hastened home, finding the stranger in the valley. Aram asked why he had returned. He answered that he had rejoined his comrades, who were "cruising" around the country. Perhaps Aram had heard of their exploits last night.

"Ha, was that villainy yours, Houseman?"

"Villainy!" repeated Houseman, in a tone of sullen offense. "Come, Master Aram, these words must not pass between you and me, friends of such date, and on such a footing."

"Talk not of the past," replied Aram, with a livid lip, "and call not those whom Destiny once drove down her dark tide, in a momentary companionship, by the name of friends. Look you, Houseman, I cannot live and have my life darkened by your presence."

Houseman answered that he and his comrade would leave

as soon as they had gathered their plunder. Aram passionately insisted he must go instantly. Houseman replied he would starve were he to leave his mates. Aram offered to make it possible for him to do so and Houseman named three hundred pounds as his price, but Aram did not possess such a sum. Finally after a stormy parry of words it was agreed that they should meet in two days at a secret spot called Devil Crag; it might then be possible for Aram to make a satisfactory arrangement with Houseman.

The next morning the village was in consternation, for a still bolder robbery had been committed. It wrung Aram's soul to see with what utter trust Madeline clung to him. His mind grew black with the thought of what an awful interest he had in the prevalent outrages; how he might be dragged into a share of their ruin if the robbers were caught. That afternoon he asked Lester whether he could lend him a portion —about three hundred pounds—of Madeline's dowry. The Squire replied that he should have six hundred the next day. He also said that he intended to give his daughter double that sum. As they turned homeward, the Squire remarked that he must take precautions against burglary, because the three hundred guineas were hidden in a bureau in the parlor. As Lester said this, they heard steps on the other side of the hedge as if someone had been standing there listening. In a few minutes they saw two strangers in carters' frocks. Their humble answers, however, disarmed the Squire. As he and Aram reached the manor-house, it began to rain heavily. Madeline lovingly overpowered Aram's desire to return home.

The sisters talked late that night, for the wedding-day was close at hand. As the clock struck one, Ellinor was startled by a sound of footsteps near a window below. Madeline calmed her sister, and went to arouse her father. The noise grew louder; a pistol-shot was heard. Another minute, and the whole house was stirring. They found Aram standing in the parlor, a pistol in one hand, a sword in the other. A wedge was fixed in the bureau which held the money. On the floor was a broken bludgeon, and near the window were drops of blood. Aram was very pale, and was muttering to himself. When he perceived the others he fiercely ordered the servants to get water to wash out the blood. He said he had heard the scraping of a file ; had gone down stairs, and had discovered two men standing by the bureau. They had hurled a bludgeon at him and then fled before his pistol.

Aram left his sleepless room early in the morning, and hurried to his home. He had determined that if he could not bind Houseman to secrecy he would surrender Madeline. He did not believe that Houseman could have known of the attack on *that* house; but the tempting thought came that if he *had* been there a shot might have freed Aram, without crime, forever. He walked all day, struggling with his thoughts. Devil's Crag was as lonely a spot as one could find, and haunted by many a wild tradition. At the appointed hour, Aram was joined by Houseman, who suggested that they should gain the cave below.

"The cave!" said Aram, starting.

"Ay, ay! but not Saint Robert's," answered Houseman, grinning. "Come, give me your hand, I will conduct you through the thicket—that is your left hand," observed Houseman, an angry suspicion in his tone, "give me the right."

"As you will," said Aram, "but for fourteen years I have not given this right hand, in pledge of fellowship, to living man; you alone deserve the courtesy—there!"

The conference, which was not without storminess, ended by Aram's promising to pay Houseman 150 guineas a year, half of which was to be paid to Houseman's little motherless daughter, who lived with her grandmother. For this sum Houseman promised to leave England forever. As soon as the business should be completed, they arranged to meet for a last interview at Houseman's quarters in London.

On his meager information, it was no easy matter for Walter to obtain a clue to his father's benevolent Colonel. But a clever lawyer discovered that a Colonel Elmore of Knaresborough had died, leaving one Daniel Clarke the sum of a thousand pounds and the house in which the Colonel had resided. Also he discovered that a Mr. Jonas Elmore, the only surviving executor of the will, lived now about fifty miles from York. Walter at once set out to consult with this gentle man. He soon learned that Mr. Clarke had received his legacy, and had sold the house for an additional seven hundred and fifty pounds. The Colonel had bequeathed some jewels to Mr. Elmore, who, having no use for them, had consulted with Mr. Clarke. He offered to purchase them, believing he could turn them into a profitable speculation. A bargain was struck: Mr. Elmore sold him the greater part of the jewels for a little more than a thousand pounds. Mr. Clarke was pleased with his purchase, and borrowed the rest of the jewels, wishing to consider whether he should buy them also. Three days later, in the middle of the night, Mr. Clarke had left Knaresborough: neither he nor the jewels were heard of more. A man named Houseman, an acquaintance of Clarke's, had declared that Clarke had borrowed a considerable sum from him; he accused Clarke of decamping to avoid payment.

The day after the fearful meeting at Devil's Crag, Aram went to London. He found that, in order to secure the annual sum for Houseman, it was necessary to strip himself of everything. He sought Lord ——, who once had made him dazzling offers, which he had refused, and petitioned him to grant him a small annuity so that he could continue his studies. The Earl, affected by the humble amount for which Aram asked, and appreciating his dignified and just claim, at once agreed to bestow the annuity. With a light step, Aram then sought Houseman, whose quarters were in one of the most squalid parts of London. Aram gave him a paper, which secured to Houseman the sum he demanded. At last Aram could breathe freely, for Houseman promised to depart for France at daybreak. Houseman also felt sanguine; he was assured of a competence and safety abroad; and his child would never want. But Aram had only just gone when Houseman received a letter, containing the news that his child was dying. Ruffian that he was, he had the redeeming trait of parental love. "What's money, what's ease," he thought, "if—if!"—and he dashed out of the house.

Aram, his face aglow with joy, hastened home to Madeline. The change in him completed her happiness. The days rolled on until it was the eve before their marriage.

Walter had at length reached Knaresborough, the place where

his father was last seen! If no further clue could be discovered, his inquiries must cease at this spot. The following morning he found his landlord in his garden, who said that he had taken to gardening through the kind interest of a beloved scholar who formerly lived there—a Mr. Aram! This news was startling to Walter. The host also had known Mr. Clarke, who he suspected had been a victim of foul play. He suspected that a man named Houseman had murdered him, as he was the last person seen with Mr. Clarke. But when Houseman was finally examined he deposed that he had spent the evening with Eugene Aram; that leaving Aram's house he had met Clarke; he walked a little way with him, but the latter seemed annoyed and confused, so he had left him. Walter asked the landlord whether he meant that this abandoned character was intimate with Aram. The landlord replied that Houseman was a distant relative of Aram's, whom he could not always shake off.

"And no suspicion rested on Aram?"

The host turned round in amazement. "Heavens above, no! One might as well suspect the lamb of eating the wolf!"

But Walter was not satisfied, when he recollected Aram's peculiar habits. These suspicions were not allayed by the clergyman, who arrived shortly to announce the death of Houseman's little girl. He confided to Walter that Aram's acquaintance with Houseman was suspected, not of partaking of the murder, but of sharing some part of the jewels. He had undergone an examination, which was kept secret on account of the universal respect felt for him, and had been satisfactorily acquitted. Since then the woman at whose house Aram had lodged had dropped hints that she could tell a tale, and that Aram's life was in her power. The curate and Walter then sought Aram's old lodging house. By the promise of five guineas they induced the old woman to tell her incriminating story. She said that late that fatal night she had seen Houseman and Clarke going upstairs to Mr. Aram's room. This had aroused her curiosity; she had listened at the keyhole, and heard Clarke say, "It will soon be morning, and we must get off." Presently all three left the house. About five o'clock Aram and Houseman returned. Finding her up, they both glowered at her; she heard Houseman say if she told anything they would shoot her. That same morning she found several bits of cloth and linen, and a handkerchief with some blood on it, in Aram's grate. She showed Houseman the handkerchief, and asked him what had become of Clarke, and he had answered:

"Hark ye! I know not what you mean: but, as sure as the devil keeps watch for souls, I will shoot you through the head if you ever let that d——d tongue of yours utter a single word about Clarke, or me, or Mr. Aram!"

The old woman said she had been glad when they left the town, for she was sure that they had murdered Clarke. The curate and Walter decided that not a moment should be lost. On the way to the house of an able magistrate, they were attracted by a crowd of people. A peasant told them that a big wooden chest had been dug up. As he spoke, a shout of horror broke from the crowd. Walter and the curate quickened their steps, and beheld lying on the sward a bleached and mouldering skeleton! One said it must be the bones of a Jew peddler, who had disappeared fourteen years before. "Nay," screeched another, "they must be the bones of Daniel Clarke." The crowd agreed to this. Horrified, Walter silenced the people.

"And what do you here, fool?" said a voice abruptly. It was Richard Houseman. "Ha! Human bones! and whose may they be, think ye?"

The people answered they thought they were Daniel Clarke's.

"Clarke's?" repeated Houseman, "Ha! ha! they are no more Clarke's than mine!"

"Behold!" shouted Walter, seizing Houseman, "Behold the murderer!"

An electric conviction darted through the crowd. "Seize him! Houseman is the murderer!"

"Murderer!" faltered Houseman, trembling in the iron hands of Walter—"I tell ye these are not Clarke's bones!"

"Where, then do *they* lie?"

Pale, confused, reading his condemnation in all eyes, Houseman gasped: "Search Saint Robert's Cave, in the turn at the entrance!"

To this desolate spot the crowd hurried. Houseman was dragged into the cavern. He pointed to a spot; with the head placed to the right lay what once had been a human body!

"Can you swear," said the priest, "that these are the bones of Clarke?"

"Before God, I can swear it! But *I* did not do the deed; *I* am not the murderer."

"Speak out!—whom do you accuse?" said the curate. Drawing his breath hard, and setting his teeth, Houseman replied:

"The murderer is Eugene Aram!"

"Aram," shouted Walter; "O God! Thy hand hath directed me hither!"

It was the morning of the wedding. Before her glass stood the beautiful form of Madeline Lester. Ellinor, with trembling hands, was braiding up her sister's rich hair. Suddenly they heard swift carriage-wheels. Two chaises whirled by the window and stopped at the porch. "It is—it is— Good God! it is Walter, but how pale he looks!" cried Ellinor.

"And who are those strange men with him?" faltered Madeline.

Alone, Eugene Aram was absorbed in thoughts of the great change coming into his life. At last he was to have peace and happiness with memory defied. All was safe. *He* would not return; the dead slept without a witness. Outside the joyful peal of his marriage-bells rang forth, then it ceased. Aram noticed a little group of men approaching the house. Trembling, he sank into a chair, while a sound of voices and loud knocking came from downstairs. Then he heard Walter Lester calling "Murderer!" "Great God!" he murmured, "can he have learned—"

"Murderer!" cried Walter, "*my* hand shall seize the murderer!"

For a moment Eugene thought of escape; then his mind triumphed. He withdrew the bar; the door was burst open. Even Walter fell back before the lofty calm of Eugene Aram. But at his question as to what they wanted, Walter cried out, "Seize him!" Aram demanded by what authority this outrage was committed. Walter accused him of being the murderer of Daniel Clarke, whose real name was Geoffrey Lester, his father, the brother of him whose daughter Aram was to have called his wife. Aram replied that that was indeed a dreadful accusation, but that he could not understand it. Lester was completely overcome; he believed in Aram's innocence, whose calmness shattered even Walter's confidence in his own suspicion. Aram, anxious to end the scene, motioned to the officers to proceed. The little group started for the magistrate's, Lester assuring Aram that he would have instant acquittal. Aram's thoughts were only for Madeline: he begged Lester to go to her and in some way explain his arrest. Suddenly they saw Madeline hastening towards them: she flung herself on Aram's breast, begging to know what it all meant. Aram told her that he had been accused of murder. She demanded the name of the accuser. Aram answered, "Behold him—your cousin!" With a piercing look, Madeline denounced Walter. The woe, the horror he was about to inflict on all he most loved had not faced Walter until now. More gently, Madeline begged him to own he had erred, saying that he could not come to them on *this* day with such a lie. Walter answered at last:

"Let him prove his innocence—pray God he do! I am not his accuser. His accusers are the bones of my dead father!"

"Your father!" said Madeline, staggering back. "Now I know what a shadow has appalled us all. Eugene, did you ever see Geoffrey Lester?"

"Never, as I believe, so help me God!"

Aram begged Madeline to leave them, while he should go to disprove the charges. Madeline replied her place was at his side now more than ever. The Lesters accompanied Aram to Knaresborough. There he underwent an examination. He denied most of the particulars in Houseman's evidence, but his commitment was made out, and he was removed to York Castle to await his trial. The event created an unequaled sensation throughout the country. During his imprisonment Aram's mood fluctuated. Sometimes they thought the horrible suspicion had shaken his nerves. To Madeline he would cry out to know whether at the worst she still loved him. For eight whole months Madeline had to endure the most awful suspense. Gradually her health failed; everyone saw that she was doomed. Aram was not sanguine of acquittal; he insisted on being his own counsel. The day of the trial came. Madeline robed her now shrunken form in her bridal gown—she looked a bride, but the bride of no earthly nuptials. Houseman was first arraigned on his former indictment and acquitted. He gave evidence against Aram. The prisoner then stood at the bar! Houseman was called upon, and told, in a choked voice, that on the night of the crime he had gone to Aram's house about eleven o'clock, and stayed about an hour. Three hours later he was passing the house with Clarke, Aram was outside, and asked them to come in. Clarke was to leave at daybreak, to make away secretly with some property, and Aram proposed to accompany him. Aram and Houseman both went with Clarke. When they came to the field where St. Robert's Cave was, Aram and Clarke went into it. As they neared the cave, Houseman saw Aram and Clarke quarreling. Aram struck Clarke and Clarke fell. Houseman immediately left them. The next morning he asked Aram what he had done with Clarke. Aram did not answer, but vowed vengeance if he mentioned the affair to anyone. This was Houseman's evidence. A few minor witnesses were summoned, and at last it was Aram's turn. He gave an eloquent and artful defense, not explaining away the allegations, but dwelling on the improbable and contradictory evidence of Houseman.

The jury found the prisoner guilty.

Aram received his sentence calmly. Madeline lived but a few hours after she reached home. Her last words were, "Tell him that I never felt how deeply I—loved him—till all—the world—had—deserted him!"

Aram had already heard these tidings, when Walter, quivering with emotion, came to his cell to entreat him to whisper but one word of confession, and he would forgive him from the depth of his soul. Finally Aram said he would confess to his ear alone the tale he had expected to take with him to the grave. He would write out the story which Walter must not read until he (Aram) was no more, and Walter must swear to confide the tale to none till Lester himself had died. Promptly at the hour agreed upon before his execution, Aram handed Walter the written record of his life, and obtained from Walter the pardon that one man may grant another.

In the paper Aram showed how the passion for knowledge had seized him when he was thirteen. He became haunted with the ambition to enlighten the world. But he was poor; his genius was sacrificed to keep him from famine. He asked himself how he was to obtain money. He could not beg for it. Then he met Houseman, whose highwayman's philosophy first disgusted, then poisoned, his mind. He sought to escape from it and plunged deeper into his books. Suddenly a gigantic discovery in science flashed into his mind. A handful of gold would buy the necessary books and implements. The tempter spoke to him. Then came the stranger Clarke, who was in every way repellent. This man's vices were more loathsome than the villainies of Houseman. Aram was further goaded into hatred by having Clarke insult him, and by hearing awful stories of his crime against a young and helpless girl. Houseman told him that Clarke was about to purloin some jewels, and suggested that he and Aram should ease Clarke of his booty, and divide the spoils. Aram fell beneath the temptation, and the plot was arranged. On the fatal night they accompanied Clarke out of town. Then followed the rest. Aram did not strike the blow, as he never designed to murder the man; there was crime enough in a robber's deed. Houseman divided the booty, burying Aram's share.

On the day of execution, Aram was found lying on his bed, unable to speak above a whisper. He had opened the veins in his arm with a concealed instrument and was bleeding to death. Resolved not to cheat the scaffold of its due, the officials bore him to the fatal spot, and the dire preparations were made; but suddenly Aram struggled in their grasp, threw himself back, and a bright, triumphant smile lighted his face. With that smile the haughty spirit passed away, and the law's last indignity was wreaked upon a lifeless body.

GODOLPHIN (1833)

This work was first published anonymously. Bulwer says: "This novel was begun somewhere in the third year of my authorship and completed in the fourth. It was, therefore, composed almost simultaneously with *Eugene Aram*, and afforded to me at least some relief from the gloom of that village tragedy. It is needless to observe how dissimilar in point of scene, character, and fable, the one is from the other: yet they are alike in this—that both attempt to deal with one of the most striking problems in the spiritual history of man, viz., the frustration or abuse of power in a superior intellect originally inclined to good. . . . In *Eugene Aram*, the natural career of genius is arrested by a single crime; in *Godolphin*, a mind of inferior order, but more fanciful coloring, is wasted away by the indulgence of those morbid sentiments which are the nourishment of egotism and the gradual influence of the frivolities which make the business of the idle." It is said that Bulwer took Lord Byron as a model for *Godolphin*.

THE moonlight shone through the window of a small room and fell upon a bed, the curtains of which were drawn back and showed the form of a man past middle age propped by pillows. By his side stood a girl of about thirteen, of regal beauty and appearing much older.

"Constance," said the invalid, "I shall die this night."

"O God! My father—my dear, dear father!" the girl cried. "I will go for the doctor—"

"No, child, no; I loathe the thought of help. They denied it to me while it was yet time. They left me like a dog, and like a dog I will die! I would not have one iota taken from the justice—the deadly and dooming weight of my dying curse . . . Let me kiss thee my girl. Poor Constance! You will have good friends when I am dead! They will be proud enough to be kind to Vernon's daughter, when Death has shown them that Vernon is a loss. You are very handsome. Your poor mother's eyes and hair; my father's splendid brow and lip; and your figure even now so stately! They will court you: you will have lords and great men enough at your feet; but you will never forget this night, nor the agony of your father's death-bed face, and the cruel brand they have burned in his heart. And now, Constance, give me the Bible in which you read to me this morning; that will do! Stand away from the light and fix your eyes on mine, and listen as if your soul were in your ears."

The dying man then told his daughter how he became the tool of certain lords who sent him to Parliament, flattered him with friendship, and forsook him when he was no longer useful to the party. Later he was seized for debt and rescued from prison by a tradesman whom he had once befriended and by whom he was now aided.

"Child, girl as you are," he added, "you I consider pledged to record to fulfil my desire—my curse! Lay your hand on mine; swear that through life to death,—swear! You speak not! Repeat my words after me." Constance obeyed:— "Through life to death, through good, through ill, through weakness, through power, you will devote yourself to humble to abase that party from whom your father received ingratitude, mortification and death! Swear that you will not marry a poor and powerless man, who cannot minister to the ends of that solemn retribution I invoke! Swear that you will seek to marry among the great; not through love, not through ambition, but through hate and for revenge! You will seek to rise that you may humble those who have betrayed me! In the social walks of life you will delight to gall their vanities; in state intrigues you will embrace every measure that can bring them to their eternal downfall. For this great end you will pursue all means. What! You hesitate? Repeat, repeat, repeat! You will lie, cringe, fawn and think vice not vice, if it brings you one jot nearer to Revenge! With this curse on my foes, I entwine my blessing, dear, dear Constance, on you—you who have nursed, watched, all but saved me! God, God bless you, my child!" And Vernon burst into tears.

On the death of her father, Constance was left without a near relative. Deserted in his last days, Vernon was honored at his death: he was buried in Westminster Abbey with pomp, and a distant connection, Lady Erpingham, took Constance to live with her and educated her.

Constance was not only accomplished, but she inherited

her father's eloquence. With a dark, bold and passionate genius, which in a man would have led to the highest enterprises, she linked the feminine love of secrecy and scheming.

Percy Godolphin, a singular and talented boy of sixteen, defied his father with regard to returning to school, begging to be allowed to visit his patron Saville; but he was sent back to school, from which he escaped and was soon on the highroad to London. At the invitation of a pretty actress he took a seat beside her in the stagecoach which soon appeared.

This led to Godolphin's remaining with the company of actors for a time and to his falling in love with the lively leading lady, Fanny Millinger; but he refused to become an actor, and, leaving his new friends surreptitiously, he was soon under the roof of his friend, Saville, in London.

Through Saville's influence Godolphin was gazetted a cornet in the —— Life Guards, and soon launched into the full tide of *good society*. Saville was deemed the most consummate man of the world, wise and heartless. He was the most seductive of tutors. He had wit, *bon ton*, and control over the great world; and it was much to Godolphin's credit in the world that he was the *protégé* of a man who had so great a character for profligacy and gambling as Augustus Saville.

"Young, romantic, high-spirited, with the classic features of an Antinoüs and a very pretty nack of complimenting and writing verses, Percy Godolphin soon became, while yet more fit in years for the nursery than the world, 'the curled darling' of that wide class of high-born women who have nothing to do but hear love made to them."

Fanny Millinger played in London, and Godolphin became fascinated with the stage and with her; but the attachment was only passing. One night, on returning from the theater, he found a letter from his father announcing that a relative had left him twenty thousand pounds on condition that he would leave the Guards and reside with his father, or leave London until he attained his majority.

The desire to remove Godolphin from Saville's influence was the reason for this conditional bequest. Six hundred a year was allowed him during his minority. He insisted on sharing this with his father, and at the age of seventeen, "the young

Godolphin saw the shores of England recede before him and felt himself alone in the universe—the lord of his own fate."

Meanwhile Constance Vernon grew in beauty. She was thrown with her father's party; and, with her vow ever before her, she resolved to marry for station and power. She took a passionate interest in politics, and the play of her brilliant, satirical and cultivated mind gained for her even more admiration than her beauty and accomplishments. She still lived with her devoted relative, Lady Erpingham.

One day Constance suggested that they should visit Godolphin Priory, which was not far from Lady Erpingham's castle, and was a picturesque ruin.

While Lady Erpingham was talking to the cicerone of the Priory, Constance wandered down the lawn and followed a little brook into leafy shades. There she saw, idly dropping pebbles into the stream, a young man, dressed in deep mourning. His traveling cap of sables set off his beautiful light brown hair; his handsome features were perfectly chiseled; his complexion was pale and wan; and his head betokened intellect. Constance gazed at him a moment, and then she, "the most self-possessed and stately of human creatures, blushing deeply and confused, though unseen, turned lightly away." She soon learned that this was Percy Godolphin, and felt a vague interest respecting him spring up in her mind: but she checked it, "for it was a sin in her eyes to think with interest on a man neither rich nor powerful."

Lady Erpingham invited Godolphin to spend a week at Wendover Castle. Constance and Godolphin walked, rode and talked together, and Lady Erpingham saw, with secret delight, what she believed to be a growing attachment.

One day they arrested their horses in a sylvan scene and Godolphin made an indistinct confession of his love. Constance, although it was her happiest moment, changed the subject and quickened her horse's pace. Godolphin soon returned to his lonely home.

Lord Erpingham arrived at Wendover Castle, and when the ladies spoke of Godolphin, told them that he had known him in Italy, where he lived a mysterious life and was friendly with a sorcerer.

In honor of the Earl's visit, his mother gave a ball. Constance, with her black hair worn in the classic style, her snowy neck and arms glittering with jewels, her red, dewy lips, dazzling teeth, delicate sea-shell complexion and dainty foot, was greatly admired. On entering the drawing-room she looked for Godolphin. Lord Erpingham instantly claimed her hand for a dance. A duchess, jealous for her daughter, accused Constance of being engaged to Godolphin, which she denied. He overheard her. Later in the evening he once more declared his love. Constance proposed that they should meet on the morrow in the western chamber, but gave him no hope. While waiting for her at noon the next day, Godolphin noticed that Constance resembled the portrait of her father which hung there. Constance entered. She had been weeping; though self-possessed, her majestic mien was gone. She told Godolphin that, were she free to obey her heart, she would gladly and proudly follow his fortunes, in his poverty to soothe, in his reverses to console him and in his prosperity to triumph with him. "But—but," she cried, "it must not be."

Godolphin pleaded with passionate eloquence and softly kissed her cheek. The fate of both at that instant hung on a hair. "How different might the lot, the character of each have been, had Constance's lips pronounced the words that her heart already recorded! And she might have done so; but as she raised her eyes, the same object that had before affected Godolphin came vividly upon her, and changed, as by an electric shock, the whole current of her thoughts. Full and immediately before her was the picture of her father." She tore herself away from Godolphin, threw herself on her knees before the picture, prayed for forgiveness and rose a new being. She told him of her father's life, "he, who pursued the path that you would tread; who, through the same toil, the same pursuit that you would endure, used the same powers and the same genius that you would command. . . . Could I doom another victim to the same fate? No, no! fly from me—from the thought of such a destiny. Marry one who can bring you wealth, and support you with rank; *then* be ambitious, if you will. Leave me to fulfil my doom—*My Vow;* and to think.

however wretched I may be, that I have not inflicted a permanent wretchedness on you."

Godolphin returned to London, where he saw much of Saville and Fanny Millinger, who had formed a friendship with Godolphin's patron. Godolphin's ambitions were killed; his career was closed. With Constance all his aspirations after earthly honor were linked, and by her were broken. He felt his old philosophy, the love of ease, the profound contempt of fame, return; and one day when he read in the morning paper the announcement of her marriage to the Earl of Erpingham, he cried: "The dream is over!"

Constance, Countess of Erpingham, was a great success. Erpingham House was the *rendezvous* of the most brilliant people in London and Constance's cleverness quadrupled her husband's political importance.

Four years before these events, on his first visit to Italy, Godolphin had formed a friendship with an astrologer named Volktman, a widower, with a young daughter as peculiar in temperament as he himself. Her eyes were black, her hair bright auburn, and she had a wild beauty. This girl, Lucilla, took a great fancy to Godolphin and learned English from him with surprising facility. "Scarce accountably to himself, a certain tender and peculiar interest in the fortunes of this singular and bewitching child grew up within him: the stars had told him her fate was to have affinity with his." One evening, he found the astrologer and his daughter greatly dejected. The astrologer told him he would soon leave Rome, as disaster threatened his father. The next day Godolphin was summoned home by his father's last illness.

Lucilla Volktman was fifteen years old when her father, busy with his calculations, referred to "the foreigner." Questioning the stars, he discovered that they would soon see him. At that moment, the door opened and the Englishman entered!

Godolphin became a daily visitor at the astrologer's abode. Volktman's health had declined in the four years and he grew weaker daily. One evening he fell asleep forever. Lucilla's anguish was increased by her unsympathetic relatives, who took possession of the house and control of Lucilla. She confided her troubles to Godolphin, who now intended to leave Rome. Lucilla passionately confessed her love; and Godolphin left her with an effort.

Wandering to the beautiful grotto of Egeria to calm himself, he again met Lucilla. She begged him once more to let her follow him. Godolphin, transported beyond himself by her devotion, kissed her passionately; "then suddenly, as if stung by some irresistible impulse, he tore himself away and fled the spot."

Godolphin left Rome; but at Terracina, to his amazement, he was joined by Lucilla, who had followed him. "It is fated, and I resist no more," was Godolphin's exclamation.

By the side of one of the Italian Lakes, Godolphin and Lucilla fixed their abode; and "here the young idealist for some time imagined himself happy: he felt the magnet of a Home." They lived in the enjoyment of this life of retreat for more than two years. Lucilla had one daughter, who died a few weeks after her birth. Godolphin now made a visit to Rome, where he saw Saville, who invited him to meet him in the Coliseum, where he was going to escort a rich widow. The latter proved to be Constance! "She loves me still," said Godolphin; "Shall I fly to her feet? Shall I press for hope? And, oh! what, what happiness!—but Lucilla!"

Constance and Godolphin spent many hours together. Constance seemed more worthy of love than ever. Torn as he was by a thousand conflicting emotions, Godolphin received a letter from Lucilla, complaining of his short notes and begging him to return to her. Godolphin resolved to return; but he had promised to escort Constance to Tivoli the next day, and there wild emotion conquered him. Constance had clung closer and closer to him; finally clasping her to his heart, he exclaimed: "Here, here, my early—my only love, I feel, in spite of myself, that I never utterly, fully, adored you until now!"

Lucilla came to Rome and was admitted to Godolphin's apartments. He was out; but she read his farewell letter to Constance, left lying on the table. It was enough; she fled. On his return, Godolphin found Lucilla's name written on a piece of paper. He endeavored to find her by every means; but to no purpose. At last a letter from her was delivered to

him, in which she generously begged him to go to Constance.
He traced her to a convent, but she would not see him. Godolphin and Constance were married at Rome. Godolphin told
Constance Lucilla's history, and Constance sympathized in
the feeling with which he told it. They returned to London.
Godolphin became a man of pleasure and patron of the arts.
Constance was bitter in her disappointment regarding his lack
of ambition, but could arouse in him no motive for exertion.
Constance became a favorite with the King and the court
circles. Godolphin seldom accompanied her to the festivities
at Windsor. They began to drift apart. He still visited Saville
and also Fanny Millinger, who told him of a wonderful astrologer, Madame Liehbur, who had just come to London. Stainforth Radclyffe, a politician and much like Constance, whom
he deeply loved, had formed a friendship with Godolphin.
Very delicately he told Constance that Godolphin still loved
her. She found this true when she begged Godolphin to spend
the summer in ——shire. "At Wendover Castle?" he asked.
"We have never been there since our marriage," said Constance,
evasively. He agreed, and there tender recollections reawakened
his love.

At this period Lord John Russell brought forward the
Bill for Parliamentary Reform. Constance was delighted,
for she saw it would crush her father's party. "This was the
happiest time of her life—she was happy in the renewal of her
love, happy in the approaching triumph of her hate."

One night Godolphin became alarmingly ill. He was
tormented by terrible dreams of Lucilla. "Is it mockery,"
he asked Constance, "or can the living Lucilla really be in
England? And have these visions, these terrors, been part of
that mysterious sympathy which united us ever, and which
her father predicted should cease but with our lives?"

A strange suspicion came into Constance's mind. She
went to see Madame Liehbur. Constance and Lucilla met
face to face. Constance gave the half-mad Lucilla her affection.
They talked of Godolphin, and Lucilla, closing her eyes as if
to shut out some horrid vision, said: "My last hour is at hand,
and imminent, dark and deadly danger clings fast to *him!*"

Constance did not tell Godolphin of this interview. Godolphin now resolved to enter politics, although he was not of Constance's party; but Constance contrived to get him elected to Parliament.

Constance and Godolphin now went to the country; but instead of driving into the grounds of Wendover Castle, the carriage climbed the hill. To Godolphin's joy and amazement, his father's home had been artistically restored by his wife, the loving labor of years having been given to the work.

For a time they lived in happy seclusion; but at length decided to conciliate their neighbors by a *fête*. While dressing for this entertainment, a servant brought Godolphin this letter from Lucilla: "Percy Godolphin, the hour has arrived; once more we shall meet. I summon you, fair love, to that meeting— the bed of death. Come." He learned from the messenger that she was at The Chequers.

Godolphin called for his fleetest horse and without alarming Constance rode away.

The astrologer's expiring daughter lay in a mean room in the village inn. One tiny light accentuated the gloom, and through the window flashed the lightning of the approaching storm. A gleam of intelligence lighted Lucilla's face. She put her finger to her lips, smiled and said: "Hark! he comes!" In another moment Percy Godolphin clasped her in his arms.

Lucilla closed her dying speech with: "Beware, beware, Percy! The rush of waters is on my ear—the splash, the gurgle! Beware!—Your last hour is at hand!" Pointing to one star shining through the window, she cried: "Thine, thine, Godolphin, it summons thee; farewell, but not for long!"

Soon that strange, unearthly spirit was perhaps with the stars, for the unveiling of whose mysteries it had so vainly yearned.

In the blackness of the midnight storm Godolphin missed the ford. His horse shrank from the rushing tide and a gipsy tried to warn him; but he did not hear him. The riderless steed arrived at the porch of the Priory, where the pale, anxious Constance awaited Godolphin. At daybreak his corpse was found in the shallows of the ford.

Nydia sighed. "You have but lately returned? and you are well?"

"I am well. How you have grown, Nydia! Next year you will be thinking what answer to make to your lovers."

A blush and a frown passed over Nydia's cheek and brow. "I have brought you some flowers," she said. "They are poor, but they are fresh-gathered."

"They might come from Flora herself," he said, kindly. "Poor Nydia!" he thought, as she passed into the viridarium, "thine is a hard doom! Thou seest not the earth—nor the sun—nor the ocean—nor the stars;—above all, thou canst not behold Ione."

One day Arbaces found Glaucus seated by the side of Ione, while her handmaids sat at a little distance. The Egyptian gazed on the pair with a brow from which all the usual stern serenity had fled; but, recovering himself, he slowly approached them with a step so soft and echoless that it was unheard. Both started, as they recognized his cold, sarcastic face.

"You are a sudden guest," said Glaucus, rising, and with a forced smile.

"So ought all to be who know they are welcome," replied Arbaces, seating himself.

"I am glad to see you together," said Ione, "for you are formed to be friends."

But the two did not show any desire to propitiate each other, and after a short and embarrassing conversation, Glaucus took his leave of Ione.

When he was gone, Arbaces asked abruptly: "This young profligate, this Glaucus, how didst thou know him? Hast thou seen him often?" And the priest fixed his gaze steadfastly on Ione, as if he thought to penetrate into her soul.

"I have known him only within this last week or so; but why these questions?"

"He is a base insinuator! But yesterday he boasted openly, in the public baths, of your love to him. He said it amused him to take advantage of it."

"Impossible! How heard you this base slander?"

"Think no more of it," said he, rising, "but let it be a warning voice to tell thee how much prudence thy lot requires."

Arbaces left her resolved to visit her—to watch her—
every day. No sooner had his shadow glided from her presence
than the haughty Ione burst into passionate tears.

Apæcides, the brother of Ione, tired of the delusions and
trickery of the worship of Isis, had sought consolation elsewhere. He had made the acquaintance of one Olinthus, who
was suspected of adherence to the new and atheistical creed
which set up one God over all the gods, held by the company
who called themselves Christians. Arbaces, who heard of
his dissatisfaction with the rites of Isis, reasoned with him,
told him that these rites were only symbolical, and invited him
to his house to share the higher mysteries. There he overwhelmed his senses with a splendid spectacle and with the
fascinations of wine and woman until Apæcides succumbed
to the pleasures that surrounded him.

"Drink, feast, love, my pupil!" said the Egyptian, who
appeared clad in a dazzling robe studded with jewels and
crowned with roses. "Blush not that thou art passionate and
young. That which thou art, thou feelest in thy veins: that
which thou shalt be, survey!"

With this he pointed to a skeleton between the statues of
Bacchus and Venus. "Start not! that friendly guest admon-
ishes us but of the shortness of life, and summons us to *enjoy*."

Nydia, the blind flower-girl, was the slave of Burbo, a
relative of the priest Calenus, who kept a low tavern, the
resort of gladiators and prizefighters. Burbo had picked her
up at a bargain from a slave merchant, who told him that
she was a Thessalian of good birth, but concealed the fact
of her blindness. When the tavern-keeper found out the fraud
that had been played on him, he was furious, and the poor girl
felt the effects of his anger. But he became reconciled to his
purchase when he found he could employ her as a flower-
girl; for the best people took a fancy to her, and she came
home every night laden with sesterces, which Burbo, or his
wife Stratonice, transferred to his leather bag. Among others
who had treated the poor girl with kindness was Glaucus, and
she had conceived for him an affection which, if not love,
may be likened to that of a dog for its master. One night
Glaucus and Clodius were at Burbo's for the purpose of inspect-